American Casino Guide

2003 Edition

Written and Edited By
Steve Bourie

<u>Contributing Writers</u>

Anthony Curtis
Bob Dancer
Larry Edell
John Grochowski
H. Scot Krause
Max Rubin
Frank Scoblete
Jean Scott
Tom Ski
Henry Tamburin

This book is dedicated to the memory of Scott Barr.
A truly great guy who will forever be missed by his friends and family.

American Casino Guide - 2003 edition

Published By:
Casino Vacations
P.O. Box 703
Dania, Florida 33004
(954) 989-2766
Fax (954) 966-7048

e-mail: webmaster@americancasinoguide.com
web site: americancasinoguide.com

ISBN: 1-883768-12-8
ISSN: 1086-9018

Table of Contents

About Your Guide

This guide has been written to help you plan your visit to casino gambling areas and also to help you save money once you are there. The first edition of this guide began 12 years ago as an eight-page newsletter and it has continued to grow each year as casino gambling has spread throughout the country. We have listed information on all of the states that offer any type of traditional casino table games or slot machines (including video lottery terminals). We have also included stories to help you understand how casinos operate; how video poker and slot machines work; how to make the best plays in blackjack, craps, roulette and baccarat; and how to take advantage of casino promotional programs. Additionally, we have included a casino coupon section that should save you many times the cost of this book.

Besides listing general information about each casino, this guide also notes those casinos that offer free fun books as well as those that have casino marketing departments. Knowing this information can be very helpful. As an example: almost every large casino has a "comp" program whereby you can get free rooms, food, shows, gifts or cash based upon your level of play at their table games or slot machines. Just call the casino and ask for their marketing department for details on their current programs. Another program many casinos offer is a free fun book. These are coupon books that contain free and discounted offers on various items such as: bets, food, drinks, shows, rooms, souvenirs and more. This guide lists all of the casinos that offer fun books, plus details on how to get them.

A good suggestion to save you money when visiting a casino is to join their slot club. It doesn't cost anything and you would be surprised at how quickly those points can add up to earn you gifts, cash, food or other complimentaries. Also, as a slot club member you will usually receive periodic mailings from the casino with money-saving offers that are generally not available to the public.

When using this guide please remember that all of the listed room rates reflect the lowest and highest prices charged during the year. During holidays and peak periods, however, higher rates may apply. Also, since the gambling games offered at casinos vary from state to state, a listing of available games is found at the start of each state heading. We hope you enjoy your guide and we wish you good luck on your casino vacation!

Your Best Casino Bets - Part I

by Henry Tamburin

The majority of casino players leave too much to chance when playing in a casino. To put it bluntly, they do not have a clue as to how to play. They are literally throwing their money away with little chance of winning. Luck most certainly has a lot to do with your success in a casino but what really separates the winners from the losers is the skill of the players. Granted, there is no guarantee that you will win, but on the other hand, there is no guarantee that you must lose. My objective in this article is to educate you on the casino games so that at the very least, you'll be able to enjoy yourself in the casino with a minimum risk to your bankroll.

Let's begin our understanding of casino gambling by learning how casinos win as much as they do. They don't charge admission, and they certainly don't depend on the luck of their dealers to generate the income they need to pay their overhead. In fact, they guarantee themselves a steady income by having a built in advantage, or house edge, on every bet. Think of it as a very efficient hidden tax that generates them a guaranteed daily profit.

Here's an example of how this works. Suppose we take a coin and play heads or tails. Every time you lose a flip of the coin you pay me $1. Every time you win a flip, I pay you 90¢. Would you play? I hope you said no. Here's why. In this simple game I would have an advantage over you and I created that advantage by not paying you at the true odds of one-to-one (or $1).

Casinos do this very same thing to create their advantage. They simply pay off winning bets at less than the true odds. For example, the true odds of winning a bet on number 7 on roulette are 37-to-1 (the latter means you have 37 chances to lose vs. one chance to win). If you get lucky and the roulette ball lands in the number seven slot, you'd expect the casino to pay you 37 chips as winnings for the one chip you bet on number 7 (37- to-1 payoff). If they did that, the casino's advantage would be zero. However, as I mentioned above, the casinos create their advantage by paying off winning bets at less than true odds. In the case of our bet on number 7, the winning payoff is 35 chips (instead of 37 chips). The two chips the casino quietly kept is what pays their bills. Mathematically, the casino advantage is 5.26% on this bet which simply means day in and day out, the casino expects to win (or keep) 5.26 % of all money wagered in roulette.

The casino games with the lowest casino advantage (less than 1.25%) and your best bets are blackjack, craps, baccarat, and video poker. Now don't sell the ranch and run over to your nearest casino just yet. These games, plus table poker, are your best bets but you must learn how to play these games properly to enhance your chances of winning. Here are some tips to get you started:

BLACKJACK - This is your best casino game, but you must learn how to play your hands (when to hit, stand, double-down, split, etc.). This is known as the basic strategy. Learn it and you can reduce the casino's advantage to virtually zero. And if you learn how to keep track of the cards as they are played (i.e. card counting) you can actually turn the tables on the casino and have the edge over them! Do not try to play blackjack if you haven't learned the correct basic strategy. If you do, your chances of winning are slim.

CRAPS - The game of craps intimidates most casino players because of the complicated playing layout and the multitude of bets. In fact craps is an easy game to play. And it also has some of the best bets in the casino (and also some of the worst). Your best bet is the pass line with odds and come with odds. Next best is a place bet on six or eight. Stay away from all other bets on the layout because the casino's advantage is too high.

ROULETTE - Every bet on the American roulette layout (with 0 and 00 on the wheel) has a high casino advantage. That goes for bets straight up on numbers that pay 35 to 1, as well as even money wagers on red or black. Atlantic City players get a break. If you bet on an even money payoff bet and 0 or 00 hits, you lose only half your wager. This cuts the casino's advantage in half. Also, some casinos offer a European layout with only one zero. This is a better bet than wheels with 0 and 00.

BACCARAT - Many casinos offer a low stakes version called mini-baccarat. Not a bad game to play. If you bet on the bank hand, the casino's edge is only 1.17%. And when you play baccarat, there are no playing decisions to make which makes the game very easy to play.

BIG SIX WHEEL - Stay away from spending a lot of time (and money) at this game. The casino's advantage is astronomical (11% to 26%). Its drawing card for the novice player is the low minimum bet ($1). Save your money for the better games.

CARIBBEAN STUD POKER - This popular cruise ship game has found its way to land and dockside casinos. Unlike regular table poker where players compete against each other, in this game the players play against the house. But the rules favor the casino and their advantage is about 5%. The part of this game that appeals to players is the progressive jackpot side bet. You should not make this side bet, however, unless the jackpot exceeds $280,000 for the $1 ante and the $1 jackpot bet.

PAI GOW POKER - Strange name for a casino game. The game is a cross between Pai Gow, a Chinese game of dominoes, and the American game of seven-card poker. Players are dealt seven cards and they must arrange (or set) their cards into a five-card poker hand and a two-card poker hand. Skill is involved in setting the two hands which can help reduce the casino's advantage.

SLOT MACHINES - Casinos earn more money from slot machines than all the table games combined. The casino's advantage varies from one machine to another. Typically the higher denomination machines ($1 and up) pay back more than the nickel, quarter and fifty cent machines. Slots are not your best bet in the casino, but here are a few tips: Always play the maximum number of coins the machine will accept or you won't be eligible for a bonus payoff for the jackpot. Don't waste hours looking for a machine that's "ready to hit." Join the slot clubs. They are free and you'll be rewarded with discounts and other freebies. Machines that have lower jackpots pay smaller amounts more frequently which means you normally get more playing time for your money. Some casinos now certify their machines to return 98% or more and these machines are your best bets.

VIDEO POKER - Your best bet if you enjoy playing slot machines. Skill is involved as well as learning to spot the better payoff machines. Check the full house, flush payoff schedule. On machines that pay on jacks or better the better paying machines pay nine coins for a full house and six coins for the flush for each coin played. These machines are known as 9/6 machines. They are readily available; seek them out.

KENO - This casino game has a very high casino advantage (usually 20% and up). Stay away if you are serious about winning.

RED DOG - This is the casino version of the old acey-deucey. The stakes are low, but the casino edge is a wee-bit steep (3.5%). If you play, only make the raise wager when the spread between the two cards is seven or more.

SIC BO - This is an oriental game in which players bet on the outcome of the roll of three dice. There are lots of bets on the layout, some that pay odds of 150-to-1. However, most have a very high casino advantage. Your best bet is a bet on the big or small wager.

LET IT RIDE - This casino table game is based on the all-American game of poker. Like Caribbean Stud Poker, players compete against the house rather than against each other. What makes this game so unique is that the players can remove up to two of their initial mandatory three bets if they don't think they can win. The objective is to end up with a five-card poker hand of at least 10's or higher. The higher the rank, the greater the payoff; up to 1,000-to-1 for the royal flush. The casino edge is about 3% and about 70% of the hands will be losing hands. If you are lucky enough to catch a high payoff hand, be smart, push your chair back, and take the money and run!

Henry Tamburin has more than 27 years experience as a casino player, author, columnist and instructor. He has written more than 500 articles on casino gambling for numerous national gaming publications. He is also the author of numerous books and instructional videos. You can visit his web site at http://www.smartgaming.com. Ordering information for his books and videos can be found on page 148 .

Your Best Casino Bets - Part II

by Steve Bourie

In the previous story Henry gave you his choices for your best casino bets based on which ones offer you the best mathematical odds. Now, Henry is a great mathematician who is truly an expert at crunching numbers to figure out what the theoretical odds are, but what about real life? By this I mean - at the end of the week, or the month, or the year, how much does a casino really make from blackjack, or craps, or roulette? Sure, you can do the math to calculate the casino advantage on a bank hand in mini-baccarat as 1.17%, but at the end of the day what percent of those bets on mini-baccarat actually wind up in the hands of the casino? Is it precisely 1.17%? or is it less? or is it more? And, if you knew how much the casino truly averaged on all of the games it offered, which one would turn out to be your best bet based on that information?

To find the answer to this question I began my search by looking at the annual gaming revenue report issued by Nevada's State Gaming Control Board. It lists the win percentages, based on the drop (an explanation of this term later), for all of the games offered by the casinos and you might be surprised at which game had the lowest win percentage. Go ahead and take a guess...nice try, but you're wrong! The answer is bingo, where casinos only won 2.01% of the money they handled! The first column below lists the actual win percentages based on the "drop" (an explanation of "drop" follows shortly) for Nevada's various games for the fiscal year from July 1, 2001 through June 30, 2002:

GAME	WIN %	ADJUSTED WIN %
Keno	27.68	27.68
Race Book	16.71	16.71
Big-Six Wheel	45.65	9.13 (2001 Figures)
Caribbean Stud Poker	28.74	5.75
Sports Pool	5.53	5.53
Slot Machines	5.38	5.38
3-Card Poker	24.93	4.99
Roulette	23.46	4.69
Pai Gow Poker	22.74	4.55
Let It Ride	22.07	4.41
Pai Gow	19.58	3.92
Baccarat	15.95	3.19
Mini-Baccarat	14.05	2.81
Craps	13.24	2.65
Twenty-One	13.11	2.62
Bingo	2.01	2.01

Usually bingo would rank as one of the games with the worst odds, but not in Nevada where it's sometimes used as a "loss leader." Just like your local Kmart runs especially low prices on a couple of items to bring you into the store where they believe you'll buy some other items, Nevada casinos use bingo to bring people into their casinos, believing that while they're there they'll play other games and also develop a loyalty to that casino. Actually, some years the casinos offering bingo actually lose money on the game rather than make money. So, if you're a bingo player Nevada casinos are the best places you'll ever find to play your game.

Before we go on to the other games though you'll need a brief explanation of how the win percentages are calculated and we'll start off with a basic lesson in how casinos do their accounting.

Casinos measure their take in table games by the *drop* and the *win*. The *drop* is the count of all of the receipts (cash and credit markers) that go into the drop box located at the table. Later, an accounting is made to see how much more (or less) they have than they started with. This amount is known as the *win*.

What the first column in the table shows you is how much the casinos won as a percentage of the drop. For example, on the roulette table for every $100 that went into the drop box the casino won $23.46 or 23.46%. What it doesn't tell you, however, is how much the casinos won as a percentage of all the bets that were made. In other words, the drop tells you how many chips were bought at that table, but it doesn't tell you how many bets were made with those chips. For example, if you buy $100 worth of chips at a blackjack table and play $10 a hand you don't bet for exactly 10 hands and then leave the table, do you? Of course not. You win some hands and you lose some hands and if you counted all of the times you made a $10 bet before you left the table you would see that your original $100 in chips generated many times that amount in bets. In other words, there is a multiplier effect for the money that goes into the drop box. We know that for every dollar that goes into the drop box there is a corresponding number of bets made. To find out exactly what that number is I asked Henry for some help. He replied that there is no exact answer, but during a 1982 study of the roulette tables in Atlantic City it was discovered that the total amount bet was approximately five times the amount of the buy-in. This means that for every $100 worth of chips bought at the table it resulted in $500 worth of bets being made.

The multiplier effect for the money that goes into the drop box is also dependent on the skill of the player. A blackjack player that loses his money quickly because he doesn't know good playing strategy will have a much lower multiplier than a player who uses a correct playing strategy. For purposes of this story, however, we'll assume that they balance each other out and we'll also assume that all games have the same multiplier of five. We can now return to our win percentage tables and divide by five the percentages for those games that have a multiplier effect. These new adjusted numbers lets us know approximately how much the casinos actually won as a percentage of the amount bet on each of those games. Keep in mind, however, that besides bingo there are three other game categories that do not need to be adjusted: keno, race book and sports pool. They need no adjustment because there is no multiplier factor involved. On these particular games the casinos know the exact total of the bets they take in and the exact total of the bets they pay out.

After calculating our adjusted win numbers we can now go back and take another look at which games are your best casino bets. The worst game, by far, is keno with its 27.68% edge. Next comes the race book with 16.71%. Traditionally, the Big-Six wheel would come next with a casino win of about 45% which adjusts to 9.13%. However, the Nevada Gaming Control Board stopped releasing numbers on this game in 2002 so we are using old numbers from the 2001 report. This is followed by Caribbean stud poker at 5.75%.

Sports betting has a win rate of 5.53% but that number actually deserves a closer look because there are really six different types of bets that make up that 5.53% figure: football - 4.49%; basketball - 5.67%; baseball - 3.24%; sports parlay cards - 32.41%; pari-mutuel sports - 14.39%; and other sports - 7.92%. As you can see, all sports bets carry a relatively low house edge, except for sports parlay cards which you may want to avoid.

Next are slot machines at 5.38%; three-card poker at 4.99%; roulette at 4.69%; pai gow poker at 4.55%; let it ride at 4.41%; and pai gow at 3.92%.

Finally, we come to the four best casino bets that all have roughly the same edge of less than four percent: baccarat at 3.19%; minibaccarat at 2.81%; craps at 2.65%; and twenty-one (blackjack) at 2.62%.

So there you have it. After discounting bingo, blackjack is your best casino bet! Henry said it was the a good game to play and he was right!

An important thing to keep in mind, however, is something else that Henry said about the game of blackjack: "you must learn how to play your hands." You should remember that of all the table games offered in a casino (other than poker), blackjack is the only one that is a game of skill. This means that the better you are at playing your cards, the better you will be able to beat the house average. The 2.62% figure shown is just an average and if you learn the proper basic strategies you should be able to cut it down even more. Good luck!

Casino Comps

by Steve Bourie

In the world of casino gambling a "comp" is short for complimentary and it refers to anything that the casino will give you for free in return for your play in their casino.

Naturally, the more you bet, the more the casino will be willing to give you back. For the truly "high roller" (those willing to bet thousands, tens of thousands or even hundreds of thousands on the turn of a card) there is no expense spared to cater to their every whim, including: private jet transportation, chauffeur-driven limousines, gourmet chef-prepared foods, the finest wines and champagnes, plus pampered butler and maid service in a $10 million penthouse suite. But what about the lower-limit bettor?

Well, it turns out that pretty much any gambler can qualify for comps no matter what their level of play and if you know you're going to be gambling anyway, you might as well ask to get rated to see what you can get on a comp basis.

When you sit down to play be sure to tell the dealer that you want to be rated and they'll call over the appropriate floorperson who will take down your name and put it on a card along with information on how long you play and how much you bet. The floorperson won't stand there and constantly watch you, instead they'll just glance over every once in awhile to see how much you're betting and note it on the card. If you change tables be sure to tell the floorperson so that they can continue to track your play at the new table.

Usually a casino will want you to play for at least three hours and virtually all casinos use the same formula to calculate your comp value. They simply take the size of your average bet and multiply it by: the casino's advantage on the game you're playing; the decisions per hour in your game; and the length of your play in hours. The end result is what the casino expects to win from you during your play and most casinos will return about 40% of that amount to you in the form of comps.

So, let's say you're a roulette player that averages $20 a spin and you play for four hours. What's that worth in comps? Well, just multiply your average bet ($20), by the casino's advantage in roulette (5.3%) to get $1.06, which is the average amount the casino expects to make on you on each spin of the wheel. You then multiply that by the number of decisions (or spins) per hour (40) to get $42.40, which is the average amount the casino expects to make on you after one hour. Then, multiply that by the total hours of play (4) to get $169.60, which is the average amount the casino expects to make on you during your

4 hours of play. Since the average casino will return about 40% of that amount in comps you should qualify for $67.84 in casino comps.

One thing to keep in mind about comps is that you don't have to lose in order to qualify. The casino only asks that you put in the time to play. So, in our example if, after 4 hours of gambling, our roulette player ended up winning $100, they would still be eligible for the same amount of $67.84 in comps.

The last thing to mention about comps is that some casino games require skill (blackjack and pai gow poker), or offer various bets that have different casino advantages (craps) so those factors are sometimes adjusted in the equation when determining the casino advantage in those games. Just take a look at the chart below to see how the average casino will adjust for skill in blackjack and pai gow poker as well as for the types of bets that are made in craps.

Game	Game Advantage	Decisions Per Hour
Blackjack	**.0025 (Card Counter)** **.01 (Good Basic Strategy)** **.015 (Soft Player)**	**70**
Roulette	**.053**	**40**
Craps	**.005 (Pass Line/Full Odds)** **.01 (Knowledgeable)** **.04 (Soft)**	**144**
Baccarat	**.012**	**70**
Mini-Baccarat	**.012**	**110**
Pai Gow Poker	**.01 (Knowledgeable)** **.02 (Average)**	**25**

Comp City U.S.A.

by Max Rubin

Casino Comps have always been synonymous with Las Vegas, high rolling, and living large. Certainly everyone who plays the high and fast game—and there aren't that many of them—has come to expect to be treated like a potentate at the casino's expense. But most gamblers still don't realize that the overwhelming majority of the billions of comp dollars dished out by casinos every year are spent on the average guy, and you don't have to risk a spare $10,000 to beat the system.

Fact is, the comp system is designed to reward gamblers at every level. Even if you play nickel slots or blackjack at $5 a hand, your action makes you eligible for something in the grand comp plan. The trick to getting your share is to understand what you're entitled to and then get more.

What Gets What - The first step is to size up your threshold for risk and to determine how much money you've got to play the game with. Casinos have one simple goal: take your money. That means that how much you wager—or how much they think you wager—is the prime determinant in how much in comps they're willing to give you. But you've gotta be careful. The strategy isn't to increase the amount that you gamble to get comps. On the contrary, it's to stay at your normal level, get the comps you qualify for, and use them to enhance your result (by either mitigating losses or augmenting wins). The following provides a good overview of what you can expect to get.

At the lowest levels, you'll have to be content with little comps, things like comped parking and funbook freebies. You get those just for showing up.

The next rung on the comp ladder is free drinks, which even the lowly single-nickel slot player (or someone who pretends to be) can get by flagging down a cocktail waitress. You only have to step up your play a little—quarter slots and $5-$10 table games—to graduate to the next level, which is where it starts getting good. These comps include free snack bar food, breakfasts in the coffee shops, and rounds of drinks at the bar. Double that action and you'll start getting the best buffets, dinner in the coffee shops, invitations to low-level events, and the little-known but highly valuable "casino rate" on a room (a discount that can knock up to 50% off the retail price). The two-fold secret to getting these comps is simple: If you play table games, ask for them. If you play machines, join the slot club.

It's no mystery that casinos give better comps to bigger players, and if you regularly bet $25-$100 a hand, or plug dollars into machine, you can look forward to gourmet meals and free seats in the showrooms in all but the most elegant Vegas megastores. Once you graduate to the $100-$350 bet level, it's essential to get "rated" if you're playing table games, which means the pit bosses have to log all of your action. If you're playing multi-coin dollar machines and use your VIP card, they're already tracking every coin you shove down the gullet of the no-armed bandits, so all you have to do is put in your hours to be put in a suite.

Beyond the $350-a-hand table game and $5-a-pull machine level, the sky's the limit for comps: private multi-room penthouse suites, limo rides, $500 rounds of golf, trips to the Super Bowl, shopping sprees at Neiman's, the works. Many of the high rollers who get this treatment have casino lines of credit in excess of $1 million, and at these levels, a strange symbiotic bond is forged between the casino and the gambler. The casino is happy because its winnings far exceed the expense of hosting the gambler. The gambler is happy because he considers the attention and status he receives a fair trade for the risk he's willing to take (and the losses he's willing to fade).

The biggest change in the evolution of the comp system over the past five years is that you can now get the comps you want where you want. There are now very few major cities in America that are more than 100 miles from a bona fide big-bet store, and earning comps has become easier—geographically at least—than ever before.

Some of the newer venues—especially in California, where they're still getting their feet wet and don't have sophisticated management or comp-tracking systems, and places like Illinois and Mississippi, which have brutal tax structures that don't leave much for the masses—make it fairly tricky to earn comps on the Vegas level. But that's not to say you can't get a comp-bang for your gambling buck outside Nevada. You can, and in some places with inadequately trained staffs and/or outdated comp systems, it actually gets easier. You just have to be more diligent in doing the research necessary to know which casinos are ripe for the taking.

Comp Wizardry - Now that you know that the prizes are out there—and everywhere—you might be wondering how well you can play the comp game. The bottom line is, anyone with a lick of sense can play it well. You can master perfect basic strategy blackjack, which is the skill-level you need to achieve, for about $2 (use one of the cards they sell in virtually every casino gift shop), and you can learn how to exploit the loopholes in every casino's comp system by reading my book, *Comp City, A Guide to Free Casino Vacations*. The book details the step-by-step techniques used by "comp wizards" to beat casinos at their own game by getting a dollar's worth of comps for every dime they lose. Short of taking this crash course in comp strategy, just asking for meals and tickets and line passes, and using your rating card every time you play is 90% of what you need to know in 95% of America's casinos, especially at the lower levels. They're giving away millions every day. Don't miss out on your share.

Max Rubin is a former casino idustry executive and author
of the book "Comp City - A Guide to Free Casino Vacations."
Ordering information for his book can be found on page 22.

Taking Advantage of Slot Clubs

by H. Scot Krause

Slot Clubs originated in Atlantic City over 20 years ago as a way to begin recognizing and rewarding the casino's good players. Today, slot clubs are the casino's most powerful marketing tool and the player's best benefit the casino has to offer. It's the best of both worlds for both the player and the casino.

To begin, perhaps the word "club" is a little misleading, since there are no dues to pay, meetings to attend or any of the usual aspects associated with joining a club. You do get a slot club membership card (also called a player's card) which is your key to unlocking the benefits and rewards of the casino you're playing in.

Typically, your slot club membership card is a plastic card, with your identifying number on it, that you will use while playing at any of the casino's slot or video poker machines or while playing table games. It resembles a credit card, but only in its appearance, and is in no way an actual credit card. I mention that because there are some people who actually, mistakenly believe they will be inserting a credit card into their slot machine and play on credit, and therefore they refuse to get their player's card and are basically denied any and all benefits they are entitled to!

So let's start at the beginning and walk through the slot card program, when and why to do it and discuss some benefits, rewards and perks.

When you enter any casino for the first time, ask someone immediately where you can find the slot club or players club booth before you put any money at play. At the booth, or club, you should find a rather friendly group of employees who will get you started, signed up and get your card for you pronto.

You'll probably need to fill out a short application form or at least give your identification card to the clerk. It's simply a way to register the card in your name. You usually don't need to give your social security number if you don't want to, but always give your birthday and anniversary dates when asked. They help identify you with the casino in case others have your same name and many times the birthday benefits are nothing short of fantastic.

Always ask the slot club personnel about how to use the card and any other current promotions or benefits in addition to using your card. There will usually be a brochure or literature available that you can take explaining all the club benefits. There may also be a sign-up bonus such as a free gift or free points when you register. Be sure to ask. Sometimes an easily obtainable coupon may be required, and the clerks can tell you where or how to get one. Finally, I like to request two cards when I join, and you might like to do the same. You'll find that you may lose one, or want to play two machines at one time. That's it! You're on your way.

When you're out on the casino floor, you'll notice a slot on the machines that your card fits into. When you decide which machine you want to play, put your card in the slot and leave it in the entire time you play that machine. (Note: Take a moment to look for the card reader slot and not the bill acceptor. If you accidentally put your card in the bill acceptor you'll probaly strip the magnetic reader off your card and it won't work).

Most machines will have some type of reader that will display your name, points earned or at least let you know your card has been accepted. It's not a swipe card, and you must leave it in the machine while you play. It's simply counting the coins, or credits, that go through the machine while you're playing and giving you credit in the form of points for the amount of money that cycles through the machine. (Some casinos consider time on the machine as well as money being cycled, but that is a little more rare than in years past). Now, while your playing, you'll be earning valuable points that become redeemable for anything from cashback to restaurant complimentaries (refered to as "comps") show tickets, gifts, reduced room rates or free rooms, to almost any amenity you may want or require.

Be sure to keep your card in the machine until you have completed your play and cashed all coins out of the machine. Some clubs base their points on a coin-out system, rather than coin-in. Of course, these rewards are based on total play and your rewards may vary according to point formulas created exclusively for the casino at which you're playing. I do caution you not to continue to play beyond your comfortable gambling range and budget just to earn a point level or comp. Let the comps fall in place as you play or when you return again in the future. Which brings me to another interesting thought. I've heard players refuse to get a card because they believe they won't return to the casino again. First of all, you never know what your future plans may hold. Second, you may earn enough points while you're on this trip to at least earn a small comp or some cash back before you leave. You'll at least get on the casino's mailing list for future specials and events. You may win a jackpot that will allow you to return sooner that you originally thought was possible. And finally, with as many consolidations and buy-outs as there are in the casino business today, the casino you're playing at today may be owned by someone else tomorrow, who may in turn, be closer to your home, and you'll be able to use your points with them. There's just no good excuse not to get a player's card at any casino you visit.

Here are a couple other tips when you plan to visit a casino and need to get a slot club card. Sometimes you can apply or sign-up in advance by mail registration or visiting the casino's website on the Internet. They will often mail you the card in advance or have it already prepared for you when you get to the casino. Call and ask ahead of time for this service and you'll save time and won't have to stand in long lines when you hit the casino floor. Sometimes, when you receive your card by mail or Internet sign-up, you'll get additional offers, coupons, gifts and funbook offers along with it.

Many casinos now employee slot club ambassadors, cash hosts, or enrollment representatives who will sign you up on the casino floor, making it even easier for you to enroll in the club. They often have additional incentives or perks they can give you when you sign up with them. You might also check to see if a card you have from another casino might work where you're playing now. Many casino corporations are beginning to combine their clubs to offer you benefits at any of their respective properties. We're sure to see more of this as consolidations and mergers continue to take place.

Now, let's take a little closer look at the benefits and reasons why you want to belong to these slot clubs. Obviously, the casinos want your business and will go to great lengths to have you return. In addition to the points you're earning while playing, which will entitle you to various comps as mentioned previously, your most valuable asset from joining the slot club will be your mailing list advantage. Offers to slot club members are mailed often and repeatedly for room specials, many times even free room offers, meal discounts (two for ones), and often other free offers. We've been mailed match play offers, double and triple point coupons, show and movie theater tickets, spa specials, gifts and gift certificates, drawing tickets, and a myriad of other offers.

The casino offers are based on levels of play, and better offers including lavish parties, Superbowl and New Year's Eve invitations, free participation to invited guest slot tournaments, limousine services, and even free round-trip airfare, are offerd to the casino's best players. Don't rule yourself out just because you don't think you'll reach those levels of play to be awarded those opportunities. Everyone is rewarded in some way for even the most nominal play. Just wait until your birthday rolls around and I can almost guarantee you'll get some fabulous offers from the casinos to spend your celebration with them!

Finally, we'll now take a look at some of the myths regarding slot clubs and player's cards and dispose of them accordingly. Here are some of the arguments I've heard against slot club cards, or excuses as to why players don't use them...

"I never win when I play with my card." The truth is your results would be the same regardless if you had a card in or not. There is no relation between the card counting coins through the machine and what comes up on the screen when you push the button. The card just records how much money is wagered. It has no memory of whether you have won or lost and it doesn't care.

"I don't want to be tracked," or "I don't want the casino to know how much I'm playing," or "I don't want the IRS to have my records." In fact, you do want the casino to track you so you can be rewarded for your play. They have no way of knowing you, or how they can help and reward you unless they know who you are, what you're playing and how much you're spending. The IRS does not have access to your gambling activities, but you, in fact, do. The slot club can provide you with a year end win-loss record of your play that may help you offset wins with losses for tax purposes.

"I don't need a card, I'm a local," or "I'm a tourist." Basically, you're one or the other, but either way you still should have a card. The casino's computers usually separate locals from tourists and tailor their offers accordingly. If you're going to play anyway, get a card!

"I always lose those cards." You can always have another card made. Get extras made. Why play without it? It's like losing your wallet. The card has so much value for you, yet you leave it in the machine. You don't forget your airline frequent flier card at the airport, or your grocery savings card when you go shopping, do you?

"I don't need a card, I'm leaving in an hour." It doesn't matter how long you will be staying or how soon you will be leaving. Remember that all-important mailing list, and that you just might return some time in the future or play at a sister property somewhere else. (Don't worry. Most casinos do not sell their mailing list names. They want you for themselves and are very selfish!)

All-in-all, I've never heard of one good reason not to join a slot club. In fact, I hope I've given you enough good reasons to always join every slot club at every casino you ever visit. Good luck and happy slot clubbing!

H. Scot Krause is employed in the casino business and has worked in entertainment and marketing. He has visited casinos from the Bahamas and Atlantic City, to Mississippi, and currently resides in Las Vegas, Nevada, with his wife, Donna. He writes promotional articles about Las Vegas and currently has a weekly column called "Vegas Values" which can be viewed at: www.americancasinoguide.com

Slot Clubs And Comps

by Steve Bourie

Before you start playing any kind of electronic gaming machine in a casino, whether it be a slot, video poker, video blackjack, or video keno machine, you should first join the casino's slot club to reap the rewards that your play will entitle you to. What is a slot club you ask? Well, it's very similar to a frequent flyer club, except that in these clubs you will earn cash or comps (free food, rooms, shows, etc.) based on how much money you put through the machines.

Virtually every major casino in the U.S. today has a slot club and joining is quite simple. Just go to the club's registration desk, present an ID, and you'll be issued a plastic card which is very similar to a credit card. When you walk up to a machine you'll see a small slot (usually at the top, or on the side) where you should insert your card before you start to play. The card will then record how much money you've played in that particular machine and then, based on the amount you put through, you will be eligible to receive cash (sometimes) and comps (always) back from the casino. Naturally, the more you gamble, the more they will give back to you.

Some casinos will give you a free gift, or some other kind of bonus (extra slot club points, free buffet, etc.) just for joining and since there's no cost involved, it certainly makes sense to join even if you don't plan on playing that much. As a club member you'll also be on the casino's mailing list and you'll probably be receiving some good money-saving offers in the mail. Additionally, some casinos offer discounts to their club members on hotel rooms, meals and gift shop purchases.

While almost no casino will give you cashback for playing their table games, virtually all casinos will give you cashback for playing their machines. The amount returned is calculated as a percentage of the money you put through the machines and it basically varies from as low as .05% to as high as 1%. This means that for every $100 you put into a machine you will earn a cash rebate of anywhere from five cents to $1. This may not seem like a great deal of money but it can add up very quickly. Additionally, some casinos (usually the casinos with the lower rates) will periodically offer double, triple or quadruple point days when your points will accumulate much more rapidly.

One other point to make about cashback is that the vast majority of casinos (about 90%) offer a lower cash rebate on their video poker machines than they do on their slot machines. Generally, the rate is about one-half of what the casino normally pays on its slot machines. As an example, on the Las Vegas Strip all of the following casinos offer their slot players a rebate of .67% but reduce that rate to .33% for video poker play: Treasure Island,

Mirage, New York New York, Excalibur, Luxor, Bellagio, Aladdin and Mandalay Bay. The reason for the reduced rate is that video poker is a game of skill and knowledgeable players can achieve a greater return on video poker games than they could on slots. Since the casino will make less money on video poker games they simply reduce their cash rebates accordingly. This is very important to keep in mind, especially if you're a bad video poker player, because you'll probably only be earning half the cash rebate you could be getting by just playing the slots.

Of course, the best situation is to be a smart video poker player and to find a casino that offers the same cash rebate to all of its player regardless of what kind of machine they play. This way you could be playing a good video poker game, combined with a good cash rebate, and this will allow you to be playing at a near 100% level! Quite a few of the "locals" casinos in Las Vegas that have low cash rebates (.05% to .15%) offer the same rate of return regardless of the type of machine. There are no casinos in Atlantic City that treat slot and video poker players equally for cash rebates.

One final point to make about cash rebates is that not all clubs will allow you to get your cashback immediately. In Atlantic City, for example, most of the casinos will send a voucher to your home address which you must bring back to the casino (usually within 90 days) to receive your cash. There are no casinos in Las Vegas that do this but you should make it a point to ask if your cashback from the slot club is available immediately. If not, you may find yourself being mailed a voucher that is worthless to you.

While not every casino's slot club will give you back cash it is standard for every slot club to allow you to earn "comps" for your machine play. "Comps" is short for complimentaries and it means various things that you can get for free from the casino: rooms, meals, shows, gifts, etc.

Once again, the comp you will earn is based on the amount of money you put through the machines but it is usually at a higher level than you would earn for cashback. After all, the real cost to a casino for a $15 meal is much less than giving you back $15 in cash so the casinos can afford to be more generous.

When it comes to casino slot club comp policies they basically fall into one of three categories. Some casinos have clubs that allow you to redeem your points for either cash at one rate, or comps at a reduced rate that will cost you fewer points. In these clubs, for example, you might have a choice of redeeming your 1,000 points for either $10 in cash or $20 in comps.

Another option (one that is commonly used by many "locals" casinos in Las Vegas) is for the casino to set a redemption schedule for each particular restaurant, or meal. For example: breakfast is 800 points, lunch is 1,200 points and dinner is 1,600 points. These are popular programs because players know exactly what is required to earn their comp.

At the other extreme is the practice of many casinos to base their comps on your total machine play but not to tell you exactly what's required to achieve it. At the Mirage, Caesars Palace and Treasure Island in Las Vegas, for example, you will earn cashback at a set schedule but you'll never quite know what you need to earn a food comp. You just have to go to the slot club booth, present your card, and ask if you can get a buffet or restaurant comp. The staff will then either give it to you or say you need some more play on your card before they can issue you a food comp.

And which casinos have the best slot clubs? Well, that would really be dependant on what's most important to you. If you're visiting from out of town you would probably want a slot club that's more generous with room comps so you could save money on your accomodations. However, if you're going to be playing at a casino near your home you would be more interested in which casino offers the best cashback rate and food comps. Whatever the situation, be sure to give most of your play to the casino that offers the best benefits for you and you'll soon be reaping the rewards of slot club membership!

Using Casino Coupons

by Jean Scott

Jean Scott is one of the country's most renowned and successful low rollers. She belongs to slot clubs. She participates in promotions and drawings. She uses funbooks. She befriends slot hosts. The Las Vegas Advisor pegged her the Queen of Ku Pon in 1994 and in 1995, the CBS news magazine **48 Hours** *aired an entire hour-long segment revolving around her, in which Dan Rather dubbed her the Queen of Comps. She has appeared in segments on* **Hard Copy** *and* **Dateline** *about how to beat the casinos, plus she frequently appears in* **Discovery Channel** *and* **Travel Channel** *programs about casino gambling.*

An overwhelming majority of gamblers in a casino are playing negative-expectation games, meaning the house has the mathematical edge, and they will usually lose money in short order. Remember, you can only win in the long run if you're not giving the casino that little "admission fee," its edge, on every bet. That's not to say it's not possible to win on a negative-expectation game one day, or one trip, or even for several trips in a row. But in the long run, if you play negative-expectation games, the house edge will see to it that you're a long-term loser.

Couponing affords you the opportunity to turn things around and have the edge in your favor. For example, if you're lucky enough to have a blackjack coupon that makes your first card an automatic ace, you're playing with a whopping 52% edge. No, you won't win on every coupon, no matter how big the edge, but you will get to the winning long-term much faster.

Therefore, because couponing takes the edge away from the casino and gives it to you, it is possible to gamble with a much smaller bankroll. Because you always have the edge, and sometimes quite a large one, you'll likely become an overall winner more quickly than playing a regular game without a coupon. Of course, you must make coupon bets that are compatible with your bankroll. If you have only a couple of hundred dollars, you better stick with $5-$10 and/or one-bet coupons. It takes a larger bankroll to play some large-bet or extended-time-play coupons, i.e. $25 matchplays or getting paid double for blackjack for the first hour of play. But if you make an effort to track down a lot of those smaller coupon plays, you'll be surprised how soon you can build up your bankroll for the bigger plays that yield even greater profits.

Couponing is an extremely important tool even for casino visitors who are playing positive-expectation games. For the skillful video poker player at the quarter level or the blackjack card counter who makes only low-level bets, couponing may be the first line of defense against the casino edge. My husband Brad and I played quarter video poker for many years, and all during that time our per-hour profit rate in couponing far exceeded what we had in video poker and became an important contributor to building our gambling bankroll so we could progress to higher denomination play.

Coupons for free or reduced-price food, drinks, hotel rooms, or shows are "found" money if you're not getting these amenities comped. I've known couples that paid full-price for a show when there was a 2-for-1 coupon in the unopened freebie magazine right in their hotel room. People are given a coupon book when they check into a casino hotel-and the maid finds it on the dresser after they check out, a coupon for $5 in free coin, with no playing requirement, still intact. (And guess who the maid sometimes knows that loves "leftover" coupons!)

Casinos used to be famous for their bargain-priced meals, rooms, and show tickets, but this is changing quickly; Las Vegas especially is going upscale. So if you're are on a limited budget, you'll find that the time and effort you spend looking for the non-gambling coupons will allow you to afford some of the higher-price splurges. Even though we play enough to get all the free drinks we usually want in a casino, I always carry a few drink coupons in my purse in case we want to meet friends in the lounge and not face a big bar bill. Now let's take a look at the different kinds of coupons offered to gamblers.

Matchplay - Whether it says "$5 matchplay" or "Bet $5 and We Will Pay You $10 If You Win," it means the same: The casino is giving you money. However, you can't take this money and stick it in your pocket. The "free" money must be used for a bet and comes with a condition: You must risk some of your own money at the same time.

Here's how it works: We'll use as an example the most common matchplay-a $5 coupon for blackjack. You go to a blackjack table and sit down at an empty space, placing your coupon on the betting circle for your seat, with a $5 bill on top of the coupon. Some casinos let that bill play; some exchange it for a $5 chip. In either case, you now have a $10 bet riding on this hand-your own $5 investment plus an extra bet of $5 that the casino has given you by "matching" your bet. If you win, the casino pays off at $10. If you lose, the casino merely takes away the coupon and the $5 of your own money that you put up.

This is how it works in general for all table games and all denominations of matchplay coupons. If you have a $25 matchplay, then the casino matches that amount and you have a $50 bet. You're paid off at $50 if you win, while giving up only your own $25 (and the coupon) if you lose. You will win about half the time on matchplay bets, depending on the game and the type of bets you make. A rule of thumb to figure out the value of a matchplay coupon is to cut the amount in half and subtract the house edge, which averages around 3%, depending on the game, the bet, and/or your skill level. I usually just subtract 10 cents on a $5 matchplay as a round figure. This renders a $5 matchplay worth about $2.40-plus. A $25 matchplay is worth about $12-plus ($25 divided by 2 minus 50 cents).

Non-Even-Money Matchplay Coupons - Almost all matchplays can be used only on even-money bets. However, if you get one that allows non-even money bets, the optimal use is to bet it on the longest longshot available-like straight-up on a number at roulette.

Example: If you're betting a $100 matchplay (use it once and lose it whether you win or lose) at single-zero roulette, taking a shot at straight-up on a number yields an expected value (EV) of $94.59 ($3,500 payoff/37 possible outcomes). If you bet on the banker at baccarat, your EV is about $49.47.

The problem is that you pay for your extra EV on this bet in roulette with *extreme* variance, but if you expect to get many more of these matchplays, it can make sense to maximize your EV in this way.

Lucky Bucks - This kind of coupon generally adds a dollar or two extra on an even-money bet. For example, with a 7-for-5 coupon, you put down the coupon with a $5 chip or bill and if you win, you're paid an extra $2. Like matchplays, you win on average about half the time, so the coupon is worth just a few cents less than half the bonus, about 97 cents.

There are also occasional 3-for-2 and 2-for-1 lucky bucks, but you often can't find a table with minimums that allow you to bet that small, and you're usually not permitted to use them with a larger bet even if you explain that you still only expect the same dollar bonus. I've given up trying to educate dealers (and even pit bosses) that this is actually to their advantage, since I'm putting more money at risk for the same measly bonus. (I guess I'm getting too old to argue over small change. Brad says it's about time!)

First Card Is An Ace - Put this coupon in the betting spot on a blackjack table with the bet listed on the coupon (usually $5) and it becomes your first card, a valuable ace. The dealer skips you on the first-card deal around, then gives you a second card. You play out the hand the same as if you were dealt a first-card ace, getting paid immediately if you're lucky to score a blackjack. Otherwise you hit, stand, split, or double as usual.

This coupon gives you an enormous 52% edge, although a bit more long term than other coupons, since you often have to split or double, which involves putting more money at risk. But it still doesn't take too many of these coupons to become an overall winner and to make this your favorite coupon, as it is mine.

Free Play - This is usually a coupon you get as a bonus reward for past play at a casino and an incentive to come back, sometimes referred to as bounce-back cash. If the coupon is for slot play, you usually have to go to the slot club to have credits activated on a slot or video poker machine and you have to play them through once before you can cash out your winnings.

If the coupon is for chips, you usually get special non-negotiable chips at the cage. These chips cannot be exchanged for cash, like regular chips, but must be played. These chips are usually *not* matchplay, but can be bet alone, with no money of your own at risk. When you win a bet with this kind of chip, you're paid in regular chips that you *can* cash in. You can usually continue to bet with these special non-negotiable chips until you lose them; therefore their worth is the face value of the chip.

Read the rules for all free-play coupons carefully and note any special in-structions or restrictions. They're often date specific. The table-game chips might be "for one play only," and the ones for slot credits might specify or exclude certain machines

Slot Machines

by Steve Bourie

Virtually anyone who visits a casino, even for the first time, is familiar with a slot machine and how it operates: just put in your money, pull the handle and wait a few seconds to see if you win. It isn't intimidating like table games where you really need some knowledge of the rules before you play and it's this basic simplicity that accounts for much of the success of slot machines in the modern American casino.

As a matter of fact, the biggest money-maker for casinos is the slot machine with approximately 65 percent of the average casino's profits being generated by slot machine play. As an example, in Nevada's fiscal year ending June 30, 2002 the total win by all of the state's casinos was a little more than $9.3 billion. Of that amount, slightly more than $6.2 billion, or almost 67 percent, was from electronic machine winnings.

With this in mind, you must ask yourself, "can I really win money by playing slot machines?" The answer is a resounding yes...and no. First the "no" part: in simplest terms a slot machine makes money for the casino by paying out less money than it takes in. In some states, such as Nevada and New Jersey, the minimum amount to be returned is regulated. In Nevada the minimum is 75 percent and in New Jersey it's 83 percent. However, if you look at the slot payback percentages for those particular states in this book you will see that the actual average payback percentages are much higher. In New Jersey it's about 92 percent and in Nevada it's about 95 percent. Even though the actual paybacks are higher than the law requires, you can still see that on average for every $1 you play in an Atlantic City slot machine you will lose 8¢ and in a Las Vegas slot machine you will lose 5¢. Therefore, it doesn't take a rocket scientist to see that if you stand in front of a slot machine and continue to pump in your money, eventually, you will lose it all. On average, it will take you longer to lose it in Las Vegas rather than Atlantic City, but the result is still the same: you will go broke.

Gee, sounds kind of depressing, doesn't it? Well, cheer up because now we go on to the "yes" part. But, before we talk about that, let's first try to understand how slot machines work. All modern slot machines contain a random number generator (RNG) which is used to control the payback percentage for each machine. When a casino orders a slot machine the manufacturer will have a list of percentage paybacks for each machine and the casino must choose one from that list. For example, a manufacturer may have 10 chips available for one machine that range from a high of 96% to as low as 85%. All of these chips have been inspected and approved by a gaming commission and the casino is free to choose whichever chip it wants for that particular brand of machine.

In almost all instances, the casino will place a higher denomination chip in a higher denomination machine. In other words, the nickel machines will get the chips programmed to pay back around 87% and the $25 machines will get the chips programmed to pay back around 96%. A casino can always change the payback percentage, but in order to do that it must go back to the manufacturer to get a new RNG that is programmed with the new percentage. For this reason, most casinos rarely change their payback percentages unless there is a major revision in their marketing philosophy. And what exactly is a random number generator? Well, it's a little computer chip that is constantly working (as its name implies) to generate number combinations on a random basis. It does this extremely fast and is capable of producing hundreds of combinations each second. When you pull the handle, or push the spin button, the RNG stops and the combination it stops at is used to determine where the reels will stop in the pay window. Unlike video poker machines, you have no way of knowing what a slot machine is programmed to pay back just by looking at it. The only way to tell is by knowing what is programmed into the RNG.

Okay, now let's get back to the "yes" part. Yes, you can win money on slot machines by using a little knowledge, practicing some money management and, mostly, having lots of luck. First, the knowledge part. You need to know what kind of player you are and how much risk you are willing to take. Do you want to go for the giant progressive jackpot that could make you a millionaire in an instant or would you be content walking away just a few dollars ahead?

An example of a wide-area progressive machine is Nevada's Megabucks where the jackpot starts at $7 million. These $1 machines are located at more than 125 Nevada casinos around the state and are linked together by a computer. It's fine if that's the kind of machine you want to play, but keep in mind that the odds are fairly astronomical of you hitting that big jackpot. Also, the payback percentage is lower on these machines than the average $1 machine. During Nevada's fiscal year ending June 30, 2002 Megabucks averaged around 88% payback while the typical $1 machine averaged a little more than 95%. So, be aware that if you play these machines you'll win fewer small payouts and it will be very difficult to leave as a winner. Unless, of course, you hit that big one! If you really like to play the wide-area progressive machines your best bet is probably to set aside a small percentage of your bankroll (maybe 10 to 15 percent) for chasing that big jackpot and saving the rest for the regular machines.

One other thing you should know about playing these wide-area progressives is that on most of them, including Megabucks, you will receive your jackpot in equal payments over a period of years (usually 25). You can avoid this, however, by playing at one of the casinos that link slot machines at their own properties and will pay you in one lump sum. The Circus Bucks slots at Circus Circus casinos in Nevada offer this as well as the Million Dollar Babies at Caesars Palace. There is also a wide-area progressive slot system called Cool Millions which will pay the first one million dollars immediately.

Knowledge also comes into play when deciding how many coins to bet. You should always look at the payback schedule posted on the machine to see if a bonus is payed for playing the maximum number of coins that the machine will accept. For example, if it's a two-coin machine and the jackpot payout is 500 coins when you bet one coin, but it pays you 1,200 coins when you bet two coins, then that machine is paying you a 200-coin bonus for playing the maximum number of coins and you should always bet the maximum two coins to take advantage of that bonus. However, if it's a two-coin machine that will pay you 500 coins for a one-coin bet and 1,000 coins for a two-coin bet, then there is no advantage to making the maximum bet on that machine and you should only bet the minimum amount.

Knowledge of which casinos offer the best payback percentages is also helpful. When available, we print that information in this book to help you decide where to go for the best return on your slot machine dollar. You may want to go to the Las Vegas Strip to see the free pirate show at Treasure Island, but take a look at the slot machine payback percentages for the Strip area casinos in the Las Vegas section and you'll see that you can get better returns for your slot machine dollar by playing at the off-Strip area casinos.

The final bit of knowledge you need concerns slot clubs. Every major casino has a slot club and you should make it a point to join the slot club before you insert your first coin. It doesn't cost anything to join and as a member you will be able to earn complimentaries from the casinos in the form of cash, food, shows, drinks, rooms or other "freebies." When you join the club you'll be issued a card (similar to a credit card) that you insert in the machine before you start to play and it will track how much you bet, as well as how long you play. Naturally, the more money you gamble, the more "freebies" you'll earn. Just make sure you don't get carried away and bet more than you're comfortable with just to earn some extra "comps." Ideally, you want to get "comps" for gambling that you were going to do anyway and not be pressured into betting more than you had planned.

Now let's talk about money management. The first thing you have to remember when playing slot machines is that there is no skill involved. Unlike blackjack or video poker, there are no decisions you can make that will affect whether you win or lose. It is strictly luck, or the lack of it, that will determine whether or not you win. However, when you are lucky enough to get ahead (even if it's just a little) that's where the money management factor comes in. As stated earlier, the longer you stand in front of a machine and put in your money, the more likely you are to go broke. Therefore, there is only one way you can walk away a winner and that's to make sure that when you do win, you don't put it all back in. You really need to set a "win goal" for yourself and to stop when you reach it. A realistic example would be a "win goal" of roughly 25 percent of your bankroll. If you started with $400, then you should stop if you win about $100. The "win goal" you decide on is up to you, but keep in mind that the higher your goal, the harder it will be to reach it, so be practical.

And what if you should happen to reach your goal? Take a break! Go have a meal, see a show, visit the lounge for a drink or even just take a walk around the casino. You may have the urge to keep playing, but if you can just take a break from the machines, even it's just for a short time, you'll have the satisfaction of leaving as a winner. If, later on, you get really bored and find that you just *have* to go back to the machines you can avoid a total loss by not risking more than half of your winnings and by playing on smaller denomination machines. If you made your winnings on $1 machines, move down to quarters. If you won on quarters, move down to nickels. The idea now is basically to kill some time and have a little fun knowing that no matter what happens you'll still leave as a winner.

And now, let's move on to luck. As stated previously, the ultimate decider in whether or not you win is how lucky you are. But, is there anything you can do to help you choose a "winning" machine? Not really, because there is no such thing. Remember, in the long run, no machine will pay out more than it takes in. There are, however, some things you could try to help you find the more generous machines and avoid the stingy ones. Keep in mind that all slot machine payback percentages shown in this book are averages. Some machines are programmed to pay back more and some machines are programmed to pay less. Also, like everything else in life, machines have good cycles where they pay out more than average and bad cycles where they pay out less than average. Ultimately, what you want to find is a high-paying machine in a good cycle. Of course if I knew how to find that machine I wouldn't be writing this story, instead I'd be standing in front of it with a $100 bill in my hand and looking for the change attendant. So, I guess you'll have to settle for my two recommendations as to how you *might* be able to find the better paying machines.

First, is the "accounting" method. With this method you start with a pre-determined number of coins and after playing them you take an accounting of your results. If you have more than you started with you stay at that machine and start another cycle. Just keep doing this until the machine returns less than you started with. As an example, let's say you start with 20 coins. After playing those 20 coins you count how many you got back. If it's more than 20 you start over again with another 20 coins and then do another accounting. If, after any accounting, you get back less than the 20 you started with, stop playing and move on to a different machine. This is an especially good method because you have to slow down your play to take periodic accountings and you will always have an accurate idea of how well you are doing.

The other method is even simpler and requires no math. It's called the "baseball" method and is based on the principle of three strikes and you're out. Just play a machine until it loses three times in a row, then move on to another machine. Both of these methods will prevent you from losing a lot in a machine that is either set for a low payback or is going through a bad cycle; yet both can still allow you to take advantage of a high payback machine or one that is going through a good cycle. Good luck!

The Slot Manager - 2003

by Steve Bourie

As stated in the previous story, the average U.S. casino makes about 65% of its profits from gaming machines but an interesting bit of information is that it didn't used to be that way. In fact, it used to be just the opposite! Table games were the big revenue producers for the casinos and it was usually the men who played those games while their wives were kept busy at the slot machines.

Back in the 40s and early 50s, the old mechanical slots were full of gears and springs and were actually powered by pulling the handle which started the reels spinning. One of the problems with these machines was that they were limited in the size of the jackpots they could offer because they could only accept one coin, plus the hoppers, still relying on those springs and gears, were limited in the number of coins they could pay out.

In the 60s the next generation of slots was introduced: the electromechanical. These machines still had a handle on the outside, but this time when you pulled it you activated an electric switch which started a motor to spin the reels. These machines increased the popularity of slots because they allowed multiple coin play and they also had electrically-powered hoppers that could pay out much larger jackpots.

In the 80s computer controlled slots were introduced. These new machines revolutionized the industry because everything was now controlled by a computer chip. These electronic marvels could offer progressive jackpots that were linked among different machines and it wasn't long before this new computer technology led to the introduction of a new game called video poker.

Today, the technology is so advanced that it allows slot machines that are hundreds of miles apart to be linked together by computer and offer jackpots that start at $10 million (Super Megabucks), or video poker to be played from five different decks at the same time (Five Deck Frenzy).

Although the technology constantly changes, one thing remains the same: the person responsible generally for the operation of the slot department is the slot manager. It is the slot manager who determines how the slot department will be laid out and how much the machines will be set to pay back.

As a slot player, you've probably had a few questions about how a slot department works: How do they decide where to put those slot machines out on the casino floor? Is winning purely luck? Are some machines really set to pay back more than others? And, if so, where do they put those better-paying machines? Well, the person with the answer to those questions would be the slot manager and through the years I've interviewed some who were gracious enough to sit down for an interview to answer questions about how their departments work and what goes into some of their business decisions.

In 1998 I spoke to Rich Marino, Director of Slot Operations at Luxor, the giant pyramid-shaped casino-resort in Las Vegas. Luxor is owned by Mandalay Resort Group, one of the largest gaming companies in the world. Two years later Rich became the director of slot operations at the Mandalay Bay Resort & Casino.

I'd like to address some common beliefs that players have about slot machines and here's the first one: "The casino can flip a switch to make the machines hold more." Or, "the machines are set tighter on the weekends." I've actually heard people say "there's a big convention coming this week and they're going to reset all the slots to make them tighter." Any truth to those kinds of thoughts?

Marino:There is no magic switch. The only time we change a machine is when we convert it to a newer or more popular model. And, of course, when you get a new model, then you would change the e-prom (the computer chip that controls the payback percentage) to that new model. The manufacturer initially sets all the percentages for the machines when ordered. I determine the hold percentages I want by the denomination of the machine. The hold percentage averages for the Las Vegas Strip are 11% for nickels, 6.5% for Quarters, 4.5% for dollars, and 3.5% for five dollars and above.

Also, gaming-wise to do that, it's not just going in and changing a chip. You have to go in and you actually have to take all of the money out of the machine. It's got to be returned to the cashier's cage, that money has to be counted and you have to assign a new number to that machine because that's a new machine once you change the e-prom. So, gaming regulations require you to change the statistics on the whole new machine. It's a whole day process to do that. It's not just to go in and change the chip and leave and say "okay, I've tightened them up for the weekend."

How about "the best paying machines are on the aisles?"

Marino:Not true. The best machines are on the aisle? I'll tell you what, that's a perception people have because most of them like to play machines on the aisle. They'll walk up and play the machines on the end because they don't want to play with somebody next to them. If you've got a guy playing here, here, and here, you're not going to go right next to that guy. You're going to go to the end so there's nobody next to you. That's why we've gone to these round configurations. People don't like sitting next to each other. So, we're going more and more to the round ones because people really like that a lot and these games do a lot better than the normal straight rows of slot machines. That's why I try to break them up with rounds down the middle and slants.

But as far as the tighter and the looser machines, I set them up by model types. I mean, if I have a bank of quarter machines, I'll have a Double Diamond; a Red, White and Blue; and my percentages on those quarter machines are all the same. So, it doesn't matter which machine I put where.

Then you wouldn't have a situation where a high-paying machine would be sitting next to a low-paying machine?

Marino:No. If the machines were the same denomination on a particular bank the hold percentages would be virtually the same. In my dollar machines I order everything at between 4% and 5%. So, you're talking the difference between one percentage point and that's only because certain models are only available at certain percentages. I mean, I would never put an 8% dollar machine next to one at 4%. I don't do that here. Some places might do that, I don't know. I try to give everybody an equal shot no matter what.

So, there would be very little difference between a high machine and a low machine?

Marino:If I was going to set it up that way I would put the loosest machine in the middle as opposed to the end because they get the most play. That's why it appears to be looser to the customer because it gets more play and more action and more people are playing it and it cycles more. And, it gets into those better cycles more often.

Do machines get 'hot' and pay out more frequently?

Marino:Sure they get hot, they also get cold. Through the cycle of a machine it's percentaged to pay out a certain amount over a period of time based on the number of handle pulls the machine receives. However, the hot and cold cycles are random and indeterminable.

It's my understanding that when you order a slot machine you have to tell the manufacturer what you want it to pay and each manufacturer tells you the pre-approved percentages you can choose from?

Marino:That's correct. (goes to shelf, pulls down a book and opens it to a page). This book contains all the available hold percentages for these particular models and the denomination of a machine is what determines the hold percentage I would order for it.

This is what I order quarter machines at - 92.4% - which would be right around 7.5% holding for the house. If it's dollars, I order this one (around 95%) and for twenty-fives (around 97%) or hundreds (around 98%), it goes up, like that. If it's nickels, you start down here (around 89%). That's the way it works.

Now, over a period of time, this quarter machine is going to pay back 92.42% and it's going to hold around 7.5% for the house. And when I say over a period of time, that means over 10 million handle pulls.

10 million is the life cycle? On every machine?

Marino: 10 million is the numbers of handle pulls the manufacturer has determined it would take a particular machine to achieve that 7.5% hold calculation. Getting to that number though, may take a year. That means in January, that machine might be hot, or today it may be hot. So, I may be holding...it's a volatility index they call it...for the first two months of the cycle when that machine goes out on the floor, I may be in the negative. I may be paying out 400% or 500% on that game. But, the next month it may be tighter and at the end of that cycle, it's going to hold at 8%.

Rich's answers were surprisingly candid and they certainly laid to rest some long-standing beliefs among slot players as to how slots are set up in a casino. For years slot players have always believed that some machines were set much higher than others within a casino. Rich dispelled this myth by pointing out that all of his machines within a particular denomination were set to pay back approximately the same amount. He pointed out that not all manufacturers offer the exact same percentages in their computer chips so there could be a difference of as high as 1% but you really won't find a situation where one quarter machine that's set to return 92% would be sitting next to another quarter machine set to return 82%.

If you look at the numbers from the Nevada Gaming Control Board regarding the returns on slot machines that are shown in this book it certainly corroborates what Rich was saying. After all, if the average $1 machine returns 95% how much of a difference could there be between the high and the low? Do you think half of the $1 machines are set at 99% and the other half are set at 91% in order to get that 95% average? Sorry, but it just doesn't work that way. Yes, there are differences among machines but, once again, the amount is minimal and it probably amounts to no more than 1%.

And what about the common belief that machines at the end of an aisle are set to return the most? Well, Rich killed that idea too. He explained that it just seems that end machines pay out more often simply because they're played more often.

This is similar to the "bad player" theory in blackjack where, if there's a bad player at the blackjack table who constantly makes poor decisions it will somehow affect the order of the cards and cause the good players (who make correct playing decision) to lose more often. The truth is that the bad player really has no affect on the game because sometimes his decisions will hurt you and sometimes his decisions will help you. The problem is that you only tend to remember the situations where you lost because of his poor play and you forget the times that you won because of his boneheaded moves.

This same theory can apply to slot machines at the end of an aisle. When you're playing in a casino, or just walking through, you'll only remember the times you saw people winning at machines, not losing. Since the end-of-the-aisle machines get more play, they will, of course, have more winners and people will tend to remember them as the better paying machines.

As far as constantly changing percentages on the chips to make machines "looser" or "tighter" Rich pointed out that it's not quite that simple and that changes are rarely made because of all the extra work that's involved.

In the July 1998 issue of *Las Vegas Advisor* this same subject was covered in an interview with three different Las Vegas casino slot managers and two officials from the Nevada Gaming Control Board. The *Advisor* writer discovered that there actually are some slots where the percentages can be changed by flipping a switch, but it only applies to machines that are connected together in a "bank" where they all share the same centralized chip. The vast majority of the machines in a casino, however, are not capable of this function as they each have their own internal chip.

The *Advisor* story also went on to point out that Nevada law requires casinos to do paperwork whenever a chip is changed and it must be completed within 24 hours. Also, the casino must complete additional accounting paperwork for filing with the state. Evidently, the process is so time-consuming the story concluded that "no one we talked to even had a secondhand story of a Nevada casino that frequently changes chips."

Of course, Nevada is just one gaming jurisdiction in the U.S. and not every casino is going to work in the exact same manner. Or, will it? To get some perspective on how it's done in a different market in 2002 I traveled to Atlantic City and interviewed Tom Reale, Director of Slot Operations at the Sands.

Can you explain the procedure for when you order a slot machine?

Reale: All the manufacturers provide a range of payout percentages on any particular slot machine. It's up to the operator to pick and choose the payout percentage for a machine. The manufacturers will generally provide a range payouts from 83% up to 99%. The issue with slot machines from a player's perspective is that I could have identical machines side-by-side with the same paytable and one could be set for 83% while the other one could be 99% and nobody will know the difference until we identify the particular program in each machine.

How do you decide which machines are going to pay 83% and which ones are going to pay 99%?

Reale: I guess I should start off by saying that there is nothing in this property that is set to pay 83%. Probably the tightest game we offer now is 88% to 89% and on the high end we have a couple of video poker machines out there that are holding less than 1%. Pick'em Poker for example is a machine where we only make about nine-tenths of one percent.

But as far as slot machines are concerned I guess you would follow the industry standard where the lower the denomination, the less the machine is set to pay back? Meaning the nickel machines would return around 88%-89%?

Reale: Yes; then on our 25¢ machines it's around 92%; $1 machines around 93%; $5 machines around 95%; and $25 or $100 machines around 97.5%

Do you have some machines within a particular denomination set to pay back more than others? For example, since quarter machines are the most popular, are all of them set to pay back about 92%? Or, are some set at 88% and some set at 96% so that they average out at 92%?

Reale: We do have some, about three dozen, that are set to pay over 98%, however, these machines are only located in one particular area and are clearly marked as an advertisement. On the other hand, we do have some quarter machines that are 89% and they can be found in different places throughout the casino.

So there is a definite variance in how the machines are set?

We try to keep them all within a very close range. Out of the 550 25¢ standard reel-slots we have I would say 90% of those would have to be in the 91% range. Of the remaining machines some could be as low as 89% and some as high as 93%

How about $1 machines?

Reale: On standard three-reel $1 slots we probably don't have anything tighter than 92% and most of them are 93% to 95%. On $1 multi-coin, multi-line video games where you can play up to $45 a pull, and we have a couple of dozen of them, they are all 95% or looser.

What about nickel machines? I know that traditionally, nickel machines were always set to pay the least in a casino. However, now that some multi-coin, multi-line nickel video games will allow you to bet several dollars per pull I'm wondering if that's still true? Have nickel machines loosened up?

Reale: By far. Probably the tightest nickel machines we have on the floor are five-coin reel slots that return around 88%. With the 45 and 90-coin nickel games we have them set around 92% because they're really not nickel games when someone can bet a few dollars on one pull. It's interesting because we just did some reseach on this issue and found that we have some quarter 98%

90-coin video games out there where the average bet per game is $5.17 while on regular three-coin quarter games the average bet is about 67¢ per game.

Based on what you said about nickel machines then wouldn't it make sense for a nickel player to avoid the regular three-line machines and just play three lines on a multi-coin, multi-line video game because they're probably programmed to payback a higher percentage?

Reale: Absolutely.

Then I guess I can come to the conclusion that for anyone who has the choice of playing a traditional three-line machine or a multi-coin, multi-line video game they're probably better off going to the multi game because it's set to payback more, even though they're only playing three lines at a time?

Reale: That's what I tell my relatives, so I think you're right about that.

Let's address the most prevalent rumor that many people have heard about slot machines in casinos and that is: the best machines are always located on the aisle, near the exit doors, etc. Is there any truth to that in your casino? After all, you've already said that some of your machines are set to pay slightly more than other machines within the same denomination so when deciding where to put those better-paying machines on the floor in your casino is there some particular rule you follow?

Reale: We haven't done that here. We have tried many different things over the years and we've actually had two machines sitting side-by-side at both extremes of the payscale (one at the highest and one at the lowest) to see, performance-wise, which would do better and in some cases the looser game did better and in other cases the tighter game did better. But we have found that, in general, the looser the percentage, the more play that game will get. The coin-in increases and in most cases the win seems to go along with that.

So you wouldn't have any particular policy about putting your better-paying machines in a specific location?

Reale: We do have a couple of carousels in looser percentages that we have positioned purposely in high-traffic areas.

Are they marked as high-paying machines?

Reale: No. They aren't marked because they're not extremely loose which would be 97% or looser. These are loose for their particular denomination. They're quarter machines in the 93% to 94% range. So, to get back to your original question, we do have a couple of carousels in high-traffic areas but we don't have all the entrances and high-traffic areas covered.

So there could be some higher-paying machines located just about any-where?

Reale: Yes. There are some buried in with all of the other other machines.

Any words of advice for slot players?

Reale: I would just say that in order to appreciate the fastest cycle of any particular slot machine players should always look for a machine that has the lowest top jackpot. For example, let's say you have two machines side-by-side and one machine offers a 600-coin jackpot as the top award and the other machine offers a 6,000-coin jackpot as the top award. Well, you're going to appreciate the payout percentage of the machine with the lower jackpot because it will cycle faster. You have to realize that the odds of hitting the 6,000-coin jackpot are a lot greater than the 600-coin jackpot, so you should always play the machine with the lower top jackpot for your own benefit. That doesn't mean that you can't walk up to a machine and hit a million-dollar jackpot because people do hit them but the odds of hitting a lower jackpot are much, much better simply because they cycle faster.

The talk with Tom confirmed that there really isn't much difference between Las Vegas and Atlantic City as far as how frequently slot machine payback percentages are changed. Basically, they aren't. Once they're set, they stay that way because it's just too much trouble to keep changing it.

Actually, it's an even bigger problem to change payback percentages in New Jersey because casinos in that state aren't allowed to go into a machine and change a chip on their own. They must first notify the state's regulators that they want to make the change and then an Electronics Specialist from the Division of Gaming Enforcement must be present to supervise the changing of the chip. Gaming regulations aren't quite that strict in Nevada where casinos are free to change the chips on their own. However, even though Nevada casinos don't have to notify the state before changing a chip, they are required to make sure they only use a chip that has been previously approved by the state and they're also required to complete paperwork notifying regulators of the change.

And what have we learned from all of this? Well, besides seeing that casinos don't constantly change the paybacks on their machines so they can increase their winnings at a moments notice, hopefully, we've also learned that casinos are a business and the decision as to what the payback percentage on their slot machines should be is simply a function of that machine's cost to the casino.

If you think about it, most slot machines take up about the same amount of space and all of them probably require the same amount of electricity and routine maintenance. Now, if the operating costs are basically the same, then it only makes sense that a casino needs to take more out of a nickel machine, percentagewise, than a quarter machine in order to cover its costs. As an example, casinos know they need to keep 11% on a nickel machine because the profit on a five-coin pull is only about 3¢ (25¢ x .11), whereas a quarter machine can be set to keep only 8% because the profit on a three-coin play on that machine is 6¢ (75¢ x .08).

So, if you're looking for a better return from a slot machine it seems that the best thing you can do is play a higher denomination machine (assuming you can afford it). Just remember that nickel machines return the least, $100 machines return the most and plan your gambling budget accordingly.

An Interview With IGT

by Steve Bourie

On January 24, 2001 I took a tour of International Game Technology's headquarters in Reno, Nevada. IGT is the world's largest manufacturer of slot machines and the tour was arranged by IGT's Public Relations Manager, Rick Sorensen.

While it was interesting to tour the huge one million square-foot facility, the best part was saved for last when I got to sit down with one of IGT's chief software engineers to ask questions about the inner workings of their games.

The company was originally founded as A-1 Supply, Inc. in 1952 by Si Redd, who later went on to invent the video poker machine. The company went public as IGT in 1981 and it currently controls about 70% of the gaming machine market. IGT had revenues of slightly more than $1 billion in 2000, has offices in major gaming centers throughout the world and employs more than 3,600 people.

All of IGT's machines are produced at its Reno plant (except for some pachisuro machines in Japan) and Sorensen explained that IGT had moved to this new facility just three years earlier because previously, due to its tremendous business growth, the company had been forced to spread itself out among 17 different buildings in Reno.

Evidently, IGT plans on continuing that pace as it constantly brings out new machines. "We used to come out with about 25 new slot games and maybe two new video poker games a year," says Sorensen. "But since Joe Kaminkow, our Vice President of Engineering and Design, came on board we had about 40 new games last year and this year it was about 68." The company produced 107,000 machines in 2000 and currently turns out approximately 400 machines per day on its assembly line.

When it comes to new types of slot machines the entire process, from conception to finished product, can take up to one year. "The first step is to decide on the theme that you want and to brainstorm what the symbols are going to be and what the bonus round is going to be like," say Sorensen. "The engineers then go to work on that and come up with the computer programs that are going to propel the machine. The artwork glass is simultaneously designed and when we finally get all of the design elements together, then we put together a prototype machine."

Of course, not all of IGT's new games are successful. "I'm not sure what the success rate is but we're doing a lot better than we used to," says Sorensen.

"When we came out with 25 new games maybe 8 to 10 of those would do real well. But we do testing in casinos before they ever get out to the general public. We will test them at specific casinos sites and see if the earnings are matching what the best games are doing. If they're not, then we have to go back to the drawing board."

If he had to guess at the success rate, Sorensen believes "it's better than half of the machines" and if things don't go well they can always bring back a machine for further refinements. "Not very often will we let a game theme just go," he says. "Once in awhile we have something that simply isn't going to work for us but usually, with a little bit of changing and a little bit of tweaking, we can get it where we want it to be."

After our tour of the plant I met James Vasquez, IGT's Firmware Engineering Manager, for my interview. Jim explained that there are more than 200 people in the Firmware Engineering Department and he only oversees the people that program IGT's video games, such as the Game Kings. The reel-spinning games are done by another manager in Firmware Engineering.

What's your background?

Vasquez: I have a bachelor's degree in electrical engineering from the University of Nevada at Reno. I started working at IGT eight years ago in the reel-spinning slot group, did S-Plus games for two or three years, then I was the lead guy in the Vision Slots firmware team.

Vision Slots are Double Diamond, Cherry Pie, Racing 7's, Temperature's Rising, etc?

Vasquez: Yes. I was in charge of the spinning reel portion of that firmware design and then I switched over to the I-Game which includes: Game King Poker, Triple Play, Five Play, Ten Play, Fifty Play. All of those games come from my group.

Is there a difference between programming a reel-spinning slot and a video slot?

Vasquez: I would say the more significant difference is between our older 8032-based products, meaning the S-plus product line and our newer product lines: the Vision Series, S-2000 and Game King video.

From a programming standpoint is whether or not you're programming on our 8032 microprocessor. It's just an older technology. Our newer product lines are all based on the I-960 processor series. It's still an Intel chip but its a 32-bit chip and it's faster. The architecture is different and the programming is done in a higher level programming language

The machine assembly line at IGT's world headquarters in Reno, Nevada.

In the old days when you had a mechanical slot with three reels I understand that someone could calculate the odds of winning if they knew how many times each symbol appeared on a reel. Can you explain the difference between that old system and the current "virtual reel" technology?

Vasquez: Have you read the Telnaes patent? That is the main patent that IGT has covering that technology. That's the one that was the center of the lawsuit that was public between us and Williams. That patent, in and of itself, will give you a lot of explanation on how it works.

I guess there wasn't a simple answer to this question so, following Jim's advice, a few weeks after our interview I did some research on the Telnaes patent, as well as the IGT versus Williams lawsuit.

U.S. patent #4,448,419 was issued May 15, 1984 to Inge S. Telanaes of Reno, Nevada. The patent is for "a gaming machine of the type utilizing rotating reels which carry on the periphery a plurality of indicia, a brake to stop the reels at a selected position and a random number generator for selecting the reel-stopping position. Numbers are assigned to the reel-stopping positions and entered into the random number generator with each number being entered one or more times to control the payout odds of each particular stopping position being selected, thereby enabling any odds to be set without changing the physical characteristics of the machine."

The patent later goes on goes on to state: " it is the purpose of this invention to increase the capability of the designer to include high payoffs without increased physical size of the machine...it should be noted that players perceive larger machines as being less 'good' in terms of winning and payout chances... thus, it is important to make a machine that is perceived to present greater chances of payoff than it actually has within the legal limitations."

The Telnaes invention was revolutionary because it solved a major problem in allowing slot machines to offer big jackpots. Previously, slot machine jackpots were limited by two factors: the number of reels and the number of stops on each of those reels. Thus, if you had a three-reel machine with 28 stops on each reel the maximum number of combinations possible on that machine was 21,952 (28 x 28 x 28 = 21,952). The only way to offer a larger jackpot was either to add more reels or more stops on each reel. If you added one more reel to our example it would bring the maximum number of combinations up to 614,656 (28 x 28 x 28 x 28 = 614,656). Add another reel and it rises to 17,210,368 (28 x 28 x 28 x 28 x 28 = 17,210,368). As you can see, it was actually possible to award very large jackpots back then but in order to do it you would have to keep adding reels (or stops) to the machines and, as noted in the patent wording, players were hesitant to play on machines with too many reels. Additionally, it required additional labor on the machines to add more reels.

With the Telnaes invention it no longer mattered how many "physical" stops were on a reel. Instead, each machine had "virtual" reels and the slot manufacturer could simply program a computer chip with the number of stops it wanted on each reel. Keep in mind though that IGT's Telnaes patent only applied to slot machines with physical reels and not to slots with video reels. Slot manufacturers using video reels were free to program in as many stops as they wanted because they weren't limited by the physical size of the reels. The problem with video reel slots, however, was that they weren't popular with slot players. The overwhelming majority of players wanted to see spinning reels and that proved to be a bonanza for IGT.

By controlling the Telnaes patent IGT was the only manufacturer that could offer huge jackpots on reel-spinning machines and they began to dominate the slot industry. In 1986 they introduced Megabucks which was the first slot machine to offer progressive jackpots starting in the millions of dollars.

In 1993 WMS Gaming (Williams) introduced its Model 400, a reel-spinning slot machine that, similar to Telnaes' invention, manipulated the odds of winning rather than relying on the physical number of stops on each reel. According to court documents, WMS claimed to effect that manipulation by use of a different method which they claimed was covered under their own Durham patent. According to WMS, their Durham patent used "a different approach to calculating payoffs than the Telnaes patent. In the Telnaes patent, the stop positions of the reels are determined first and then the payoff is calculated based on the stop positions. In the Durham patent, the payoff is calculated first and then the stop positions that represent that payoff are chosen." Not surprisingly, IGT thought otherwise and brought a patent infringement suit against WMS early the following year.

In 1996 a federal judge ruled in IGT's favor and they were awarded $10.75 million in actual damages, which was tripled to $32.25 million because the court believed that WMS had willfully violated IGT's patent. WMS appealed the decision but agreed in December 1999 to pay $28.67 million to IGT to settle the suit.

IGT does currently license its Telnaes patent to other slot manufacturers but only for reel stops up to a limited number. This way IGT is still the only manufacturer able to offer multimillion dollar jackpots on reel-spinning machines such as Megabucks. The Telnaes patent will expire in February 2002.

Is there a minimum number of stops you program onto a reel?

Vasquez: We have different games with all different numbers of stops. Some have 64 stops, 128 stops, 256 stops, 70 stops, whatever we need to do to get the payback percentage, or hold percentage, dialed in to what the casino is asking for.

You adjust the number of winning and losing combinations?

Vasquez: We adjust the probability of any symbol showing up on a per reel basis. We never look at games as a combination. I am not going to tell you that I am going to pick this combination and display this combination. Instead, I am going to tell you that this blue 7 has these odds on this reel. When you see 22 stops on a reel, each stop has a certain probability of coming up. Even though physically you see 22 stops, each stop with virtual reel technology has its own probability of landing on the payline. The combination is just the sum of the three stops. We don't dial in combinations per se that's just done by figuring out the red 7 has a 1-in-30 chance, the blue 7 has a 1-in-30 chance and the white 7 has a 1-in-30 chance.

So even though you have a reel with 22 stops on it each symbol doesn't necessarily have a 1-in-22 chance of showing up?

Vasquez: That's what virtual reels are all about. Otherwise you could never pay a $10,000 coin award.

Is there a minimum number of stops on each reel?

Vasquez: The minimum number of stops would be 22 and it would go up from there.

Is there a maximum of stops?

The maximum number is programming limitations. Whatever the code is designed to handle. It does vary from game to game.

Can you give a brief explanation of how the RNG works?

With a random number generator you are always calling numbers and discarding numbers until player interaction occurs and then you actually use the numbers instead of discarding them.

At what point does the player interaction occur and the random number generator actually stop?

The program will pull the number from the random number generator when the game is started by pushing the deal/spin button or by pressing max bet.

On a linked progressive system like Megabucks what happens when someone hits the big jackpot? Does the machine automatically lockup?

A signal is sent to the control room to reset the meters everywhere and the winning machine meter stays locked up to the amount that was won on it. There is a lag time because the state is all linked together, so from the time the machine hits to the time it actually gets to every machine to reset their meters is probably in the order of under a minute.

I have a question on Wheel of Fortune machines where you have to push a second button in order to determine your bonus. Is the amount of that bonus predetermined, or does it really matter when you push that second button?

Yes it matters. We don't lock in the stops for the bonus wheel until you push the second button and then we pull the number. We don't try to pull numbers all at once. Even from a poker game standpoint between the two pushes on your deal and your draw there are two separate calls to the random number generator.

In some other bonus games, such as Party Time, the player is given a screen with multiple choices that allow them to keep adding to their bonus until they choose a losing symbol. On those games is that bonus predetermined or not?

Its not predetermined. It's pure luck whether you choose a winning or losing box on the screen and how much you win.

Are there any of your machines that have a bonusing feature that's pre-determined ahead of time?

I believe there are none. I couldn't give you a 100% guarantee on all IGT games because I wasn't here for every single one. There may be a game that was done years ago that I wasn't involved with that may do it differently. Our philosophy is, "look we're showing you, the player, at the end what you could have won and we are not lying to you. That is really what you could have won. We want the player to feel that really is what you could have won if you did it just right."

I see that you have a new game of checkers coming out. Is that completely based on skill? And if so, do you see the future of the machines moving more into the field of skill games?

There will definitely always be a market for skill games. The skill games that we make now are still mainly card games. Checkers will be one of the first skill games in quite a while that doesn't have anything to do with cards. The "gotcha" with the skill games is that we still have to decide what the field of return is going to be on these checker games - we have an idea and we expect it to be similar to poker, we have held tournaments, and stuff so we have an idea.

Let's talk about the difference between video poker and slot machines. It's my understanding that with video poker you can't control the number of winning and losing combinations programmed into the computer chip, instead its based on a 52-card deck with a fixed number of combinations. Is that correct?

Vasquez: Yes, assuming there are no wild cards. There are some games coming out that will use four decks but it will tell you that it uses four decks. That will be a specialty game but every standard poker game uses one deck.

When the cards are dealt is it done on a serial basis where it's similar to cards coming off the top of a deck? Or, parallel where there are five cards dealt face up and one card is unseen underneath each of the initial five cards?

Vasquez: It's serial and the five later cards aren't determined until there is more player interaction at the time of the draw.

They aren't determined at the time of the deal?

Vasquez: No. They're determined at the time of the draw. That varies with the jurisdictional regulation actually. Some lottery jurisdictions tell you that you have to draw all 10 at once. Different jurisdictions write into their rules how they want it done, specifically on poker, because it's a simpler game and they understand it. They say they either want all 10 done at once, or however they want.

How is it done in Nevada? All ten at once, or five and five?

Vasquez: In Nevada it's five and five.

How do you determine the payback percentage on a video poker machine?

Vasquez: We have our own optimizer that says what we think perfect strategy will return on the game and we expect a two to four percent dip on how people will actually play the machine. We put two numbers on our parameter sheet and that is typically the standard. When we give the game to the casino we say this is what the absolute maximum is, per our optimization, and this is what we expect the field of return to be: somewhere between two and four percent lower than that. That two to four percent is a guess.

And some games can actually return more than 100%?

Vasquez: Yes. But that's a jurisdictional regulation. Nevada doesn't regulate over 100% payback percentage. Most other states don't allow an optimal 100% payback.

If someone had an idea for a game could they submit it to IGT?

Vasquez: Oh yeah.

What would be the procedure for that?

Vasquez: There are several different ways. They can get in touch with Joe Kaminkow, our Vice President of Cool Games, or they could also submit it through our website at www.igt.com. We get stuff through the site all the time and usually I send them on to Bob Bittman in engineering who is Joe's boss.

Have you ever accepted an idea from someone outside the company?

Vasquez: Triple Play Video Poker from Action Gaming. That idea came from outside of IGT and was brought to us. He had his own patent on that game concept.

It sounds like that idea came from a big company. Have you ever accepted an idea from an individual?

Vasquez: That was how Action Gaming started. A guy named Ernie Moody who, I think, was a casino operator in Colorado, had these ideas and he kept going back to the drawing board and he came up with Triple Play Poker. He sent it to us and we said 'whoa, you're onto something here.' That's evolved into his own company. He comes up with his own ideas and we come up with the hardware and software for it. So, it does happen!

Shortly after my visit I was able to get some statistics from IGT on the percentages that some of their slot machines are set to payback to players. The following list shows those machines and the range of percentages that can be programmed into the random number generator on each machine. Keep in mind that casinos generally set their slot paybacks based on each machine's denomination. Therefore, nickel machines will probably be set towards the lower number and $5-$25 machines will be set towards the higher number.

Red White and Blue	85.03% - 97.45%
Texas Tea	87.00% - 97.00%
Addams Family	92.50% - 93.50%
I Dream of Jeannie	86.01% - 96.97%
Austin Powers	88.00% - 98.00%
Tabasco	85.00% - 98.03%
The Munsters	85.00% - 98.00%
Creature From The Black Lagoon	88.00% - 98.00%
Triple Lucky 7's	83.94% - 98.02%
Pink Panther	88.00% - 95.00%
Neon Nights	87.53% - 98.03%
Cleopatra	87.00% - 97.00%
Catch A Wave	85.02% - 98.03%
My Rich Uncle	85.00% - 98.00%

IGT has a website at www.igt.com that contains a wealth of information about the company. Visitors to that site can obtain information on most of the company's products and also access a list of current MegaJackpot totals for machines in 18 states, plus Iceland (if the jackpot gets high enough you might want to pack up the bags and head over there!). All major IGT games are listed: Megabucks, Wheel of Fortune, Elvis, Quartermania, Fabulous Fifties, Slotopoly, Quarters Deluxe and some others. The company also has a toll-free number (888-448-2946) for current information on MegaJackpot totals for machines in Nevada only.

If you're going to be in Reno and would like to take a tour of IGT's headquarters you would need to make advance arrangements by calling (775-448-7777) and asking for George Terry in the facilities department. According to Sorensen "we don't do a lot of individual tours but, time permitting, we would try to accommodate them."

Slot Tournaments

by Steve Bourie

Slot tournaments are special contests arranged by casinos where participants who get the highest scores on slot machines within an allotted amount of time, or credits, are awarded cash or prizes. Some slot tournaments are offered free of charge but most require an entry fee.

Virtually every casino today offers slot tournaments and they're used by each casino's marketing department as a promotional tool to generate more business for the casino. An interesting thing about slot tournaments is that they aren't necessarily designed as money-making events for the casino.

Some casinos will give back all of the entry fees in the form of prizes and some won't. Those casinos that give back all of the money are happy to have the tournament's contestants in their hotel rooms and playing in their casino. The thinking at these casinos is that the tournament is generating extra business and they don't have to make money off the tournament itself. These are the best kinds of tournaments to play in but they aren't always easy to find. In other instances the casinos look at tournaments strictly as a money-making venture and they'll keep part of the entry fees for themselves. In either case, tournaments can sometimes provide extra value to you and they are occasionally worth looking into.

Each month *Las Vegas Advisor* gives information on upcoming tournaments in that city and many gaming magazines do the same for all of the major casinos throughout the country. These publications don't list much more than the required entry fee so you'll have to call each casino for more information on the specifics. You can probably get that information over the phone but it's best to ask for a brochure to be mailed to you. This way, you'll have an official written record of the tournament rules and regulations.

When looking at the prize structure of the tournament be sure to add up the total cash value of all the prizes and compare it to the total amount of money the casino will be getting in entry fees. For instance, if the entry fee is $200 and they're limiting the tournament to 200 entrants then the casino is generating $40,000 in entry fees. Are they offering that much in cash prizes? If so, then it's a good tournament. If they're only offering $25,000 in cash, then the casino is keeping $15,000 and you may want to shop around for a different tournament that offers you more "equity." By equity we mean the value you'll be receiving in relation to the cost to enter. Positive equity means the casino is giving back more in cash and benefits than it's charging to enter the tournament. Negative equity means just the opposite: the casino is charging more than it's giving back in cash and benefits. You should always try to find a positive equity tournament.

Another thing you'll need to add into the equation when considering your equity are the extra "freebies," or discounts, that the casino will add to the package. Most casinos will host a welcoming party for the contestants, plus a free lunch or dinner and an awards banquet at the end when the winners are announced. Generally, all casinos will also offer a discounted room rate to tournament participants and some will even throw in a surprise gift for everyone. If you don't need a room then that benefit won't add anything to the value you'll be receiving but for some players a discounted room rate could mean the difference between a positive and negative equity situation. Each tournament is different and you should be sure to add up the total of all the benefits you'll receive when deciding which tournament you want to enter.

One more thing to keep in mind when looking at a tournament's structure is how the prizes are distributed. If too much is given to the top finishers that leaves less to be distributed among the other contestants. The chances are pretty good that you're not going to win one of the top prizes so it will help if the lower-tier prizes are worthwhile.

One last thing to remember about tournaments is that in many of them it pays to enter early. Most tournaments offer an "early-bird" discount if you enter by a certain date and the entry fee rises after that date. The discount can be as high as 25 percent and, once again, the reduced rate could make the difference between a positive and a negative equity situation.

Once you've found the tournament that offers you the most equity you'll need a strategy for winning. What's the best strategy? Get lucky! Slot tournaments are pure luck and there really isn't anything you can do to help you win. So, just keep pushing that spin button and hope for a good score!

Personally, I only like to play games of skill (like blackjack and video poker) so I usually don't play in slot tournaments. There was, however, one instance where I played in a tournament because of the value it offered. A few years ago my friend Marvin and I were planning a trip to Las Vegas to attend the World Gaming Congress and Expo at the city's main convention center. This event is held each year and it's the world's largest trade show for the casino industry. The event took place during the middle of the week but we also wanted to stay over for the weekend. Unfortunately, the room rates are much higher on weekends and the hotels usually don't discount their rates very much on those days. After calling around to check rates we decided to look in the *Las Vegas Advisor* to find out about slot tournaments.

Boulder Station was having its *All Treats, No Tricks* slot tournament that same weekend. The entry fee was $199 but by entering before a certain date, the fee was reduced to $149 and there was a total of $40,000 in prize money up for grabs. The rules required 268 entrants, or else the total prize money could be reduced, but based on that required number the casino would be receiving $39,932 in prize money (assuming all early entrants) and awarding $40,000 in prize money which made this a slightly positive equity situation. Additionally, everyone received a t-shirt, a welcoming cocktail party, lunch at the *Pasta Palace,* an awards celebration and a reduced room rate of $25 for Friday and Saturday evening.

We had stayed at Boulder Station before and we both liked the property very much. We called the hotel's reservation department and they told us it would be $99 per night on Friday and Saturday. That was $198 for the two nights, plus 9% tax, for a total of $215.82 By entering the slot tournament our cost would be $149, plus $50 for the room for two nights, plus 9% tax (only on the room), for a total of $203.50 Hey, you want to talk about positive equity? This thing was great! Not only were they giving back all of the prize money, but in this case it was actually cheaper to enter the slot tournament than to get the room by itself!

The rules allowed us to enter as a team for the $149 fee and that also got us into the activities together. At the welcoming party we had an unlimited choice of alcoholic beverages or sodas, plus a large selection of finger sandwiches and other snacks. The *Pasta Palace* is a good restaurant and we had a great lunch there.

We weren't very lucky in the tournament and didn't finish high in the standings. Actually, we received the lowest cash prize which was $40. That brought our actual cost for the room and the tournament down to $163.50 which was still $52 cheaper than just getting the room by itself. Plus, we got the t-shirt, welcoming party and lunch as an added bonus.

As you can see, we saved some money by entering the slot tournament and we also had a lot of fun. You can do the same thing by checking out some of the tournaments that are available the next time you're planning a trip to a casino. Just use the toll-free numbers in this book to call the casino marketing departments, or pick up the latest issue of *Las Vegas Advisor,* or a general gaming magazine, for information on current tournaments.

Video Poker

by Steve Bourie

Okay, who knows the main difference between video poker and slot machines? C'mon now, raise your hands if you think you know it. If you said "a slot machine is a game of luck and video poker is a game of skill" then you are correct! When you play a slot machine there is no decision you can make which will affect the outcome of the game. You put in your money; pull the handle; and hope for the best. In video poker, however, it is your skill in playing the cards which definitely affects the outcome of the game.

Okay, who knows the other major difference between video poker and slot machines? Well, you're right again if you said "you never know what percentage a slot machine is set to pay back, but you can tell a video poker machine's payback percentage just by looking at it." Of course if you knew that answer then you also knew that video poker machines almost always offer you better returns than slot machines (provided you make the right playing decisions).

Now for those of you who didn't know the answers to those two questions, please read on. You others can skip the rest of this story as I am sure you're eager to get back to your favorite video poker machine.

First, let's cover the basics. Video poker has virtually the same rules as a game of five card draw poker. The only difference is that you have no opponent to beat and you can't lose more than your initial bet. First, you deposit from one to five coins in the machine to make your bet. You are then shown five cards on the video screen and your goal is to try to make the best poker hand possible from those cards. Since it is a draw game, you are given one opportunity to improve your hand. This is done by allowing you to discard from one, up to all five cards from your original hand. Of course, you don't have to discard any if you don't want to. After choosing which cards you want to keep (by pushing the button below each card), you then push the deal button and the machine will replace all of the other cards with new cards. Based on the resulting final hand the machine will then pay you according to the pay schedule posted on the machine. Naturally, the better your hand, the higher the amount the machine will pay you back.

That's pretty much how a video poker machine works from the outside, but what about the inside? Well, I had a few questions about that so I visited International Game Technology, which is the world's largest manufacturer of video poker machines (as well as slot machines), in January 2001 and spoke to their chief software engineer, James Vasquez. The full story story is in the slot machine section of this book, so I'll just refer here to some video poker questions which I asked.

Let's talk about the difference between video poker and slot machines. It's my understanding that with video poker you can't control the number of winning and losing combinations programmed into the computer chip, instead its based on a 52-card deck with a fixed number of combinations. Is that correct?

Vasquez: Yes, assuming there are no wild cards.

When the cards are dealt is it done on a serial basis where it's similar to cards coming off the top of a deck? Or, parallel where there are five cards dealt face up and one card is unseen underneath each of the initial five cards?

Vasquez: It's serial and the five later cards aren't determined until there is more player interaction at the time of the draw.

They aren't determined at the time of the deal?

Vasquez: No. They're determined at the time of the draw. That varies with the jurisdictional regulation actually. Some lottery jurisdictions tell you that you have to draw all 10 at once. Different jurisdictions write into their rules how they want it done, specifically on poker, because it's a simpler game and they understand it. They say they either want all 10 done at once, or however they want.

How is it done in Nevada? All ten at once, or five and five?

IGT: In Nevada it's five and five.

The talk with Jim Vasquez confirmed that in most regulated jurisdictions video poker machines use a Random Number Generator to shuffle a 52-card deck and then choose five cards to display to the player. (By the way, when played without wild cards, there are exactly 2,598,960 unique five-card poker hands possible.) Then, when the deal button is pushed, the next group of cards is chosen and dealt to the player.

One point must be made here regarding random outcomes in video poker machines. Please note that *gaming regulations* always require video poker machines to have random outcomes. You should be aware that there are casinos operating in places that *do not* have gaming regulations. Examples are cruise ships which operate in international waters, some Indian reservations that are not subject to state regulations, and virtually all Internet casinos. You should also be aware that the technology exists for machines to be set so they do not act randomly. These machines can be actually programmed to avoid giving the players better hands and they wind up giving the house a much bigger advantage. These machines are illegal in Nevada, New Jersey, Colorado and all other states that pattern their gaming regulations after those states. You may, however, come across them in unregulated casinos.

One final point you should keep in mind - IGT is not the only manufacturer of video poker machines. There are quite a few others and they may engineer their machines to work in a different manner. Their RNG may not stop in the same way and their draw cards may be dealt differently. IGT, however, is by far the largest and it is the type of machine you will most often encounter in a casino.

Now that you understand how a video poker machine works let's learn how to pick out the best paying ones. In the beginning of this story it was mentioned that "you can tell a video poker machine's payback percentage just by looking at it." That's true, but it takes a little bit of knowledge to know the difference among all the different types of machines. An example of some of the different machines available are: Jacks or Better, Bonus, Double Bonus, Double Double Bonus, Joker Poker and Deuces Wild. To make it even more confusing, not only are there different machines, but each of those machines can have a different pay schedule for the same hand.

Fortunately, every video poker machine's payback percentage can be mathematically calculated. Not only does this let you know which machines offer you the best return, but it also tells you the best playing decisions to make on that particular machine based on the odds of that combination occurring. The bad news, however, is that it's fairly impossible to do on your own so you'll have to either buy a book that lists all of the percentages and strategies or buy a computer program that does the work for you. Take a look at the tables on the next few pages and you'll see some different types of video poker games and their payback percentages (when played with maximum coin and perfect strategy). For those of you with a computer, *Bob Dancer Presents Win Poker* can determine the exact payback percentage for any video poker machine. It retails for $29.95 (see ad in ths book) and besides calculating percentages it will also allow you to play video poker on different types of machines and analyze hands to show you the expected return for each play. You can set the game to automatically show you the best decision each time or you can set it to just warn you if you make a wrong decision on your own. It's so simple that my 14-year-old son plays it and I'm confident he can play better than the average Las Vegas visitor. "I'm going for the flush, dad!"

If you have no desire to get quite that serious about learning video poker then I'll try to provide some general tips to help you out. First, you'll need to find the machines that offer you the highest returns. One of the best is the 9/6 Jacks or Better machine. Of course, you're probably wondering "what exactly is a 9/6 Jacks or Better machine?" Well, the Jacks or Better part refers to the fact that you won't win anything from the machine unless you have at least a pair of Jacks. The 9/6 part refers to the payback schedule on this kind of machine. As stated earlier, each machine can have a different payback schedule and there are at least 20 different kinds of payback schedules available on Jacks or Better machines. In Las Vegas the two most common Jacks or Better machines you will find are 8/5 and 9/6. Here's a comparison of their pay schedules (per coin, for five-coin play):

Hand	9/6	8/5
Royal Flush	800	800
Straight Flush	50	50
4-of-a-Kind	25	25
Full House	9	8
Flush	6	5
Straight	4	4
3-of-a-Kind	3	3
Two Pairs	2	2
One Pair J's	1	1

As you can see, the schedules are identical except for the better payoffs on the 9/6 machines for Flushes and Full Houses. The payback on a 9/6 machine is 99.5% with perfect play, while the 8/5 machines return 97.3% with perfect play. Of course, it doesn't make any sense to play an 8/5 machine if a 9/6 machine is available. Yet, in Las Vegas you'll see lots of people playing an 8/5 when a 9/6 can often be found in the same casino. The reason they do that is because they don't know any better; you do. Always look for the 9/6 machines. They can be found in every downtown Las Vegas casino and most, but not all, Strip casinos. In other states, including New Jersey, they won't be found as easily. On a trip to Mississippi I found a few, but it took some searching and not every casino had them.

One other common machine you will come across is an 8/5 Jacks or Better progressive. These feature the same 8/5 pay table as above except for the royal flush which pays a jackpot amount that is displayed on a meter above the machine. The jackpot will continue to build until someone hits a royal flush; then it will reset and start to build again. If the jackpot on a 25¢ machine is above $2,240 (for five coins) then you should play it. If it's below $2,240 then stick to the regular 9/6 machines.

Another good tip is to restrict your play to the same kind of machine all the time. Each video poker machine has its own particular strategy and what works best on a Jacks or Better machine is definitely much different from what works best on a Deuces Wild machine. I usually only play 9/6 Jacks or Better machines because that is what I practice on and I automatically know the best decision to make all the time. Keep in mind that when you calculate the payback percentage for a video poker machine the number you arrive at is based on perfect play. As an example, a 9/6 Jacks or Better video poker machine has a 99.5 percent payback with perfect play. This means that, theoretically, it will return $99.50 for every $100 played in the machine, but

Jacks or Better Pay Table Variations
(Per coin with maximum coin played and perfect strategy)

### 9/7 (at Stratosphere)		### 9/6 with 4,700 coin jackpot	
Royal Flush	800	Royal Flush	940
Straight Flush	50	Straight Flush	50
4-of-a-kind	25	4-of-a-kind	25
Full House	*9*	*Full House*	*9*
Flush	*7*	*Flush*	*6*
Straight	4	Straight	4
3-of-a-kind	3	3-of-a-kind	3
2 Pair	2	2 Pair	2
Jacks or Better	1	Jacks or Better	1
Payback	**100.8%**	**Payback**	**99.90%**

### 9/6 with 4,000 coin jackpot		### 8/5	
Royal Flush	800	Royal Flush	800
Straight Flush	50	Straight Flush	50
4-of-a-kind	25	4-of-a-kind	25
Full House	*9*	*Full House*	*8*
Flush	*6*	*Flush*	*5*
Straight	4	Straight	4
3-of-a-kind	3	3-of-a-kind	3
2 Pair	2	2 Pair	2
Jacks or Better	1	Jacks or Better	1
Payback	**99.54%**	**Payback**	**97.28%**

### 7/5		### 6/5	
Royal Flush	800	Royal Flush	800
Straight Flush	50	Straight Flush	50
4-of-a-kind	25	4-of-a-kind	25
Full House	*7*	*Full House*	*6*
Flush	*5*	*Flush*	*5*
Straight	4	Straight	4
3-of-a-kind	3	3-of-a-kind	3
2 Pair	2	2 Pair	2
Jacks or Better	1	Jacks or Better	1
Payback	**96.15%**	**Payback**	**95.00%**

Bonus Poker Pay Table Variations
(Per coin with maximum coin played and perfect strategy)

7/5 Bonus

Royal Flush	800
Straight Flush	50
Four Aces	80
Four 2s 3s 4s	40
Four 5s-Ks	25
Full House	*7*
Flush	*5*
Straight	4
3-of-a-kind	3
2 Pair	2
Jacks or Better	1
Payback	**98.02%**

8/5 Bonus

Royal Flush	800
Straight Flush	50
Four Aces	80
Four 2s 3s 4s	40
Four 5s-Ks	25
Full House	*8*
Flush	*5*
Straight	4
3-of-a-kind	3
2 Pair	2
Jacks or Better	1
Payback	**99.17%**

9/6 Double Bonus

Royal Flush	800
Straight Flush	50
Four Aces	160
Four 2s 3s 4s	80
Four 5s-Ks	50
Full House	*9*
Flush	*6*
Straight	5
3-of-a-kind	3
2 Pair	1
Jacks or Better	1
Payback	**97.81%**

9/7 Double Bonus

Royal Flush	800
Straight Flush	50
Four Aces	160
Four 2s 3s 4s	80
Four 5s-Ks	50
Full House	*9*
Flush	*7*
Straight	5
3-of-a-kind	3
2 Pair	1
Jacks or Better	1
Payback	**99.11%**

10/7 Double Bonus

Royal Flush	800
Straight Flush	50
Four Aces	160
Four 2s 3s 4s	80
Four 5s-Ks	50
Full House	*10*
Flush	*7*
Straight	5
3-of-a-kind	3
2 Pair	1
Jacks or Better	1
Payback	**100.17%**

10/7 Triple Bonus

Royal Flush	800
Straight Flush	50
Four Aces	240
Four 5s-Ks	120
Four 2s 3s 4s	75
Full House	*10*
Flush	*7*
Straight	4
3-of-a-kind	3
2 Pair	1
Kings or Better	*1*
Payback	**98.52%**

Deuces Wild Pay Table Variations
(Per coin with maximum coin played and perfect strategy)

Short Pay		Full Pay	
Natural Royal Flush	800	Natural Royal Flush	800
Four Deuces	200	Four Deuces	200
Wild Royal Flush	25	Wild Royal Flush	25
5-of-a-kind	15	5-of-a-kind	15
Straight Flush	9	Straight Flush	9
4-of-a-kind	*4*	*4-of-a-kind*	*5*
Full House	3	Full House	3
Flush	2	Flush	2
Straight	2	Straight	2
3-of-a-kind	1	3-of-a-kind	1
Payback	**94.34%**	**Payback**	**100.76%**

Not So Ugly (NSU) Deuces		Deuces Deluxe	
Natural Royal Flush	800	Natural Royal Flush	800
Four Deuces	200	Four Deuces	200
Wild Royal Flush	25	Natural Straight Flush	50
5-of-a-kind	*16*	Wild Royal Flush	25
Straight Flush	*10*	5-of-a-kind	15
4-of-a-kind	*4*	Natural 4-of-a-kind	10
Full House	*4*	Wild Straight Flush	9
Flush	*3*	Wild 4-of-a-kind	4
Straight	2	Full House	4
3-of-a-kind	1	Flush	3
Payback	**99.73%**	Straight	2
		3-of-a-kind	1
		Payback	**100.34%**

only if the player makes the correct decision every time. If you make mistakes, and most players do, the return to the casino will be higher. If you play several different kinds of machines it becomes increasingly harder to remember the correct play to make and you will make mistakes. Therefore, it only makes sense to memorize the correct decisions for one kind of machine and to always play on that same kind of machine (of course, in order to learn those proper strategies, you may want to buy that book or software).

Now that you've decided which machines to play, you'll need some help with strategy. On the next two pages are charts that will give you an excellent simple strategy for both 9/6 and 8/5 video poker machines. These charts were derived from calculations using the *Bob Dancer Presents Win Poker* computer program and give you a near-perfect strategy. They aren't 100% perfect but they are close to it and will only be fractionally incorrect in some situations. The only difference between the two tables is shown in the poker hands that have been *italicized* in the 8/5 strategy tables.

Simple Strategy Table For 9/6 Jacks or Better

1. Royal Flush
2. Straight Flush
3. 4 of a kind
4. 4 card Royal Flush
5. Full House
6. Flush
7. 3 of a kind
8. Straight
9. 4 card Straight Flush
10. Two Pairs
11. 4 card inside Straight Flush
12. Pair of Jacks or higher
13. 3 card Royal Flush
14. 4 card Flush
15. 4 card straight with 3 high cards
16. Low Pair
17. 4 card Straight with 2 high cards
18. 4 card Straight with 1 high card
19. 3 card Inside Straight Flush with 2 high cards
20. 3 card Straight Flush with 1 high card
21. 4 card Straight with no high cards
22. 3 card Double Inside Straight Flush with 2 high cards
23. 3 card Inside Straight Flush with 1 high card
24. 3 card Straight Flush with no high cards
25. 4 card Inside Straight with 4 high cards
26. 2 card Royal Flush with no Ace or 10
27. 2 card Royal Flush with Ace and no 10
28. 3 card Double Inside Straight Flush with 1 high card
29. 3 card Inside Straight Flush with no high card
30. 4 card Inside Straight with 3 high cards
31. 3 high cards with no Ace
32. 2 high cards
33. 2 card Royal Flush with 10 and no Ace
34. 1 high card
35. 3 card Double Inside Straight Flush with no high card
36. All New Cards

Simple Strategy Table For 8/5 Jacks or Better

1. Royal Flush
2. Straight Flush
3. 4 of a kind
4. 4 card Royal Flush
5. Full House
6. Flush
7. 3 of a kind
8. Straight
9. 4 card Straight Flush
10. Two Pairs
11. 4 card inside Straight Flush
12. Pair of Jacks or higher
13. 3 card Royal Flush
14. 4 card Flush
15. 4 card straight with 3 high cards
16. Low Pair
17. 4 card Straight with 2 high cards
18. 4 card Straight with 1 high card
19. 3 card Inside Straight Flush with 2 high cards
20. 3 card Straight Flush with 1 high card
21. 4 card Straight with no high cards
22. 3 card Double Inside Straight Flush with 2 high cards
23. 3 card Inside Straight Flush with 1 high card
24. 3 card Straight Flush with no high cards
25. 4 card Inside Straight with 4 high cards
26. 2 card Royal Flush with no Ace or 10
27. 2 card Royal Flush with Ace and no 10
28. *3 high cards with no Ace*
29. *4 card Inside Straight with 3 high cards*
30. *3 card Double Inside Straight Flush with 1 high card*
31. *2 high cards*
32. *3 card Inside Straight Flush with no high card*
33. 2 card Royal Flush with 10 and no Ace
34. 1 high card
35. 3 card Double Inside Straight Flush with no high card
36. All New Cards

To use any chart just look up your hand and play it in the manner that is closest to the top of the chart. For example: you are dealt (6♣,6♦,7♥,8♠,9♣). You keep (6♣,6♦) rather than (6♦,7♥,8♠,9♣) because a low pair (#16) is higher on the chart than a four-card straight with no high cards (#21). Remember to always look for the highest possible choice on the chart when there are multiple ways to play your hand. As another example: you are dealt (8♣,8♦, J♥,Q♥,K♥). You keep (J♥,Q♥,K♥) rather than (8♣,8♦) because a three-card royal flush (#13) is higher on the chart than a low pair (#16). As a final, but radical, example of how to play your hand by the chart what would you do if you're dealt (6♥,10♥,J♥,Q♥,K♥)? Yes, you have to break up your flush by discarding the 6♥ and go for the royal flush because the four-card royal flush (#4) is higher on the chart than the pat flush (#6). When looking at the 9/6 chart there are a few things that should seem rather obvious:

1) A low pair is relatively good. Of the 36 possible hands, a low pair is #16 which means there are 20 hands worse than a low pair. If you look at the 15 hands that are better than a low pair eight of them are pat hands that require no draw. Of the other seven hands, six of them are four card hands and the remaining hand is a three-card royal flush.

2) Don't hold three cards trying to get a straight or flush. Nowhere on the chart do you see that you should hold three cards to try for a straight or flush. In some instances you should hold three cards to try for a straight flush, but *never* a straight or flush.

3) Rarely draw to an inside straight. Inside straights (6,7,_,9,10) appear only twice on the chart and only in rather bad positions: #30 (with three high cards) and #25 (with four high cards). It is much easier to draw to an outside straight (_7,8,9,10_) where you can complete your straight by getting the card you need on either end. Open end straights appear four times on the chart and in much higher positions than inside straights: #21 (with no high cards), #18 (with one high card), #17 (with two high cards) and #15 (with three high cards).

4) Don't hold a kicker. A kicker is an unpaired card held with a pair. For example (8,8,K) or (K,K,9) are examples of hands where an extra card (the kicker) is held. *Never* hold a kicker because they add no value to your hand!

If you would like to make your own video poker strategy charts there is a special software program that will allow you to do this. It's called *Tom Ski's Video Poker Strategy Master* and it allows you to generate your own video poker strategy charts on your home computer. You can make charts for full-pay Deuces Wild which can be found in many Nevada casinos (and the Copa Casino in Gulfport, Mississippi). It can also do Pick'Em which can be found in many different markets around the country, plus nine other common games.

For your information there are exactly 2,598,960 unique poker hands possible on a video poker machine (when played without a joker). On a 9/6 Jacks or Better machine a royal flush will occur about once every 40,000 hands; a

Other Video Poker Game Pay Tables
(Per coin with maximum coin played and perfect strategy)

Pick'Em Poker (five coin payout)
Royal Flush	6,000
Straight Flush	1,199
4-of-a-kind	600
Full House	90
Flush	75
Straight	55
3-of-a-kind	25
Two Pair	15
Pair 9's or Better	10
Payback	**99.95%**

All American Poker
Royal Flush	800
Straight Flush	200
4-of-a-kind	40
Full House	8
Flush	8
Straight	8
3-of-a-kind	3
Two Pair	1
Pair Jacks or Better	1
Payback	**100.72%**

Double Joker Full-Pay
Natural Royal Flush	800
Wild Royal Flush	100
5-of-a-kind	50
Straight Flush	25
4-of-a-kind	*9*
Full House	5
Flush	4
Straight	3
3-of-a-kind	2
2 Pair	1
Payback	**99.97%**

Double Joker Short-Pay
Natural Royal Flush	800
Wild Royal Flush	100
5-of-a-kind	50
Straight Flush	25
4-of-a-kind	*8*
Full House	5
Flush	4
Straight	3
3-of-a-kind	2
2 Pair	1
Payback	**98.10%**

straight flush about every 9,000 hands; four-of-a-kind about every 425 hands; a full house about every 87 hands; a flush about every 91 hands; a straight about every 89 hands; three-of-a-kind about every 14 hands; two pairs about every 8 hands; and a pair of Jacks or better about every 5 hands. The interesting thing to note here is that both a flush and a straight are harder to get than a full house, yet a full house always has a higher payback than either of them. The majority of the time, about 55% to be exact, you will wind up with a losing hand on a 9/6 machine.

The next bit of advice concerns how many coins you should bet. You should always bet the maximum amount (on machines returning 100% or more) because it will allow you to earn bonus coins when you hit the royal flush. Example: For a royal flush on a 9/6 machine with one coin played you receive 250 coins; for two coins you get 500; for three coins you get 750; for four coins you get 1,000 and for five (maximum) coins you get 4,000 coins. This translates into a bonus of 2,750 coins! A royal flush can be expected once every 40,400 hands on a 9/6 machine; once every 40,200 hands on an 8/5 machine; and once every 32,700 hands on an 8/5 progressive. The odds are high, but the added bonus makes it worthwhile. If you can't afford to play the maximum coins on a positive machine then move down to a lower denomination machine. And, if you absolutely insist on playing less than the maximum, be sure to play only one at a time. It doesn't make any sense to play two, three or four coins, because you still won't be eligible for the bonus.

One important thing to keep in mind when you look at the total payback on these video poker machines is that those numbers always include a royal flush and the royal flush plays a *very* big factor in the total return. As a matter of fact, the royal flush is such a big factor on video poker machines that you are actually expected to lose until you get that royal flush. Yes, even by restricting your play to video poker machines with a more than 100% payback you are *still* expected to lose money until you hit a royal flush. Once you hit that royal flush it will bring your cash back up to that 100% level but until it happens you should be fully aware that you are statistically expected to lose money.

According to video poker expert Bob Dancer, "on a 25¢ Jacks or Better 9/6 machine you will lose at a rate of 2.5% while you are waiting for the royal to happen. Another way to look at this is quarter players who play 600 hands per hour can expect to lose about $18.75 per hour, on average, on any hour they do not hit a royal." You really have to keep in mind that there are no guarantees when you play video poker. Yes, you are expected to get a royal flush about once every 40,000 hands but there are no guarantees that it will happen and if you don't get that royal flush it could cost you dearly.

A final tip about playing video poker concerns slot clubs. Every major casino has a slot club and you should make it a point to join the slot club before you insert your first coin. It doesn't cost anything to join and as a member you will have the opportunity to earn complimentaries from the casinos in the form of cash, food, shows, drinks, rooms or other "freebies." When you join the club you'll be issued a card (similar to a credit card) that you insert in the machine before you start to play and it will track how much you bet, as well as how long you play. Naturally, the more money you gamble, the more freebies you'll earn. Just make sure you don't get carried away and bet more than you're comfortable with just to earn some extra comps. Ideally, you want to get comps for gambling that you were going to do anyway and not be pressured into betting more than you had planned. Many clubs will also give you cash back for your play and that amount should be added into the payback percentage on the kind of machine you'll be playing. For example: at Treasure Island in Las Vegas, the slot club rebates .33% in cash for your video poker play (.67% for slots). By only playing 9/6 Jacks or Better machines with a return of 99.54% you can add the .33% rebate to get an adjusted figure of 99.87%. This means that you are, theoretically, playing an almost even game, *plus* you're still eligible for other room and food discounts on top of your cash rebate.

Choosing Video Poker Games

by John Grochowski

Way back in the early 1990s when the nationwide expansion of gambling was at its beginning and riverboat casinos were new, I asked a riverboat slot director why there was so little video poker on his floor.

``Our guests aren't ready for it,'' he told me. ``When we opened, we didn't know what everybody was going to play. We assumed it would be about normal for the Las Vegas Strip. We opened with about 17 percent video poker, and they sat there empty. All anyone wanted to play was the slots. So we dropped to 9 or 10 percent video poker.''

Things have changed. Slot directors move to other jobs at other casinos, and player tastes change. The current slot director at that same riverboat told me in 2000 that he now has 18 percent video poker, and players can't get enough of it. If he was starting from scratch, he'd turn 20, maybe even 25 percent of his floor over to video poker. What happened?

Video poker, it seems, is an acquired taste. You can see that clearly in casino gambling's capital city. Las Vegas visitors who stick to the Strip will see video poker taking up roughly 15 percent of the slot floors -- a little more in some casinos, a little less than others. But get off the Strip and check out the places that cater to the locals, places such as the Fiesta and Santa Fe in northwest Las Vegas, or Sunset Station and The Reserve to the southeast in Henderson. There you'll see row after row after row of video poker, 50 percent or more of the slot floor.

The difference is in the experience of the players. What the Las Vegas locals know, and what regular players in newer gaming markets are learning, is that they get a better run for their money on video poker than on the slots. Whereas slots on the Las Vegas Strip return an average of a little more than 95 percent of coins played to dollar players and a little less than 93 percent to quarter players, even the bad video poker games, the ones that experts warn to stay away from, return 95 percent with expert play. The good machines return 99 percent, even 100 percent or more in the long run -- although even on those machines there will be more losing sessions than winners, balanced out in the long run by the odd royal flush.

Video poker does it with a high hit frequency, too. On most Jacks or Better-based games, about 45 percent of all hands bring some return. That's a percentage slots were unable to approach until the advent of multiline, multicoin video slots, and on those games many "winners" bring returns of less than the wagers.

Not every player has access to those 100-percent machines. In new gaming markets, where demand for a place to play frequently outstrips available space, slot directors are able to use games that will maximize their profit margins. They know they can use a Jacks or Better game that pays 7-for-1 on full houses and 5-for-1 on flushes instead of a full-pay game that returns 9-for-1 and 6-for-1, and they'll still get plenty of play. There are good machines out there, too, but it's up to the player to learn to tell the difference.

JACKS OR BETTER: In video poker, when the casino wants to change the long-term payback percentage of a game, it changes the pay table. Given the same strategy, players get winning hands no more or less frequently, but some hands pay a little more or a little less.

In Jacks or Better, the base game around which many video poker variations are built, the payoffs that usually are changed are full houses and flushes. We look for games that pay 9-for-1 on full houses and 6-for-1 on flushes, with the full pay table being 250-for-1 on royal flushes (jumping to 4,000 coins with a five-coin wager), 50-for-1 on straight flushes, 25-for-1 on four of a kind, 9-for-1 on full houses, 6-for-1 on flushes 4-for-1 on straights, 3-for-1 on three of a kind, 2-for-1 on two pair and 1-for-1 on pairs of Jacks or better.

For each unit that the payoff on full houses or flushes drops, we lose about 1.1 percent of our long-term payback. On an 8-5 Jacks or Better game, with one-unit drops in both spots on the pay table, our average return drops to 97.3 percent. Drop the full house payback again to 7-for-1, and a 7-5 machine drops to 96.2 percent.

Given better options, a video poker player in the know would walk away from that 7-5 game. In Las Vegas, he might even leave the casino and look for a better deal next door or across the street. That's tough to do on a riverboat, or in a Native American casino that's miles away from the next option. So a player who finds the best video poker in a casino is 7-5 Jacks or Better has a decision to make. Does he take up table games? Does he just go home and skip his night's entertainment? Or does he sigh, decide that at least a 96-percent game is better than he'd get on the slots, and play anyway? Most take the third option.

BONUS POKER: The "bonuses" in Bonus Poker are on certain fours of a kind. Four 2s, 3s or 4s will bring you 40-for-1 and four Aces will bring 80-for-1 instead of the 25-for-1 that is standard on Jacks or Better and on the remaining quads in Bonus Poker.

Other than that, the pay table is the same as in Jacks or Better, with reduced paybacks on full houses and flushes. We look for games that pay 8-for-1 on full houses and 5-for-1 on flushes. That's a 99.2 percent game with expert play. Bonus Poker games often have 7-5 and 6-5 versions, with overall returns dropping about 1.1 percent for each unit the flush payoff drops.

There are no major strategy differences between Bonus Poker and the versions of Jacks or Better that pay 5-for-1 on the flush. Learn to play 8-5 Jacks, and you're ready for Bonus Poker.

DOUBLE BONUS POKER: If everyone could play this game perfectly and played only the best available version, the casinos would be supporting us instead of the other way around. Double Bonus Poker, which in its full-pay version pays 10-for-1 on full houses, 7-for-1 on flushes and 5-for-1 on straights, returns 100.17 percent in the long run with expert play.

The full pay table is as follows: 250-for-1 on royal flushes (jumping to 4,000 coins with a five-coin wager), 50-for-1 on straight flushes, 160-for-1 on four Aces, 80-for-1 on four 2s, 3s and 4s, 50-for-1 on four of a kind, 10-for-1 on full houses, 7-for-1 on flushes, 5-for-1 on straights, 3-for-1 on three of a kind, 1-for-1 on two pair and 1-for-1 on pairs of Jacks or better.

A few important things to note: Two pair pays only 1-for-1 instead of the 2-for-1 Jacks or Better players get. More of the overall payback is tied up in the higher end of the pay table. With five coins wagered, four Aces bring an 800-coin jackpot. I've had more than one former slot player tell me that Double Bonus is the game that pried them away from the reels, with a realistic secondary jackpot worth walking away with making the difference.

Few play at expert level, and the casinos are in no danger of losing money. There are some tricky little moves in this game that average players miss. For example, if we're dealt a full house that includes three Aces, our best play is to break up the full house and go for the fourth Ace. We'd never do that in Jacks or Better or Bonus Poker. Also, the 7-for-1 payback on flushes dictates that we hold three parts of a flush. Given 10 of diamonds, 8 of clubs, 6 of diamonds, 4 of hearts, 2 of diamonds, in 10-7 Double Bonus we'd hold the three diamonds, whereas in Jacks or Better we'd discard all five.

To change the payback percentage, the casino changes payoffs on full houses, flushes and sometimes straights. It's common to see Double Bonus games with 9-7 (99.1 percent) and 9-6 (97.8 percent pay tables), and I sometimes see pay tables as low as 8-5-4, paying 8-for-1 on full houses, 5-for-1 on flushes and 4-for-1 on straights. The 8-5-4 game pays only 94.2 percent with expert play, making it problematic as to whether a video poker player is really any better off on that game than on the reel slots.

DOUBLE DOUBLE BONUS POKER: The big change as compared to Double Bonus is that there are extra bonuses available on some fours of a kind provided the fifth card is a certain denomination. If four Aces are accompanied by a 2, 3 or 4, the usual 160-for-1 jackpot jumps to 400-for-1 -- a 2,000-coin bonanza with five wagered. If four 2, 3s or 4s are accompanied by an Ace, 2, 3 or 4, the 80-for-1 payoff jumps to 160-for-1.

Straights drop back to 4-for-1 on all versions of this game. The full-pay Double Double Bonus game pays 9-for-1 on full houses and 6-for-1 on flushes, and returns 98.9 percent with expert play.

It's not unusual to see Double Double Bonus in an 8-5 format, leaving a 96.8 percent game, and I've even seen 7-5, a 95.7 percent pay table in the long run with expert play.

One quick strategy tip: Do not hold fifth-card kickers without already having the four of a kind. If you're dealt three Aces, a 2 and a 9, discard both the 2 and the 9. Give yourself two chances to draw the fourth Ace instead of just one.

DEUCES WILD: Someday, I'm going to write a book with nothing but Deuces Wild pay tables and strategy variations. There are countless versions of Deuces Wild. Most video poker books focus on strategy for full-pay Deuces Wild, which is available only in Nevada. The 100.8 percent payback with expert play is too strong for regulators' tastes in most gaming markets, and the game has never been licensed outside Nevada. It's a great game if you can find it. Most players can't.

Let's compare it to another game that video poker fans sometimes call ``Illinois Deuces.'' It doesn't say ``Illinois'' on the machine -- it just says Deuces Wild. Manufacturers and casino operators leave it to the player to tell the difference among pay tables, if they can.

The game isn't limited to Illinois. It's available nationwide. It just has that nickname because it rose to popularity in the early '90s at the Par-A-Dice casino in East Peoria, Illinois. Look at the following pay tables, and guess which one is the full-pay game, returning 100.8 percent, and which is Illinois Deuces, returning 98.9

Variation No. 1: Natural royal flush 250-for-1 (jumps to 4,000 coins for a five-coin bet); four 2s 200-for-1; royal flush with wild cards 25-for-1; five of a kind 15-for-1; straight flush 9-for-1; four of a kind 5-for-1; full house 3-for-1; flush 2-for-1; straight 2-for-1; three of a kind 1-for-1.

Variation No. 2: Natural royal flush 250-for-1 (jumps to 4,000 coins for a five-coin bet); four 2s 200-for-1; royal flush with wild cards 25-for-1; five of a kind 15-for-1; straight flush 9-for-1; four of a kind 4-for-1; full house 4-for-1; flush 3-for-1; straight 2-for-1; three of a kind 1-for-1.

The differences look minor, right? No. 1 pays 5-for-1 on four of a kind, while No. 2 pays only 4-for-1. But No. 2 pays 4-for-1 on full houses and 3-for-1 on flushes, but up a notch from the payouts on No. 1. So which is better? It's No. 1.

Some players fall into the trap of thinking that in poker, full houses and flushes are more common than four of a kind, so No. 2 must be the better game. That's exactly what the operators want you to think. In Deuces Wild, we get four of a kind more often than full houses and flushes combined. If you have two pair and one of the pair consists of 2s, you have four of a kind. If you have three 9s, an 8 and a 2, the wild deuces doesn't become an 8 to complete a full house, it takes the place of a 9 to give you four of a kind.

One major strategy difference comes when we're dealt two pairs. If we have two 9s and two 8s, strategy tables that focus on full-pay Deuces will tell you to keep only one pair. But in Illinois Deuces, where we get less for four of a kind and more for a full house, our best play is to keep both pairs and make a one-card draw for a full house. Let's try one more variation:

Variation No. 3: Natural royal flush 250-for-1 (jumps to 4,000 coins for a five-coin bet); four 2s 200-for-1; royal flush with wild cards 25-for-1; five of a kind 16-for-1; straight flush 13-for-1; four of a kind 4-for-1; full house 3-for-1; flush 2-for-1; straight 2-for-1; three of a kind 1-for-1.

Again, we have a Deuces variation that differs from full-pay in three places on the pay table. As in Illinois Deuces, four of a kind is reduced to 4-for-1, and we know that's important. Five of a kind goes up to 16-for-1 from the usual 15-for-1, and there's a big jump on straight flushes, to 13-for-1 from 9-for-1.

Those jumps aren't nearly enough to make up the difference. This game, nicknamed ``Colorado Deuces'' but available nationwide, returns only 96.8 percent with expert play.

There's no easy road map to all the variations of Deuces Wild. The key thing to remember is that changes on the low end of the pay table in Deuces Wild or any other video poker game have a greater effect than those higher on the pay table. With few exceptions such as four-of-a-kind in Deuces Wild, hands lower on the pay table occur more frequently than those higher up. An increase on full houses to 4-for-1 helps the player much more often than a bigger increase on straight flushes, and so makes a bigger difference in the long-term return.

So it goes with any video poker game. In Double Bonus, the four-of-a-kind bonuses, the enhanced payoffs on full houses, flushes and straights all are offset by one decrease low on the pay table -- the drop from 2-for-1 to 1-for-1 on two pair. When you next find an unfamiliar pay table, be aware. Any boost high on the pay table might look attractive, but check out what you're giving up to get it.

John Grochowski is the gaming columnist for the "Chicago Sun-Times" and a contributing writer to many gaming magazines. John is also the author of several books on casino gambling.

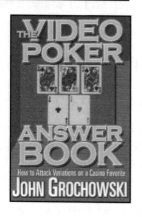

Video Poker Quiz

by Bob Dancer

In each of the combinations below, decide which one, if either, is better. Sometimes one of the two combinations will be quite a bit better than the other. Sometimes they will be tied. But in no case will one be only slightly better than the other. In other words, there are no close calls here and good players need to understand these distinctions cold!

Usually I teach that pay schedules matter a lot. And they do! But in today's quiz they are not important. When considering Jacks or Better in today's quiz, how much you get for flushes and full houses is largely irrelevant. When considering Deuces Wild, you need to know that 3-of-a-kind returns even money (and that Two Pair and all single pairs return nothing), but the exact value you receive for flushes, 4-of-a-kinds, straight flushes, etc. is irrelevant, as long as these values are somewhat close to normal.

In each case, consider the value of the combinations "before the draw."

Q1: In Jacks or Better, which is more valuable J♥J♠ or A♥A♠?

Q2: In Jacks or Better, which is more valuable J♦ or A♦?

Q3: In Jacks or Better, which is more valuable Q♣J♣ or J♣T♣? (T stands for "ten")

Q4: In Jacks or Better, which is more valuable 2♥3♥4♥ or 3♥4♥5♥?

Q5: In Deuces Wild, which is more valuable Q♠T♠ or Q♠J♠?

Q6: In Deuces Wild, which is more valuable WW5♦6♦ or WW6♦7♦? (W stands for wild card, in this case a deuce)

Q7: In Deuces Wild, which is more valuable WW5♣6♣ or WW5♣7♣?

A1: JJ is worth exactly the same as AA in Jacks or Better. They both give you your money back. Three jacks pays as much as three aces and four of one pays the same as four of the other. In various "Bonus" games, where four aces pay quite a bit more than four jacks, AA would be worth more than JJ. People who play bonus games, and are used to AA being worth more than JJ, sometimes forget to adjust their thinking when they are not playing the bonus game.

A2: J is worth more than A. Either one is equally likely to pair up, become four of a kind or a royal. But in terms of straights and straight flushes, J is quite a bit better. Other than the royal, the A can only be part of an A2345 straight flush. The J can be part of a KQJT9, QJT98 or JT987 straight flush. The same goes for straights, although you can add the AKQJT straight to both.

A3:　QJ is much better than JT in Jacks or Better. QJ has TWO high cards and JT only has ONE. This is by far the dominant fact. The fact that you can get more straights and straight flushes from JT than you can from QJ is not close to being strong enough to compensate for the extra high card.

A4:　345 is quite a bit stronger than 234. 345 is truly open-ended, and can be part of three different straight flushes: 7-high, 6-high and 5-high. 234 is too close to the bottom of the deck and can only be part of two different straight flushes: 6-high and 5-high.

A5:　QJ is identical in value to QT in Deuces Wild. Any straight, straight flush or royal flush containing QJ also must contain the T, and any of these nice hands containing QT must also include the J. The distinguishing factor between this problem and Q3 above is that in Deuces Wild, there are no such things as "high cards." No pair of cards gives you your money back in Deuces Wild.

A6:　**WW**67 is more valuable than **WW**56. The reason for this is how much room there is to move before the combination runs into the deuce. From **WW**67, there are 8 perfect cards giving you a straight flush. Specifically three cards on top (the 8,9,and T), three cards on the bottom (3,4, and 5) and the other two deuces. From **WW**56, there are only 7 perfect cards. There are still three perfect cards on top and two deuces, but now there are only two cards on the bottom (the 3 and the 4).

A7:　**WW**57 has exactly the same value as **WW**56 in Deuces Wild. We showed in the last example that there were 7 perfect cards to complete the straight flush from **WW**56. From **WW**57, you'll notice two cards on top (the 8 and the 9), one in the middle (the 6), two on the bottom (the 3 and the 4) and the remaining two deuces. This also adds up to 7 perfect cards. In any game where holding **WW**56 is correct (which would be games where the amount you receive for a flush and the amount you receive for a one-coin straight flush add up to 12 or higher), holding **WW**57 would also be correct. In any game where holding **WW**57 would not be correct (which would be games where the amounts you receive for a one-coin flush and straight flush add up to 11 or less), you would also not hold **WW**56.

Bob Dancer is a professional video poker player as well as a columnist for several gaming publications. Bob also markets a video poker software program that will allow you to practice numerous version of video poker at home on your computer. Ordering information for his software can be found on page 72.

Calculating Slot Club Cashback

by Bob Dancer

Sometimes I'll write such a thing as a certain casino has a half-percent cash slot club. But when a player goes up to the slot club booth, the slot club booth doesn't know what it's slot club pays. It's not that the people in the booth are intentionally misleading you, it's just that many casinos have brand new low-level employees working the booth and these people do not know. Even experienced employees frequently do not know. Mathematics is a foreign language for many people! They have been instructed to give you such information as: if you play four quarters, for every 25 quarters you play you get 1 point and for every 320 points you earn they give you $10 in cash back.

Say what? For a lot of players this is confusing mumbo jumbo. Let me give you a formula for converting coin countdowns into percentages.

$$\text{Cash Back Percentage} = \frac{\text{Dollars Returned}}{\text{Countdown} \times \text{denomination} \times \text{points needed}}$$

So in our formula we have

$$\frac{\$10}{25 \times \$.25 \times 320} = .005 = .50\%$$

This example was tougher than usual. Almost nobody could have done this one without a pencil and paper (or maybe a calculator), and even people with those tools would sometimes have a tough time. The casino could have reached the same half-percent figure in a number of easier-to-understand ways. For whatever reason, the systems of many casinos are unnecessarily difficult.

But frequently the situation is much easier. The Mirage, for example, tells you that you need $30 to earn a point and it takes 10 points to earn a dollar cashback. This becomes

$$\frac{\$1}{30 \times \$1 \times 10} = .0033 = .33\%$$

When casinos base things on single dollars, or you can convert their amounts to single dollars, the formula reduces to

$$\frac{1}{(\text{Countdown in dollars to earn 1 point})(\text{Points needed to earn \$1 cashback})}$$

so the Mirage example would just be $1 / (30)(10) = .0033 = .33\%$.

Many casinos have it so that $1 coin in equals 1 point. I strongly encourage this as being player-friendly. When the casino combines that with an easy to use number of points to redeem for $1 cash back [such as 200 (for .5%) or 400 (for .25%) or 500 (for .20%) or 1000 (for .10%)]. One of these numbers will usually provide the appropriate amount of cashback for most casinos and will have the added benefit of being easy to compute and understand by the players.

Common sense tells you that, everything else being equal, receiving a half percent in cash back is better than receiving a tenth of a percent. But other things are rarely equal. A half percent cash back added on to a 97 percent game isn't nearly as good of a deal as a tenth of a percent cash back added on to a 100.2 percent game.

With slot machines, it usually is impossible to calculate the average return on a given machine. A machine returning 93 percent looks identical to one re-turning 97 percent. So whether a slot club returns a tenth of a percent or a half percent is large irrelevant because the major part of what makes up the return remains invisible.

But for video poker machines, the actual average payback for any machine is available to anybody willing and able to use a computer. If you plug the values for 9/6 Jacks or Better (i.e. the game that returns 9 for a full house and 6 for a flush) into a computer program, it will tell you that the game returns 99.54%. If the best Jacks or Better machine at a particular casino returns only 6 and 5 for a full house and flush respectively, the same computer pro-gram will tell you the game returns 95.00%. Once you have this information (and have written it down so you may consult it when you visit the casino), it doesn't take a genius to conclude that any slot club with the first game can give you close to, or better than, an even game. And no slot club returns enough to make the second game into anything close to attractive.

Casinos frequently offer multiple points, such as double points on Tuesdays or triple points from midnight to 8 a.m. I've seen five times points and even ten times points at some places. Again common sense tells you that triple points at one casino must be better than double points at another. And again common sense fails you. To correctly evaluate double points you need to know the value of single points and the value of the underlying game. But once you have converted the slot club into a percentage return, doubling it and adding it on to the return for a game is very easy.

The computer program tells you the average return, IF YOU PLAY PER-FECTLY. Almost nobody does play perfectly, which is why the casinos can offer such potentially good games. And even those of us who CAN play that well very often DO NOT play that well. Maintaining your concentration in a casino setting can be difficult. And those of us who do play well actually only know a few such games perfectly. Playing less than perfectly costs. Sometimes a little. Sometimes a lot. Depends.

So in addition to taking into consideration the value of the game and the value of the slot club, you need to have some estimate of how well you play. How do you estimate this? Everybody is a little different, but the following rules of thumb might be helpful.

• Raw beginner: 95% of perfection

• Have played a lot and have figured out the strategy on your own: 97% of perfection

• Have practiced with good strategy and have the strategy card with you in the casino: 98% of perfection.

• Have practiced for at least 20 hours on a computer. 99%-100% of perfection. But this number does not need to be estimated because the computer program will tell you how accurately you are playing.

Obviously there will be a lot of personal variation from these figures. People with a lot of game-playing smarts will do better than those without this experience. And once you have gone through the considerable effort to learn one video poker game, the second one is a lot easier. After all, most of the effort in learning any video poker game comes from recognizing various kinds of straight and straight flush opportunities. Once you learn to recognize these combinations accurately, learning the rest of the strategy is relatively easy.

I've mentioned computer programs a few times here. There are some programs that do a good job of letting you know how much a particular game is worth and also providing accurate correction for your playing mistakes. Currently, the best of these is my own *Bob Dancer Presents WinPoker* and more detailed information is listed in this book about this program.

Remember, the tools are widely available for you to get as good as you want. The games are widely available that will give you a very competitive gamble, or even offer you the advantage. If EVERYBODY took advantage of this information, the games would drastically change because the casinos could not win. But you can depend upon many people not studying. You can depend upon many people preferring to play slots, where the house has a big advantage. The relevant question for you is will YOU undertake the needed amount of study and practice so YOU can win? It is truly up to you.

Bob Dancer is a professional video poker player as well as a columnist for several gaming publications. Bob also markets a video poker software program that will allow you to practice numerous version of video poker at home on your computer. Ordering information for his software can be found on page 72.

Risk of Ruin In Video Poker

by Tom Ski

A frequently asked question from video poker players is "How big must my bankroll be to avoid going broke?" The answer to that will depend on which type of game you are playing. Ideally, you would like to find a low variance game like 9/6 Jacks or Better or Pick'em Poker, combined with a high percentage return over 100% due to a special promotion or cash back. Any game that returns less than 100% would require an infinite bankroll, so we will only be looking at some common games that return over 100%. Most of these games are found in Nevada, but every now and then, one might show up in another state too.

The accompanying table shows various bankroll requirements for five different games that can often be found to pay back over 100%. The dollar amounts assume you are playing a single line 25-cent game and playing five coins per hand. The table shows how much money you would need in the long run to survive bankroll risk of ruin (RoR) rates from 1% to 25%. I think many will be surprised at just how high some of these figures appear to be. For example, a deuces wild player, with no cash back, would need a bankroll of $8810 to have a 99% chance of never going broke. This drops all the way down to $2477 if one played at a casino that offered ½ of 1% cash back, and you were willing to accept a 10% chance of going broke.

Double bonus players might be stunned to see the 1% risk of ruin bankroll is a whopping $46,343 if one were to play with no cash back. But this is due to the razor thin edge of only 17/100 of 1% advantage that the game offers with expert play. That is why it is important to try and play were cash back is offered and when there are double or triple point days as your bankroll requirement is reduced dramatically.

If one was to take a snapshot of the bottom 1% of outcomes after playing X amount of hands, the graph would start at -$1.25 on the left and proceed to gradually dip lower and lower as more hands are played. Eventually, the graph would reach a low point and then begin a steady rise as you begin to grind out the 100%+ long run return of the game. The table shows the number of hands played at which the low point is reached. The table also shows this number in terms of hours based on 700 hands per hour playing speed. This will give you an idea of how long you could expect to last on average with your 1% risk of ruin starting bankroll should you happen to be unlucky and lose it all. For example, if you had the $6404 1% RoR deuces wild bankroll with ¼ of 1% cash back, you could expect to survive on average for 420,000 hands or 600 hours of play. (assuming you were destined to go broke which will NOT happen 99% of the time). Thus, if you just plan a weekend trip to Las Vegas, you certainly don't need to bring over $6000 to play 25-cent deuces wild as you won't be playing 600 hours in your two day visit. In that case $1000 to $1500 should provide a comfortable stake to survive all but the worst-case bad streaks for a short two-day visit.

I should point out that the Jacks 8/5 progressive game has one of the highest returns on the list with a 101.44% payback, but it also has one of the highest bankroll requirements. The reason for this is that a large percentage of the total return is tied up in hitting the big 11,000-coin royal flush. This gives the game a high variance and requires a large bankroll to survive the inevitable long royal flush droughts that we all are familiar with. So just picking a game with the highest percentage return can be a mistake. It is better to find a balance between high return and low fluctuations. In general, the best game to be commonly found that fits this bill is the classic full pay deuces wild with ¼ of 1% or higher cash back. Many locals casinos in Las Vegas have plenty of these games to go around. So now you can improve your chances to win on your next gambling trip by playing a game that best suits your bankroll situation.

Risk of Ruin For Five Coin, Single-line, 25-Cent Video Poker

Game	Cash Back	Total Return	1% RoR	5% RoR	10% RoR	25% RoR	# of Hands at which 1% RoR is Greatest	@ 700 h.p.h # Hours at which 1% RoR is Greatest
Full Pay Deuces Wild	0.00%	100.76%	$8,810	$5,731	$4,405	$2,652	750,000	1,071
Full Pay Deuces Wild	0.25%	101.01%	$6,404	$4,166	$3,202	$1,928	420,000	600
Full Pay Deuces Wild	0.50%	101.26%	$4,954	$3,222	$2,477	$1,491	270,000	386
Full Pay Deuces Wild	0.75%	101.51%	$3,985	$2,592	$1,993	$1,200	185,000	264
10-7 Double Bonus	0.00%	100.17%	$46,343	$30,146	$23,171	$13,950	15,700,000	22,429
10-7 Double Bonus	0.25%	100.42%	$18,452	$12,003	$9,226	$5,555	2,600,000	3,714
10-7 Double Bonus	0.50%	100.67%	$11,303	$7,353	$5,652	$3,403	1,050,000	1,500
10-7 Double Bonus	0.75%	100.92%	$8,033	$5,226	$4,017	$2,418	550,000	786
All-American	0.00%	100.72%	$9,756	$6,346	$4,878	$2,937	840,000	1,200
Joker AK- 4000	0.00%	100.64%	$10,715	$6,970	$5,357	$3,225	1,050,000	1,500
Joker AK- 4700	0.00%	101.00%	$8,402	$5,465	$4,201	$2,529	550,000	786
Jacks 8/5 Progressive 11,000 Coin Royal	10.00%	101.44%	$26,429	$17,193	$13,215	$7,956	1,225,000	1,750

Multiply dollar figures by 4 for $1 play

Multi-Play Video Poker

by Tom Ski

Video poker has long been a favorite game of choice for many casino patrons. A great deal of work has been done analyzing payback percentages and bankroll requirements for traditional single line games. But then, a few years ago, a new variation of the game called Triple Play began to appear and it quickly spread like wildfire. Instead of playing just one hand at a time, this game would let you play the same starting hand three times. But how exactly does this variation affect the payback percentage and bankroll requirements?

To answer this question, I turned to Jazbo Burns who is one of the best video poker game theoreticians around. He wrote about this topic on his website at http://www.jazbo.com which also contains a lot of other very insightful information about video poker. Jazbo shows that the overall game percentage return is unchanged when playing triple play vs. single line play. The only difference is that you are now betting three times more money. So if you are playing a game that returns under 100%, you will lose three times more than usual, and if you are playing a game that returns over 100%, you will win three times more. But does the game require three times the bankroll?

Jazbo was able to address that question by first showing how the three hands are not independent of each other since they share the first five starting cards. And once a card is held, it is duplicated in all three hands. Thus there is a co-variance element involved in formulating bankroll considerations.

Jazbo went on to calculate the co-variance of many common video poker games. In the case of full pay 10-7 Double Bonus, Jazbo's formulas showed that while triple play allows the player to wager three times more money, the variance is only 1.24 times higher. This means that if you are faced with a choice of playing a multi-line machine at a lower denomination or a single-line game at a higher denomination, the multi-line game will require a smaller bankroll.

For example, let us suppose one could play five-line nickel 10-7 Double Bonus, or a single-line quarter version of the game. In the nickel game, you are betting five hands of five nickels each for a total of $1.25 in action. This is the same amount as the five quarters in the single line game. But the bankroll required for the five-line nickel game is less than 1/3 of the amount required for the single line quarter game.

If on the other hand, you are not concerned about a choice of denominations, but rather overall bankroll requirements within the same denomination, then single line play will always require a smaller bankroll than multi-line play. The bankroll required for triple play 10-7 Double Bonus would be 1.24 times greater than for single line offered at the same denomination, 1.48 times greater for five-play, 2.08 times greater for ten-play, and 6.88 times greater for fifty-play. The percentage increase in bankroll required for all other types of video poker games will be very nearly the same as the increase shown in this 10-7 Double Bonus example. As one other example, the increase for single line 9/6 to triple line 9/6 is around 1.22 times greater and other games will all vary around 1.21 times to 1.28 times.

So is multi-line video poker a better game to play vs. single-line play? The answer will vary depending upon different circumstances. Single-line play is always better if you are playing a game that returns less than 100% simply because you are betting less, and thus will lose less. If you are playing a positive expectation game, and you want to minimize bankroll fluctuations, you can play single-line games, or, better yet, if available, move down in denomination and play multi-line games. If you want to maximize your hourly win rate, and you have an adequate bankroll for the higher variance of multi-line games, then you should play the multi-line games. For example, if you have three times the bankroll required for a single-line quarter game, then you have enough to play a ten-line version of the same game since the ten-line version only requires a 2.08 times greater bankroll.

While 10/7 Double Bonus is usually the only positive game that can be found on multi-line games, there are times when a special casino promotion can make other games worthwhile. Such promotions might include double or triple cashback points, or a special four-of-a-kind that pays double. Limiting your play to such opportunities will help increase your chances of winning and thus making your casino visit a more enjoyable experience.

Tom Ski is an expert video poker theoretician and has written about video poker for several gaming magazines. His software program "Video Poker Strategy Master" is the only product of its kind that can generate extremely accurate strategies for almost any conventional VP game or paytable. Ordering information for his software can be found on page 78.

Blackjack

by Steve Bourie

Blackjack is the most popular casino game in America and one of the biggest reasons for that is its relatively simple rules that are familiar to most casino visitors. Blackjack also has a reputation as being "beatable" and although that is true in some cases, the vast majority of players will always be playing the game with the house having a slight edge over them.

At most blackjack tables there are 7 boxes, or betting areas, on the table. This means that up to 7 people can play at that table and each player has their own box in front of them in which they'll place their bet. Now, before you take a seat at any blackjack table the first thing you should do is to take a look at the sign that's sitting on each table because it will tell you the minimum amount that you must bet on each hand. If you're a $5 player you certainly wouldn't want to sit at a table that has a $25 minimum so, once again, be sure to look before you sit down.

Once you're at the table you'll need chips to play with and you get them by giving your cash to the dealer who will exchange it for an equal amount of chips. Be careful, however, that you don't put your cash down into one of the betting boxes because the dealer might think you're playing it all on the next hand!

After everyone has placed their bets in their respective boxes the dealer will deal out 2 cards to each player. He will also deal 2 cards to himself; one of those cards will be face up and the other face down. Now, if you've ever read any brochures in a casino they'll tell you that the object of the game of blackjack is to get a total of cards as close to 21 as possible, without going over 21. However, that really isn't the object of the game. The true object is to beat the dealer and you do that by getting a total closer to 21 than the dealer, or by having the dealer bust by drawing cards that total more than 21.

The one thing that's strange about blackjack is that the rules can be slightly different at each casino and this is the only game where this happens. If you play baccarat, roulette or craps you'll find that the rules are virtually the same at every casino in the U.S. but that isn't the case with blackjack. For example, in Atlantic City all of the casinos use 6 or 8 decks of cards that are always dealt from a little rectangular box called a shoe and the cards are always dealt face up. In Las Vegas, some casinos will offer that same kind of game while others will offer games that use only 1 or 2 decks that are dealt directly from the dealer's hand and all of the cards will be dealt face down. To make it even stranger, some casinos in Las Vegas will offer both kinds of games in their

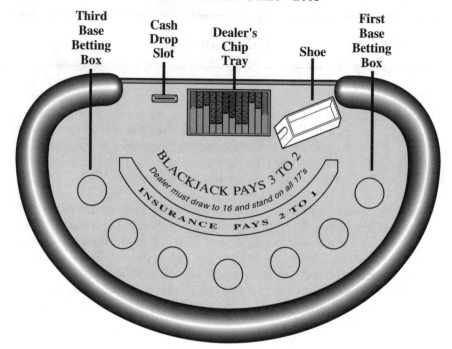

Typical Blackjack Table Layout

casinos and the rules will probably change when you move from one table to another. There can also be other rules variations concerning doubling down and splitting of pairs but we'll talk about those later. For now, just be aware that different casinos can have different blackjack rules and some of those rules will be good for you while others will be bad for you. Hopefully, after reading this story you'll know the good rules from the bad ones and which tables are the best ones to play at.

For our purposes, we'll assume we're playing in a casino that uses 6 decks of cards that are dealt out of a shoe and all of the player's cards are dealt face up. By the way, whenever you play blackjack in a casino where the cards are dealt face up don't touch the cards. In that kind of game the dealer is the only who is allowed to touch the cards and if you do happen to touch them they'll give you a warning not to do it again - so, don't touch the cards!

After the cards are dealt the players must determine the total of their hand by adding the value of their two cards together. All of the cards are counted at their face value except for the picture cards - jack, queen and king which all have a value of 10 - and the aces which can be counted as either 1 or 11. If you have an ace and any 10-value card you have a blackjack which is also called a natural and your hand is an automatic winner, unless the dealer also has a blackjack in which case the hands are tied. A tie is also called a *push* and when that happens it's a standoff and you neither win nor lose. All winning blackjacks are paid at 3-to-2, or one-and-a-half times your bet, so if you bet $5 and got a blackjack you would be paid $7.50

If the dealer has an ace as his up card the first thing he'll do is ask if anyone wants to buy *insurance*. When you buy insurance you're betting that the dealer has a blackjack by having a 10 as his face down card. To make an insurance bet you would place your bet in the area just above your betting box that says "insurance pays 2-to-1" and you're only allowed to make an insurance bet of up to one-half the amount of your original bet. So, if you originally bet $10 you could only bet a maximum of $5 as your insurance bet. After all the insurance bets are made the dealer will check his face down card and if it's a 10 he'll turn it over and all of the insurance bets will be paid off at 2-to-1. If he doesn't have a 10 underneath, the dealer will then take away all of the losing insurance bets and the game will continue. By the way, according to basic strategy, insurance is a bad bet and you should never make an insurance bet.

If the dealer has a 10 as his up card the first thing he'll do is check to see if he has an ace underneath which would give him a blackjack. If he does have an ace he'll turn it face up and start collecting the losing bets that are out on the table. If he doesn't have an ace underneath the game will continue. In some casinos, however, the dealer won't check his hole card until after all of the hands are played out.

If the dealer doesn't have an ace or a 10 as his up card the game continues and the dealer will start with the player to his immediate left to see if they want another card. If a player wants another card they indicate that with a hand signal by tapping or scratching the table with their finger to show they want another card. Taking a card is also known as *hitting* or taking a hit. If a player doesn't want another card they would just wave their hand palm down over their cards. Not taking another card is known as *standing*. The reason hand signals are used is because it eliminates any confusion on the part of the dealer as to exactly what the player wants and it also allows the security people to follow the game on the closed-circuit cameras that are hung from the ceiling throughout the casino.

Keep in mind that the hand signals will be slightly different if you're playing in a casino where the cards are dealt face down and you're allowed to pick them up. In that situation a player would signal that they wanted another card by scratching the table with the edges of the two cards they're holding. If they didn't want another card, they would simply place their two cards under the bet in their box.

In either case, if a player draws another card the value of that card is added to the total of the other cards and the player can continue to draw cards unless he gets a total of more than 21 in which case he busts and loses his bet.

When a player doesn't want any more cards, or stands, the dealer then moves on to the next player and after all of the players are finished then it's the dealer's turn to play. While each player can decide whether or not they want another card the dealer doesn't have that option and he must play by a fixed set of rules that require him to draw a card whenever his total is 16 or less and to stop when his total is 17 or more. If the dealer goes over 21 then he has busted and all of the players remaining in the game will be paid 1-to-1, or even money, on their bet.

If the dealer doesn't bust then each player's hand is compared to the dealer's. If the player's total is higher than the dealer's then they win and are paid even money. If the player's hand has a total that is lower than the dealer's hand then the player loses his bet. If the player and the dealer have the same total then it's a tie, or a push and neither hand wins. After all of the bets have been paid off, or taken by the dealer, a new round begins and new hands are dealt to all of the players.

When deciding how to play your hand there are also three other options available to you besides standing or hitting. The first is called *doubling down* and most casinos will allow a player to double their bet on their first two cards and draw only one more card. To do this you would place an amount equal to your original bet right next to it and then the dealer would give you one more card, sideways, to indicate that your bet was a double down. To double down in a game where the cards are dealt face down you would turn up your original two cards and tell the dealer you wanted to double down. Then, after you double your bet, the dealer would give you one more card face down. Some casinos may have restrictions on this bet and may only allow you to double down if the total of your 2 cards is 10 or 11, but it's always to your advantage if they allow you to double down on any two cards.

Another thing you can do is *split* your cards if you have a pair and then play each card as a separate hand. For example, if you had a pair of 8's you would place a bet equal to your original bet right next to it and tell the dealer you wanted to split your pair. The dealer would then separate your two 8's and give you one card on your first 8. Unlike doubling down, however, you are not limited to only getting one card and you can play your hand out normally. When you were finished with your first hand the dealer would then give you a card on your other 8 and you would play that hand out. Although I said that you weren't limited to just one card on your splits there is one instance where that will happen and that's when you split aces. Virtually all casinos will only give you one card on each ace when you split them. Also, if you get a 10-value card with your ace it will only count as 21 and not as a blackjack so you'll only get even money on that bet if you win. Besides splitting pairs you can also split all 10-value cards such as jack-king or 10-queen but it would be a very bad idea to do that because you would be breaking up a 20 which is a very strong hand and you should never split 10's. By the way, if you wanted to split a pair in a casino where the cards are dealt face down you would simply turn your original 2 cards face-up and then tell the dealer that you wanted to split them.

The last option you have is not available in most casinos but you may come across it in a few Las Vegas Strip casinos and it's called **surrender**. With the surrender option you're allowed to lose half of your bet if you decide you don't want to play out your hand after looking at your first 2 cards. Let's say you're dealt a 10-6 for a total of 16 and the dealer has a 10 as his face-up card. A 16 is not a very strong hand, especially against a dealer's 10, so in this case it would be a good idea to surrender your hand and when the dealer came to your cards you would say "surrender." The dealer would then take half of your bet and remove your cards. Surrender is good for the player because in the long run you will lose less on the bad hands you're dealt and you should always try to play in a casino that offers the surrender option.

All right, we've covered the basics of how to play the game of blackjack and all of the possible options a player has, so the next question is how do you win? Well, the best way to win is to become a card counter, but for the average person that isn't always possible so let's start off by taking a look at basic blackjack strategy.

Computer studies have been done on the game of blackjack and millions of hands have been analyzed to come up with a basic formula for how to play your hand in any given situation. The main principle that these decisions are based on is the dealer's up card because, remember that the dealer has no say in whether or not he takes a card - he must play by the rules that require him to draw a card until he has a total of 17 or more. Now, according to these computer calculations the dealer will bust more often when his up card is a 2,3,4,5 or 6 and he will complete more hands when his up card is a 7,8,9,10-value card or an ace. Take a look at the following chart that shows how each up-card affects the dealer's chance of busting:

Chance The Dealer's Up Card Will Bust

2	35%
3	38%
4	40%
5	43%
6	42%
7	26%
8	24%
9	23%
10	21%
Ace	11%

As you can see, the dealer will bust most often when he has a 5 or 6 as his upcard and he will bust the least amount, approximately 11% of the time, when his upcard is an ace. This means it's to your advantage to stand more often when the dealer's upcard is a 2 through 6 and hope that the dealer will draw cards that make him bust. It also means that when the dealer's upcard is a 7 through ace he will complete more of his hands and in that situation you should draw cards until you have a total of 17 or more.

Now let's show you how to play your hands by using the basic strategy and we'll start off with the *hard hand* strategy and by hard hand I mean a 2-card total without an ace. A hand with an ace is known as a soft hand because the ace can be counted as either a 1 or an 11. So, if you had an ace-6 you would have a soft 17 hand and if you had a 10-6 you would have a hard 16 hand. Later on we'll take a look at how to play soft hands, but for now we'll concentrate on the hard hand totals. Oh yes, one more thing, the basic strategy I'm going to give you applies to casinos where they deal more than one deck at a time and the dealer stands on soft 17 which is the situation you'll find in the majority of casinos today. So, keep in mind that the strategy would be slightly different if you were playing against a single deck and it would also be slightly different if the dealer hit a soft 17.

Whenever your first 2 cards total 17 through 21, you should stand, no matter what the dealer's up card is.

If your cards total 16, you should stand if the dealer has a 2 through 6 as his upcard otherwise, draw a card. By the way, 16 is the worst hand you can have because you will bust more often with 16 than with any other hand. So, if that's the case then why would you want to ever hit a 16? Well, once again, those computer studies have shown that you should hit a 16 when the dealer has 7 through ace as his upcard because in the long run you will lose less often. This means that yes, 16 is a terrible hand, but you should hit it because if you don't you will lose even more often than when you do take a card.

If your cards total 15, you should also stand if the dealer has a 2 through 6 as his upcard otherwise, draw cards until your total is 17 or more.

The same rules from 15 and 16 also apply if your cards total 14. Stand if the dealer has a 2 through 6, otherwise draw cards until your total is 17 or more. The same rules also apply if your cards total 13. Stand if the dealer has a 2 through 6, otherwise draw cards until your total is 17 or more.

When your cards total 12 you should only stand when the dealer has a 4,5 or 6 as his upcard, remember - those are his 3 weakest cards and he will bust more often with those cards, so you don't want to take a chance on busting yourself. If the dealer's upcard is a 2 or a 3, then you should take just one card and stop on your total of 13 or more. Finally, if the dealer has a 7 through ace as his upcard then you should draw cards until your total is 17 or more.

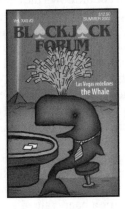

When your cards total 11 you would always want to hit it because you can't bust, but before you ask for a card you should consider making a double down bet. If the casino allows you to double down then you should do that if the dealer has anything but an ace as his upcard. After you double down the dealer would give you just one additional card on that hand. If the dealer's upcard is an ace then you shouldn't double down. Instead, you should hit the hand and continue to draw until your total is 17 or more. If the casino doesn't allow you to double down then you should just hit your hand and then, depending on your total, play it by the rules I gave you for the hands that totaled 12 through 21. So, if you had an 11 and the dealer had a 5 as his upcard, you should take a card. Then let's say you draw an ace which gives you a total of 12. Well, as I said before, if you have a 12 against a dealer's 5 you should stand and that's how you should play that hand.

If your total is 10 you would, once again, want to double down unless the dealer showed an ace or a 10. If the dealer had an ace or a 10 as his upcard you should hit your hand and then use the standard rules for a hand valued at 12 through 21. So, if you had a 10 and the dealer had an 8 as his up card you would want to double down and take one more card. If you weren't allowed to double, then you would take a hit and let's say you got a 4 for a total of 14. You should then continue to hit your hand until your total is 17 or more.

If your total is 9 you would want to double down whenever the dealer was showing a 3,4,5 or 6 as his upcard. If the dealer had a 2 as his upcard, or if he had a 7 through ace as his upcard, you should hit your hand and then use the standard playing rules as discussed before. So, let's say you had a 9 and the dealer had a 4 as his upcard you would want to double down and take one more card. If you weren't allowed to double then you should take a hit and let's say you got a 2 for a total of 11, you would then take another hit and let's say you got an ace. That would give you a total of 12 and, as I showed you previously, you should stand on 12 against a dealer's 4.

Finally, if your total is 8 or less you should always take a card and then use the standard playing rules that we already discussed.

Now, let's take a look at splitting pairs, but keep in mind that the rules for splitting will change slightly depending on whether or not the casino will allow you to double down after you split your cards. Most multiple deck games allow you to double down after splitting so that's the situation we'll cover first and then I'll tell you about the changes if you're not allowed to double down after splitting.

Basic Strategy - Single Deck

Dealer stands on soft 17 • Double on any 2 cards • Double allowed after split

Your Hand	Dealer's Upcard									
	2	3	4	5	6	7	8	9	10	A
17	ALWAYS STAND ON HARD 17 (OR MORE)									
16	-	-	-	-	-	H	H	H	H*	H
15	-	-	-	-	-	H	H	H	H*	H
14	-	-	-	-	-	H	H	H	H	H
13	-	-	-	-	-	H	H	H	H	H
12	H	H	-	-	-	H	H	H	H	H
11	ALWAYS DOUBLE									
10	D	D	D	D	D	D	D	D	H	H
9	D	D	D	D	D	H	H	H	H	H
8	H	H	H	D	D	H	H	H	H	H
A,8	-	-	-	-	D	-	-	-	-	-
A,7	-	D	D	D	D	-	-	H	H	-
A,6	D	D	D	D	D	H	H	H	H	H
A,5	H	H	D	D	D	H	H	H	H	H
A,4	H	H	D	D	D	H	H	H	H	H
A,3	H	H	D	D	D	H	H	H	H	H
A,2	H	H	D	D	D	H	H	H	H	H
A,A	ALWAYS SPLIT									
10,10	ALWAYS STAND (NEVER SPLIT)									
9,9	Sp	Sp	Sp	Sp	Sp	-	Sp	Sp	-	-
8,8	ALWAYS SPLIT									
7,7	Sp	Sp	Sp	Sp	Sp	Sp	Sp	H	-*	H
6,6	Sp	Sp	Sp	Sp	Sp	Sp	H	H	H	H
5,5	NEVER SPLIT (PLAY AS 10 HAND)									
4,4	H	H	Sp	Sp	Sp	H	H	H	H	H
3,3	Sp	Sp	Sp	Sp	Sp	Sp	Sp	H	H	H
2,2	Sp	H	Sp	Sp	Sp	Sp	H	H	H	H

- =Stand   H=Hit   D=Double   Sp=Split   *= Surrender if allowed

shaded boxes show strategy changes from chart on next page

Basic Strategy - Single Deck

Dealer stands on soft 17 • Double on any 2 cards • Double NOT allowed after split

Your Hand	Dealer's Upcard									
	2	3	4	5	6	7	8	9	10	A
17	ALWAYS STAND ON HARD 17 (OR MORE)									
16	-	-	-	-	-	H	H	H	H*	H*
15	-	-	-	-	-	H	H	H	H*	H
14	-	-	-	-	-	H	H	H	H	H
13	-	-	-	-	-	H	H	H	H	H
12	H	H	-	-	-	H	H	H	H	H
11	ALWAYS DOUBLE									
10	D	D	D	D	D	D	D	D	H	H
9	D	D	D	D	D	H	H	H	H	H
8	H	H	H	D	D	H	H	H	H	H
A,8	-	-	-	-	D	-	-	-	-	-
A,7	-	D	D	D	D	-	-	H	H	-
A,6	D	D	D	D	D	H	H	H	H	H
A,5	H	H	D	D	D	H	H	H	H	H
A,4	H	H	D	D	D	H	H	H	H	H
A,3	H	H	D	D	D	H	H	H	H	H
A,2	H	H	D	D	D	H	H	H	H	H
A,A	ALWAYS SPLIT									
10,10	NEVER SPLIT (ALWAYS STAND)									
9,9	Sp	Sp	Sp	Sp	Sp	-	Sp	Sp	-	-
8,8	ALWAYS SPLIT									
7,7	Sp	Sp	Sp	Sp	Sp	Sp	H	H	-*	H
6,6	Sp	Sp	Sp	Sp	Sp	H	H	H	H	H
5,5	NEVER SPLIT (PLAY AS 10 HAND)									
4,4	NEVER SPLIT (PLAY AS 8 HAND)									
3,3	H	H	Sp	Sp	Sp	Sp	H	H	H	H
2,2	H	Sp	Sp	Sp	Sp	Sp	H	H	H	H

- =Stand   H=Hit   D=Double   Sp=Split   *= Surrender if allowed

Basic Strategy - Multiple Decks

Dealer stands on soft 17 • Double on any 2 cards • Double allowed after split

Your Hand	2	3	4	5	6	7	8	9	10	A
				Dealer's Upcard						
17	ALWAYS STAND ON 17 (OR MORE)									
16	-	-	-	-	-	H	H	H*	H*	H*
15	-	-	-	-	-	H	H	H	H*	H
14	-	-	-	-	-	H	H	H	H	H
13	-	-	-	-	-	H	H	H	H	H
12	H	H	-	-	-	H	H	H	H	H
11	D	D	D	D	D	D	D	D	D	H
10	D	D	D	D	D	D	D	D	H	H
9	H	D	D	D	D	H	H	H	H	H
8	ALWAYS HIT 8 (OR LESS)									
A,8	ALWAYS STAND ON SOFT 19 (OR MORE)									
A,7	-	D	D	D	D	-	-	H	H	H
A,6	H	D	D	D	D	H	H	H	H	H
A,5	H	H	D	D	D	H	H	H	H	H
A,4	H	H	D	D	D	H	H	H	H	H
A,3	H	H	H	D	D	H	H	H	H	H
A,2	H	H	H	D	D	H	H	H	H	H
A,A	ALWAYS SPLIT									
10,10	ALWAYS STAND (NEVER SPLIT)									
9,9	Sp	Sp	Sp	Sp	Sp	-	Sp	Sp	-	-
8,8	ALWAYS SPLIT									
7,7	Sp	Sp	Sp	Sp	Sp	Sp	H	H	H	H
6,6	Sp	Sp	Sp	Sp	Sp	H	H	H	H	H
5,5	D	D	D	D	D	D	D	D	H	H
4,4	H	H	H	Sp	Sp	H	H	H	H	H
3,3	Sp	Sp	Sp	Sp	Sp	Sp	H	H	H	H
2,2	Sp	Sp	Sp	Sp	Sp	Sp	H	H	H	H

- =Stand   H=Hit   D=Double   Sp=Split   *= Surrender if allowed

Basic Strategy - Multiple Decks

Dealer stands on soft 17 • Double on any 2 cards • Double NOT allowed after split

Your Hand	\ Dealer's Upcard									
	2	3	4	5	6	7	8	9	10	A
17	ALWAYS STAND ON HARD 17 (OR MORE)									
16	-	-	-	-	-	H	H	H*	H*	H*
15	-	-	-	-	-	H	H	H	H*	H
14	-	-	-	-	-	H	H	H	H	H
13	-	-	-	-	-	H	H	H	H	H
12	H	H	-	-	-	H	H	H	H	H
11	D	D	D	D	D	D	D	D	D	H
10	D	D	D	D	D	D	D	D	H	H
9	H	D	D	D	D	H	H	H	H	H
8	ALWAYS HIT 8 (OR LESS)									
A,8	ALWAYS STAND ON SOFT 19 (OR MORE)									
A,7	-	D	D	D	D	-	-	H	H	H
A,6	H	D	D	D	D	H	H	H	H	H
A,5	H	H	D	D	D	H	H	H	H	H
A,4	H	H	D	D	D	H	H	H	H	H
A,3	H	H	H	D	D	H	H	H	H	H
A,2	H	H	H	D	D	H	H	H	H	H
A,A	ALWAYS SPLIT									
10,10	ALWAYS STAND (NEVER SPLIT)									
9,9	Sp	Sp	Sp	Sp	Sp	-	Sp	Sp	-	-
8,8	ALWAYS SPLIT									
7,7	Sp	Sp	Sp	Sp	Sp	Sp	H	H	H	H
6,6	H	Sp	Sp	Sp	Sp	H	H	H	H	H
5,5	NEVER SPLIT (PLAY AS 10 HAND)									
4,4	H	H	H	H	H	H	H	H	H	H
3,3	H	H	Sp	Sp	Sp	Sp	H	H	H	H
2,2	H	H	Sp	Sp	Sp	Sp	H	H	H	H

- =Stand   H=Hit   D=Double   Sp=Split   *= Surrender if allowed
shaded boxes show strategy changes from chart on previous page

As I said earlier, when your first two cards are the same most casinos will allow you to split them and play them as two separate hands so let's go over the basic strategy rules on when you should do this.

The first thing you should remember is that you always split aces and 8's. The reason you split aces is obvious because if you get a 10 on either hand you'll have a perfect 21, but remember that you won't get paid for a blackjack at 3-to-2, instead it'll be counted as a regular 21 and you'll be paid at even money. If you have a pair of 8's you have 16 which is a terrible hand and you can always improve it by splitting your 8's and playing them as separate hands.

The next thing to remember about splitting pairs is that you never split 5's or 10's. Once again, the reasons should be rather obvious, you don't want to split 10's because 20 is a great hand and you don't want to split 5's because 10 is a great hand to draw to. Instead, you would want to double down on that 10, unless the dealer was showing a 10 or an ace as his upcard.

2's, 3's and 7's should only be split when the dealer is showing a 2 through 7 as his upcard. Split 4's only when the dealer has a 5 or 6 as his upcard (remember 5 and 6 are his weakest cards!), 6's should be split whenever the dealer is showing a 2 through 6 and finally, you should always split 9's unless the dealer is showing a 7, 10 or ace. The reason you don't want to split 9's against a 10 or an ace should be rather obvious, but the reason you don't want to split them against a 7 is in case the dealer has a 10 as his hole card because in that case your 18 would beat out his 17.

If the casino will not allow you to double down after splitting then you should make the following three changes: For 2's and 3's only split them against a 4,5,6 or 7; never split 4's; and for a pair of 6's only split them against a 3,4,5 or 6. Everything else should be played the same.

Now, let's take a look at how to play *soft hands* and remember a soft hand is any hand that contains an ace that can be counted as 1 or 11. For a soft hand of 19 or more you should always stand.

For soft 18 against a 2,7 or 8 you should always stand. If the dealer shows a 9, 10 or an ace you should always take a hit and for a soft 18 against a 3,4,5 or 6 you should double down, but if the casino won't allow you to double then you should just stand.

For soft 17 you should always take a hit, but if the casino allows you to double down, then you should double against a dealer's 3,4,5 or 6.

For soft 16 or a soft 15 you should always take a hit, but if the casino allows you to double down then you should double against a dealer's 4,5 or 6.

Blackjack Books by Stanford Wong

One of the World's Leading Experts on Winning at Blackjack

Professional Blackjack - This is the 1994 revision of a classic first published in 1975. In addition to teaching card counting by means of two simple, but powerful methods, this edition includes: strategies for playing new rules such as over/under, simulation results to replace all the "best guesses" of earlier editions, plus tables of expectations. 352 pages; **$19.95**

Basic Blackjack - What blackjack neophytes need is basic strategy. It must be mastered before one goes on to card counting. *Basic Blackjack* has the most complete explanation of basic strategy available anywhere.

Example: In early 1993, blackjack players of Ramada Express in Laughlin were pleasantly surprised to find the casino had decided to pay 3:2 on five-card hands at blackjack. Those customers who had *Basic Blackjack* had only to turn to table 21 to find basic strategy for exploiting this rule.

Basic Blackjack also contains the best of *Winning Without Counting*, an out-of-print book on getting an edge at blackjack without counting cards that initially sold for $200 per copy. 224 pages; **$14.95**

Shipping Charges: $3.50 for first book and $1 for each additional book

Send Check or Money Order To:
Casino Vacations • P.O. Box 703
Dania, FL • 33004

Credit Card Orders Call Toll-Free:
(800) 741-1596
order online at:
www.americancasinoguide.com

Best Blackjack by Frank Scoblete

In precise, easy-to-understand, straightforward language, Frank Scoblete, shows you how to beat the most popular table game in the casinos today. Everything you need to know to become an expert blackjack player is in this book, including: basic strategies for single and multiple-deck games: plus, powerful but easy-to-master card-counting techniques. You'll also learn the secrets of beating options such as Over-Under 13, Red-Black 21, Super Sevens, Jackpot 21 and much, much more.

Frank also shows you the insider tricks the professionals use that can give players even greater edges. Learn how to take advantage of the sloppy dealers. Learn how to cut the cards to give you the better hands. Learn how to get the casinos to pay you extra money to play blackjack. **Best Blackjack -** 284 Pages **$14.95** + $3.50 shipping ($1 extra shipping for each additonal book). For credit card orders call toll-free **(800) 741-1596.** Or send check or money order to:

Casino Vacations • P.O. Box 703 • Dania, FL 33004

order online at: **www.americancasinoguide.com**

For soft 14 you should always take a hit, but if the casino allows you to double down then you should double against a dealer's 5 or 6.

Finally, for a soft 13 you should always take a hit, but if the casino allows you to double down then you should double against a dealer's 5 or 6.

The last thing we need to cover is surrender which, as noted before, isn't offered in many casinos but it is an option that does work in your favor and if available, you should play in a casino that offers it. The surrender rules are very simple to remember and only apply to hard totals of 15 or 16. If you have a hard 16 you should surrender it whenever the dealer has a 9, 10 or ace as his upcard and if you have a hard 15 you should surrender it whenever the dealer has a 10 as his upcard. That's all there is to surrender.

Now that you know how to play the game and you have an understanding of the basic strategy let's take a quick look at how the rules variations can affect the game of blackjack. As noted before, various computer studies have been made on blackjack and these studies have shown that each rule change can either hurt or help the player by a certain amount. For example, a single-deck game where you can double on any first 2 cards (but not after splitting pairs), the dealer stands on soft 17 and no surrender is allowed has no advantage for the casino when using the basic strategy. That's right, in a game with those rules in effect the game is dead even and neither the casino nor the player has an edge!

Take a look at the following chart and you'll see how some rules changes can hurt you or help you as a player. Minus signs in front mean that the casino gains the edge by that particular amount while plus signs mean that you gain the edge by that amount.

RULES THAT HURT YOU		RULES THAT HELP YOU	
Two decks	-0.32%	Double after split	+0.13%
Four decks	-0.49%	Late surrender	+0.06%
Six decks	-0.54%	Resplit Aces	+0.14%
Eight decks	-0.57%	Double anytime	+0.20%
Dealer hits soft 17	-0.20%		
No soft doubling	-0.14%		

As you can see, it's always to your advantage to play against as few decks as possible. The house edge goes up substantially as you go from 1 deck to 2, but the change is less dramatic when you go from 2 to 4, or from 4 to 6, and it's barely noticeable when you go from 6 to 8. You can also see that you would prefer not to play in a casino where the dealer hits a soft 17 because that gives the dealer a slight edge. You would also want to play in a casino where you're allowed to double down on your soft hands or else you would be giving another added edge to the casino.

You can also see from these charts that you would want to play in a casino where you were allowed to double down after splitting cards and you would also want to play in a casino that offered surrender. The other two rules variations that help the player are somewhat rare but they were put in to show you how these rules changes can affect your odds in the game. Some casinos will allow you to resplit aces again if you draw an ace to one of your original aces and this works to your advantage. Also, some casinos will allow you to double down on any number of cards rather than just the first two. In other words, if you got a 2- 4-3-2 as your first four cards you would then be allowed to double down on your total of 11 before receiving your 5th card. If they allow you to do this then, once again, you have a rule that works in your favor.

The point of showing you these charts is to help you understand that when you have a choice of places to play you should always choose the casino that offers the best rules. So, if you find a single-deck game with good rules you could be playing an even game by using the basic strategy, or at worst be giving the casino an edge of less than one-half of 1%.

Now, there is one way that you can actually have the edge working in your favor when you play blackjack and that's by becoming a card counter. As I said before, card counting is not for the average person but I do think it's important that you understand the concept of card counting and if you think you'd like to learn more about counting cards then it's something you can follow up on later.

Many people think that to be a card counter you have to have a photographic memory and remember every single card that's been played. Fortunately, it's not quite that difficult. Actually, the main concept behind card counting is the assumption that the dealer will bust more often when there are a lot of 10's in the deck and that he will complete more hands when there are a lot of smaller cards in the deck. Now, if you stop to think about it, it makes sense doesn't it? After all, the dealer has to play by set rules that make him take a card until he has a total of 17 or more. If there are a lot of 2's, 3's and 4's in the deck the dealer won't bust very often when he draws cards, but if there are a lot of 10's in the deck then chances are he will bust more often when he is forced to draw cards.

The card counter tries to take advantage of this fact by keeping a running total of the cards that have been played to give him an idea of what kind of cards remain in the deck. If there are a lot of 10 cards remaining in the deck then the counter will bet more money because the odds are slightly in his favor. Of course, if there are a lot of small cards remaining then the counter would only make a small bet because the odds would be slightly in favor of the dealer. Another thing that the card counter can do is to change his basic strategy to take advantage of the differences in the deck.

There are at least a dozen different card counting systems but let's take a quick look at a relatively simple one (it's also the most popular) and it's called the high-low count. With this system you assign a value of +1 to all 2's, 3's, 4's, 5's and 6's, while all 10's, Jacks, Queens, Kings and Aces are assigned a value of -1. The remaining cards: 7, 8 and 9 have no value and are not counted.

$$+1 = 2, 3, 4, 5, 6$$
$$-1 = 10, J, Q, K, A$$

When you look at these numbers you'll see that there are an equal number of cards in each group: there are five cards valued at +1 and five cards valued at -1. This means that they balance each other out and if you go through the deck and add them all together the end result will always be a total of exactly zero.

What a card counter does is to keep a running total of all the cards as they're played out and whenever the total has a plus value he knows that a lot of small cards have appeared and the remaining deck is rich in 10's which is good for the player. But, if the total is a minus value then the counter knows that a lot of 10-value cards have appeared and the remaining deck must be rich in low cards which is bad for the player. To give you an example of how to count let's say the following cards have been dealt on the first hand from a single deck:

$$2, 3, 3, 4, 5, 5, 5, 6, = +8$$
$$J, K, Q, A, = -4$$
$$Total = +4$$

As you can see, there were eight plus-value cards and four minus-value cards which resulted in a total count of +4. This means that there are now four more 10-value cards than low cards remaining in the deck and the advantage is with the player. Naturally, the higher the plus count, the more advantageous it is for the player and counters would be proportionally increasing their bets as the count got higher. The card counter would also be using the same basic strategy we spoke about previously, except for certain instances where a slight change would be called for.

On the other hand, if the count is negative, a card counter will always bet the minimum amount. Of course, they would prefer not to bet at all, but the casinos don't like you to sit at their tables and not bet so the counter has to bet something and the minimum is the least they can get by with.

There is one more important thing to explain about card counting and it's called the *true count*. The true count is a measure of the count per deck rather than a *running count* of all the cards that have been played and to get the true count you simply divide the running count by the number of decks remaining to be played. As an illustration, let's say you're playing in a 6-deck game and the count is +9. You look at the shoe and estimate that 3 decks remain to be played. You then divide the count of +9 by 3 to get +3 which is the true count. As another example, let's say you're in an 8-deck game with a count of +12 and there are 6 decks left to be played. You divide +12 by 6 to get +2 which is the true count. To put it another way, a +2 count in a double-deck game with 1 deck left to be played is the same as a +4 count in a 4-deck game with 2 decks left to be played, which is the same as a +6 count is a 6-deck game with 3 decks left to be played, which is the same as a +12 count in an 8-deck game with 6 decks left to be played.

For the card counter it is crucial to always take the running count and then divide it by the number of decks remaining in order to get the true count because all betting and playing decisions are based on the true count rather than the running count.

Of course, if you're playing in a single-deck game the running count and the true count are initially the same. The more you get into the deck, however, the more weight is given to the running count because there is less than one deck remaining. So, if the running count was +3 and only a 1/2-deck remained you would calculate the true count by dividing +3 by 1/2 (which is the same as multiplying by 2/1, or 2) to get a true count of +6. As another example, if the running count was +2 and about 2/3 of the deck remained you would divide +2 by 2/3 (the same as multi-plying by 3/2 or, 1 and 1/2) to get +3.

As you can see, the count becomes much more meaningful as you get closer to the last cards in the deck and that's why casinos never deal down to the end. Instead, the dealer will insert a plastic card about 2/3 or 3/4 of the way in the deck and when that card is reached the dealer will finish that particular round and then shuffle the cards. How far into the deck(s) that plastic card is inserted is known as the **_penetration point_** and card counters always look for a dealer that offers good penetration. The card counter knows that the further into the deck(s) the plastic card is placed the more meaningful the true count will be and the more advantageous it will be for the card counter.

So, now that you know how those card counters keep track of the cards, what kind of advantage do you think they have over the casino? Well, not too much. Depending on the number of decks used, the rules in force, and the skill of the counter, it could be as much as 2% but that would be at the high end. Probably 1% would be closer to the actual truth. This means that for every $1,000 in bets that are made the card counter will win $10. Not exactly a huge amount but there are people out there who do make a living playing the game.

If you would like to learn more about blackjack, as well as more about card counting, be sure to take a look at the some of the ads in this book for ordering information on some very helpful books, newsletters, videos and computer software.

Meet Stanford Wong - The "Guru" of Blackjack

by Steve Bourie

If you've ever read any stories about the game of blackjack you've probably heard of Stanford Wong. He's the author of numerous books on the subject, as well as the brains behind some computer software programs that can analyze the game inside and out. His most popular book, *Professional Blackjack*, is used as a bible by many professional players and is one of the best books for anyone who wants to learn how to counts cards.

I often refer to Wong's books and software programs during the course of my work and although we talk on the phone periodically I must admit that I really didn't know much about his background. In the 30 years that I've been reading about gambling I don't ever remember seeing any stories about how he came to be a blackjack expert. I thought it might be interesting to explore this subject and in early 2002 I conducted an interview with Wong by telephone from his home in La Jolla, California.

Wong was born in Georgia during World War II and his family briefly moved to a few other states before settling in Beaverton, Oregon. He began his schooling there and always had an affection for playing games. "Any new game that I would hear about I would learn the rules and I would figure out how to play it," he says. "But what always turned me on about any new game was figuring out the optimal strategy.

When I first learned tic-tac-toe for example, I really didn't want to play the game with other people, I wanted to figure out where, if I moved first, should I make my mark? Or, if I moved second, and given where you made your mark, where should I make my mark? I was probably five or six years old when I figured that out. But that was what always interested me about games: learning the strategy."

As he grew up Wong also says he spent a lot of time playing card games. "It was the sort of thing that our family and relatives did whenever they got together. There were probably a dozen different card games that my folks and I played, depending on what set of relatives, neighbors or friends we were playing with and I essentially grew up with a deck of cards in my hand. It was just a way of life and it wasn't anything we did for money, it was just a competitive sort of thing"

Wong believes he led a rather normal lifestyle and never considered playing cards to be anything other than a minor diversion until he read Ed Thorp's book *Beat The Dealer* in 1963 which suddenly gave him other ideas. "I thought 'hey this is neat!' This guy's really got something here and maybe I can make some money in the casinos," he says. "Actually, before that book came out I was doing my own work on analyzing blackjack but I really didn't do it with the idea of taking on the casinos. I just did it as a hobby because I thought it was an interesting game and I thought I could figure out what the strategy should be."

And how old was he when he developed those blackjack strategies? Just 14! "It was fun," he says. "You got to look at some of the interesting problems that were involved in calculating 'should you hit or stand on 16 against a dealer's 10?' I thought it was interesting to figure out the formulas for doing that."

Wong was 20 at the time he read Thorp's book and, not surprisingly, he turned to the book's appendix first. "Thorp had calculated all the probabilities for hitting and standing for every situation and I compared his data with the calculations I had done. I noticed that his numbers matched my numbers exactly so I thought 'hey, this guy's giving us the true information.' Actually, I had only done the calculations for deuces through 10's and I hadn't done the aces yet because they took a lot of time. At that point I abandoned the rest of my calculations because I would have been doing what he had already done and I knew his numbers were correct."

Then an udergraduate student at Oregon State University, Wong was still too young to enter a casino but he enjoyed learning how to count cards using Thorp's 10-count system. "I practiced on evenings and weekends," he says. "Since I was a student I didn't have that much time for it and I just did it as a challenge. I had to wait a few months until I was 21 before I could go to Nevada and visit the casinos."

One week past his 21st birthday Wong traveled to Reno at the start of the summer with a classmate who had also taken the time to learn card-counting. "It was interesting because we won money right off the bat," he professes proudly. "We thought 'gee, what an easy way to make money.' We just had one of those fabulous win streaks. We started with a $300 bankroll and made something like $250. Our minimum bet was $1 and our maximum was $4."

During that first weekday afternoon in Reno he strolled into the Horseshoe Casino and found he was the only customer in the place. "There wasn't even anybody playing slots," he says. "All of the dealers and the pit boss were watching me because they had nothing else to do and I didn't know how to behave because I had never watched other players. So here I am just sitting back in my chair winning hand after hand and all of these silver dollars were piling up in front of me. I had about 250 of them and finally it dawned on me that I wouldn't be able to carry them all." At that point he stopped playing and when the dealer asked him why, he said "This is all the money I can carry. If I win any more I won't have any way to carry it." Then the dealer asked if she could "give him a check for those silver dollars?" and he replied "I don't want your check. I want this money." The dealer then explained to the novice player that she would exchange his silver dollars for chips out of her rack which he could then take to the cashier's cage to be redeemed for cash. Still unsure about what she was proposing to him, Wong wondered "are they trying to cheat me or is this the normal procedure? There were no other players there that I could ask but I finally agreed to it. Then, I must have ran over to the cashier's cage because it was like I was afraid that the chips were going to lose their value by the time I got there. I was so relieved when the cashier finally gave me $20 bills for those little pieces of plastic which I wasn't sure had any real value. That's how naive I was."

Of course, the blackjack games were a little different back in that summer of 1964. "They were all single-deck games and they dealt out 50 of the 52 cards," says Wong. "They only burned one card and they wouldn't deal the last card. If you got a dealer to yourself it was a fabulous game. The rules were you could double any two cards and the dealer would hit soft 17."

Following his successful first trip Wong continued to make visits to Reno or Lake Tahoe whenever he had a break from his academic studies and the following summer he felt ready to take on Las Vegas. However, after three days in Vegas he gave up because he was discouraged by the widespread cheating which he saw. "It seemed like every place in Vegas was cheating," he says. "I couldn't find an honest game. I remember one place where I saw the dealer cheating. It was an obvious move and he noticed that I saw him do it. Suddenly, he got this big smile on his face as if I were admiring his handiwork and he was proud of what he had done. There was no shame on his part and it was just like well, that's the way we deal the game in this town." Following his experience in Vegas Wong returned to Reno to practice his skills. "There were a couple of places in Reno that cheated but we stayed away from them. The rest were all honest."

In 1965 Wong completed his undergraduate studies and the following year he received his MBA from Oregon State. He stayed there as a teacher for two more years and during that period he met and married his wife (they're still married). Naturally, he was still playing in Reno and Lake Tahoe as often as he could and in 1968 he was drafted into the Army. Following his two-year tour of duty Wong enrolled at Stanford University (located about 30 miles south of San Francisco) to pursue a PhD in finance. Being closer to Las

Vegas he decided to visit the city again and he says he "was pleasantly surprised to see that Las Vegas was dealing honest blackjack games. Somehow Las Vegas got 'cleaned up' between the years of 1965 and 1970."

For the next five years Wong visited Nevada casinos once or twice a month while pursuing his PhD and also while helping to raise his son (born in 1971) and his daughter (born in 1974). In 1974 he began teaching finance courses full-time at San Francisco State and it was during his last term at S.F. State in 1976 that Wong found himself in a bit of a dilemma. "I was making more money playing blackjack than teaching classes and I didn't want to have to go to all of the faculty meetings. I thought they were a waste of time and instead of sticking around for meetings I would rather pop over to Las Vegas," he says. Since he had signed a contract he felt obligated to continue to teach his classes but he really didn't need the money so he made a deal with the school to teach for free in return for not having to go to the meetings. The University agreed and paid him a salary of $1 for his last term of teaching at the school. That, according to Wong, was his "last *real* job."

In 1975 Wong published *Professional Blackjack* which, he says, he really didn't intend to write and the book sort of evolved. It seems that lots of people were always asking him to teach them how to count cards but he didn't have time for that. Instead, he wrote an explanation of how to count cards which he handed out to anyone who asked him for help. When those people came back with questions, he would write out the answers and then add that information to his original explanation to make it even more comprehensive. "The original write-up of how to count cards kept getting bigger and bigger," he says. "The other thing I did was that I worked out strategies on the computer that Thorp didn't have in his book. Thorp didn't cover surrender, for example, so I worked out my own surrender indexes. I also worked out strategies for games where the dealer stood on soft 17. Eventually, I looked at all of that material and thought if I put it all together, along with an explanation of how to play the game, it could be a book but it was all sort of accidental."

Once he was ready to publish his book Wong decided that he needed a pen name. After all, he had been playing under his real name in the casinos and he didn't want them to know that he was an expert in card counting. "I really liked Nevada Smith, but somebody else already had that name," he says. "I had a preference for complicated first names and simple last names so I went to my friends in the PhD program at Stanford and asked for suggestions. Denny Draper, who's now a professor at U.S.C., suggested Stanford Wong and I said 'that's it!' It's got the mystique of the Orient and it's got an academic ring. So, I have to give him credit for coming up with my name."

In 1976 Wong moved to La Jolla (near San Diego) and the following year decided he wanted to try to make a living "for a year or two" from his publishing business and playing blackjack. He finally got his Ph.D. in 1978 and initially thought he would become a college professor but, he says, "it turned out that I really enjoyed what I was doing and I was making enough money that I never got back to teaching."

Wong soon got the urge to broaden his horizons by traveling in search of good blackjack games. "I made a lot of trips to Asia," he says. "Korea had wonderful blackjack. So did Macau, Indonesia and the Philippines. They all had great games back then." When asked if his trips were successful, he responds with an enthusiastic, "oh yeah." And was he successful enough that he started getting barred? "Only at a few little Korean casinos," he says. "The problem at that time was that they just didn't have enough customers. If there were only four customers they could keep track of each customer and know exactly how they were doing. I just won too much money too fast and they said 'sorry sir, we don't want you here anymore.' I would assume that they were sophisticated enough to know that I was counting cards but their attitude was 'you're winning from us, you're too good for us, please don't play here anymore' and I could understand that."

Weary from his long trips to Asia, and eager to spend more time at home with his family, Wong resumed his visits to Las Vegas where he found that he could continue to play as long as he didn't spend too much time in any one place. He developed an index card system where he kept track of his play. He had a card for every casino with details on: the date of his visits, how many hours he played, which shift he played on, and the results of his play (dollars won or lost). Then, when he was planning his next visit he would pull out his cards and select a group of casinos where he hadn't played in a while and visit them. This way he wouldn't become too well known to any particular casino's personnel.

Wong continued to visit Vegas once or twice a month and says he continued to make money even though the casinos "did things to make the games more difficult to beat, with multiple decks being one example." "However," he says "at the same time, players developed skills too. There are skills that I have now that I didn't have in 1978. For a while there was a really good way to make money by looking for warped hole cards, especially on insurance. You just looked at the shape of the dealer's hole card and if it was bent one way it was either an ace or a 10 and if it was bent the other way it was a small card. Plus, I had no idea about 'tells' when I first started playing blackjack. That's when you use the dealer's body language to learn something about their hole card."

And did he always win? "Oh there's no such thing as always making money," he says. "Sometimes I would win and sometimes I would lose but at the end of the year I would be ahead."

Wong's comment here brought up a widespread misconception that many people have about card counters. Most people think that counters always win whenever they play but that just isn't true. "The edge that a card counter has over a casino is much, much smaller than the edge that a casino has over their players, " he explains. "The average blackjack player thinks 'every time I play I lose but as a card counter you've got an edge so every time you play you must win.' However, it doesn't work that way because the counter's edge is much smaller. Just as there are gamblers who occasionally come back as winners because they got lucky there are also card counters who get unlucky and the casino beats them. It just happens."

Wong believes that some of the best opportunities for blackjack players to-day may be in the special promotions that the casinos are continuously offering. "One of the best things now is all of the 'freebies' that the casinos are giving out," he proclaims. Anybody that plays a lot of blackjack has got more than they need in the way of room and food comps, plus many casinos are sending out coupons that are valid for cash at the cage or they're sending out matchplay offers that can be played at the tables just like cash. There's a lot of free money being given out to entice people to play. So part of the income for a professional player now, or even a regular player, is in these free cash offers. That wasn't the case 20 or 30 years ago."

When asked if there is any way a basic strategy player can come out ahead in the long run, Wong replies: "Well, it depends what you mean by come out ahead. You have to look at each individual and ask what is it that they want? There are a lot of people on our website bj21.com, for example, that don't really need the money they make playing blackjack. They're just looking for some fun. These are people who are successful as medical doctors, or law-yers, or something else outside of the world of blackjack but they're very competitive. They love Las Vegas and they really like the idea that when they go there they can stay at luxurious accommodations and eat meals in fabulous restaurants and somebody else will pay for them. So for them, as long as they're playing a game that's breakeven or better, they're happy be-cause they get to live like kings but they don't have to pay for it."

And does Wong himself play for comps? "I don't do that," he says. His pre-ferred method is to count cards and make sure he is only playing in positive decks (where the count favors the player, unlike negative decks where the count favors the casino). This means that he is constantly changing tables in search of positive situations and it's a system that is popular with card counters. The method is known as "Wonging" and, of course, it's named after him.

"I like the idea of walking around and finding positive counts," he says. "I'll sometimes play neutral counts or go to a table where a dealer is shuffling but if I get a count of -2 after the first hand, I'm gone. If it's -1 I might stick around for a second hand but I basically just stick around for positive counts. If I were to sit at one table making minimum bets in negative counts it wouldn't be worthwhile. In the first place I don't want to waste my time making minimum bets and in the second place that's going to look bad to anyone who's watching me when I hit a good count and start raising my bet. I'd rather have them see me only betting $200 a hand. I don't want them to see me sometimes betting $25 and sometimes betting $200."

But don't the casinos know him as Stanford Wong when he plays there? "Quite a few people in the casinos know me but they tend to be the higher-ups, they're not the people down on the floor" he says. "As long as I keep my bets low enough, basically the people who are watching me don't know me at all. At a lot of these places in Nevada the point where the attention starts is $100 and as long as you keep you bets under $100 you're flying under their radar. There are also some places where you can bet up to $300 or $500 before they start paying attention, so I like to bet as much as I can but the really important thing is to stay under their radar. If they'll let me bet $500 and nobody's going to care I'll stick $500 out there."

When asked if he has any words of wisdom for the average blackjack player Wong makes the point that players should be sure that they're getting the freebies that their action warrants. "If you're betting enough to earn free meals then you should make sure that the casino is paying for your meals," he says. "Also, you've got to know if you're playing with an edge and if you're not counting cards then you're not playing with an edge. If you like to play and you're not a card counter then my advice is to play as slowly as possible in order to get your comps."

By urging non-counters to play slowly Wong is referring to the fact that casinos always base their comp formulas on the amount of time you spend at the tables plus the average amount of your bets. "Typically they'll want four hours but they're going to say four hours whether it's a busy table and you're playing 40 hands an hour or it's an empty table where you're playing by yourself and putting in 200 hands an hour," he says. "If you're not counting cards make sure that you're playing at a table where there are lots of other players. It helps if they're all laughing and having a good time and the dealer's joking along with everyone and the game is moving as slowly as possible. But if you're a card counter I would advise you to do just the opposite because you want to get in as many hands per hour as possible. You would want to play at the times of day when the casino is empty and you're the only player at the table and the dealer is really fast."

Of course there are some blackjack players who believe that you don't have to be a card counter in order to have an edge over the casino. Many of these players believe that you can use money management, or progressive betting systems to overcome the casino edge but Wong doesn't believe that's possible. "That's hogwash," he says. "Money management does not give you an edge over the casino. The first thing you've got to do is count cards so you play well enough to get an edge over the casino. Once you've got that edge that's where money management comes in. But if you're not playing with an edge then proper money management says to keep your money in your pocket and don't risk it at all. "

Looking back on the start of his career in blackjack Wong says he was surprised at how things worked out. "I just thought it would be interesting to do for a while and I didn't see it as a lifetime thing. I thought I would just be doing it for a short time but it kept stretching out and stretching out."

Although he's had great success playing blackjack Wong is quick to admit that he would be "bored stiff" if that was all he did. "I just wouldn't be doing that anymore," he says. "When I first started playing the money I made was important to me because I needed it to pay bills but then I got to the point where I had plenty of money and I really didn't have to play blackjack for big money anymore. So I started asking myself what do I really want to do with my time? Do I want to sit in a smoky casino and make these boring decisions over and over again and have these huge ups and huge downs in my bankroll if I really don't need the money that badly? So I started to think of different things to do and what happened is that I got into more things that I could write about. I got into tournaments and wrote a book on that, plus books on horse racing, video poker, sports betting and now I have my own website at bj21.com. There's always something new to come along that keeps my interest up."

And is he happy with way things turned out? "Of course," he says. "I consider myself as being very fortunate in being able to do basically whatever I wanted to do for my whole adult life and what I really enjoy doing is figuring things out." There are an awful lot of gamblers out there who are glad he did!

Disturbing Trends In Blackjack

By Henry Tamburin

Over the past year changes have been made to the game of blackjack which have not been good for the player. Most of these changes occurred in Las Vegas. Let's hope they don't show up elsewhere.

The first change occurred when the majority of strip casinos decided to install continuous shuffling machines (CSM's) on their blackjack tables. These devices allowed the dealers to reshuffle after every hand, which makes card counting futile.

But CSM's not only hurt card counters; they have a negative effect on the average player. The reason is because the casinos get 20% more hands played on average per hour with these devices because there is no downtime for manual shuffles. Unless a player slows down when he plays, he will be playing more hands per hour and his potential hourly loss will increase (remember the casinos have the edge over the average player). My advice is to stay away from any CSM dealt game.

The next change occurred when the majority of strip casinos converted their rules to "dealer hit soft 17" from dealer stand on soft 17. That tiny rule change costs the player about 0.2% of his total betting action. And that assumes the player knows the changes to the basic playing strategy, which many do not.

Then came the introduction of the "new" single deck game called Super Fun 21. The game uses a single deck of cards (which most players know has better odds) and a whole bunch of player favorable rules (like doubling on any number of cards and being able to surrender even after doubling). But player blackjacks (except in diamonds) only pay even money. The latter negates all the player favorable rules resulting in a game with an 85% increase in casino's edge (up to 0.95%).

Next came the single deck game to end all single deck games. Las Vegas strips casinos were even advertising it on their marquees. It doesn't have a name but you'll know it because player blackjacks in this single deck game are paid at only 6 to 5 (or 2.4 to 2) odds instead of the usual 3 to 2 odds. That one rule change boosts the casino's edge to about 1.5%. Every player takes a hit with this game so stay away.

And finally, there's the six-deck game disguised as a double deck game. The dealer shuffles six decks but only deals two decks by hands. When you approach the table it appears to be a two-deck game but it's not. This is a deadly game for unsuspecting card counters.There is one way to stop this negative trend in blackjack. Don't play these games.

Henry Tamburin is the author of six best-selling books including Blackjack: Take The Money & Run.
For a free copy of his Blackjack Insider newsletter visit his web site at www.smartgaming.com.

Continuous Shuffling Machines in Blackjack

by Henry Tamburin

Ever since Edward Thorp published his ground breaking card counting system in 1962, skillful blackjack players have been able to get the edge over the casino by keeping track of specific cards as they are dealt by the dealer. Now a new innovation, touted as "a card counter's worst nightmare" claims to once and for all eliminate the advantage that card counters possess. The product is a new continuous multi-deck shuffler dubbed "The King" by its developer Shuffle Master Inc. of Las Vegas.

So what does this device do that threatens to make card counting obsolete? And does it have any effect on the casual blackjack player who is not card counting? Read on for the answers.

What makes this shuffler different from other automatic shufflers is that it completely randomizes the cards from a round of play with the other cards in the shuffler and then completely randomizes the delivery of the shuffled cards to the shoe. Here's how this "double randomization" process works.

After a round is over, the dealer inserts the cards into the shuffler. The cards are then randomized using an elevator system. The discards are placed on the elevator and then randomly placed into one of 19 elevator stops or shelves. The shuffler then randomly selects a shelf of cards and delivers those cards to the dealing shoe. These cards become the next group of cards dealt. The result, according to the folks at Shuffle Master, is "complete and total unpredictability."

How do these new shufflers wipe out the card counter's advantage? Card counters keep track of high and low value cards from one round to the next. They know when the remaining decks of cards in the playing shoe contain an excess of high value cards over low value cards. When this occurs the edge shifts in their favor and they increase their bets. Typically a skilled counter can gain a 1.0 to 1.5% advantage over the casino with this technique.

Essentially this new shuffler "immediately" recycles and deals cards from a 4-deck shoe on every round. More importantly, because any card can be delivered to a shelf and any shelf of cards can be delivered to the shoe, every discard re-inserted immediately following a hand has a chance to appear in the next round. The net result of this technology is that a card counter's advantage is eliminated.

How confident is Shuffle Master of the integrity of their new shuffler? A few summers ago they were offering $100,000 to anyone who could show through mathematical analysis and/or computer simulation how a player can gain the advantage using the new shuffler. Nobody claimed the 100 grand.

There is no question that this new shuffler is going to be hard to beat. Not only does it thwart card counters but also a system used by players called "shuffle tracking" where skilled players have been able to track a group of cards through the dealer's shuffling routine and know when these cards will be dispensed from the shoe. This knowledge obviously gives the shuffle tracker a big advantage over the casino. However, the "random in, random out" process of shuffling from a totally enclosed continuous shuffler makes shuffle tracking obsolete.

The continuous shuffler will not alter the odds of the game for the casual blackjack player who does not count cards. But because more hands are dealt per hour with the shuffler, a casual player's bankroll won't last as long. That's another reason why casinos like the shuffler. The game is faster and as long as they have the edge over the average blackjack player, the casino's stand to win more money per hour. In other words, if you are a casual blackjack player, the more hands you play, the more money you will lose.

Dealers who have used the new shuffler have given it mixed reviews. Some of the negatives are that it doesn't give them a break from the physically tiresome monotonous task of dealing. One dealer mentioned to me that she often likes to carry on a casual conversation with players while she shuffles the cards but with the new shuffler "it's all business all the time."

It would seem that the continuous shuffler has lots of benefits for the casinos but none for the player. It eliminates card counting and shuffle tracking for the skilled player and results in higher hourly loss rates for the casual player. Maybe that's why Shuffle Master named the new continuous shuffler "The King."

Henry Tamburin is one of America's most popular casino gaming writers and best-selling authors. For more of his winning advice visit his web site for casino players at www.smartgaming.com. Ordering information for his books and videos can be found on page 148.

Craps

by Steve Bourie

At first glance the game of craps looks a little intimidating because of all the various bets you can make but actually the game itself is very simple, so first let me explain the game without any reference to the betting.

Everyone at the craps table gets a turn to roll the dice, but you don't have to roll if you don't want to. The dice are passed around the table clockwise and if it's your turn to roll you simply take two dice and roll them to the opposite end of the table. This is your first roll of the dice which is also called the "come-out" roll. If you roll a 7 or 11 that's called a "natural" and you win, plus you get to roll again. If you roll a 2,3 or 12 those are all called "craps" and you lose, but you still get to roll again. The only other possible numbers you can roll are 4,5,6,8,9 or 10 and if one of those numbers shows up, then that number becomes your "point" and the object of the game is to roll that number again before you roll a 7.

If a 7 shows up before your "point" number does then you lose and the dice move on to the next shooter. If your "point" number shows up before a 7 does, then you have made a "pass." You then win your bet and you get to roll again. That's all there is to the game of craps.

Now that you know how to play the game, let's find out about the different kinds of bets you can make. Two of the best bets you'll find on the craps table are in the areas marked "pass" and "don't pass". When you bet on the "pass" line you're betting that the shooter will win. To make a pass line bet you put your bet right in front of you on the pass line. Pass line bets are paid even-money and the house edge on a pass line bet is 1.41% You can also bet on the "don't pass" line in which case you're betting that the shooter will lose. To make a don't pass bet you put your bet in front of you in the don't pass area. Don't pass bets are also paid even-money and the house edge on them is 1.40%

In reality, the odds are always 1.41% against the shooter and in favor of the "don't pass" bettor by that same amount. Of course, if you're a "don't pass" bettor the casinos don't want to give you a bet where you have an edge so they have a rule in effect on "don't pass" bets where on the come out roll if the shooter throws a 12, you don't win. You don't lose either, the bet is just considered a "push," or tie, and nothing happens. In some casinos they may make 2 instead of 12 the number that's a push. Just look on the don't pass line and you'll you see the word "bar" and then the number that the casino considers a push. In our illustration it says bar 12, so in this casino your bet on the don't pass line will be a push if the come-out roll is a 12. This rule is what gives the casino its advantage on don't pass bets and it doesn't matter whether the casino bars the 2 or 12 the result is the same 1.40% advantage for the house.

All right, let's say you put $10 on the pass line and you roll the dice. If you roll 7 or 11 you win $10 and if you roll 2,3 or 12 you lose $10. So, what happens if you roll any of the other numbers? Well, as I said before, that number becomes your point and you have to roll that number again before you roll a 7 in order to win your pass line bet.

Once your point is established the dealer at each end of the table will move a marker into the box that corresponds to your point number to let everyone at the table know what your point is. The marker that's used has two different sides. One side is black with the word "off" and the other side is white with the word "on." Before any point is established the marker is kept in the Don't Come box with the black side facing up until you roll a point number and then the dealer turns it over to the white side and moves it inside the box that contains your point number.

For example let's say your come-out roll is a 4. The dealer simply turns the marker over to the white side that says "on" and places it in the 4 box. This let's everyone know that 4 is your point and that you will continue to roll the dice, no matter how long it takes, until you roll a 4, which will make you a winner, or a 7, which will make you a loser.

Now, keep in mind that once your point is established you can't remove your pass line bet until you either win, by throwing your point, or lose, by rolling a 7. The reason for this is that on the come out roll the pass line bettor has the advantage because there are 8 ways to win (by rolling a 7 or 11) and only 4 ways to lose (by rolling a 2, 3 or 12). If a point number is rolled, no matter what number it is, there are then more ways to lose than to win and that's why the bet can't be removed. If you were allowed to remove your bet everyone would just wait for the come-out roll and if they didn't win they would take their bet back which would give them a big advantage over the house and, as you know, casinos don't like that, so that's why you can't remove your bet.

As previously noted, the pass line is one of the best bets you'll find, but there is a way to make it even better because once your point number is established the casino will allow you to make another bet that will be paid off at the true odds. This is a very good bet to make because the casino has no advantage on this bet.

In this instance, since your point was 4, the true odds are 2-to-1 and that's what your bet will be paid off at: $2 for every $1 you bet. This is called an "odds bet," "taking the free odds" or "betting behind the line" and to make this bet you simply put your chips directly behind your pass line bet. There is a limit to how much you're allowed to bet and for many years most casinos allowed a maximum of 2 times the amount of your pass line bet. Nowadays, however, many casinos offer 5 times odds and some casinos are even allowing up to 100 times odds. In Las Vegas, Casino Royale and Sam's Town are two casinos that offer 100 times odds.

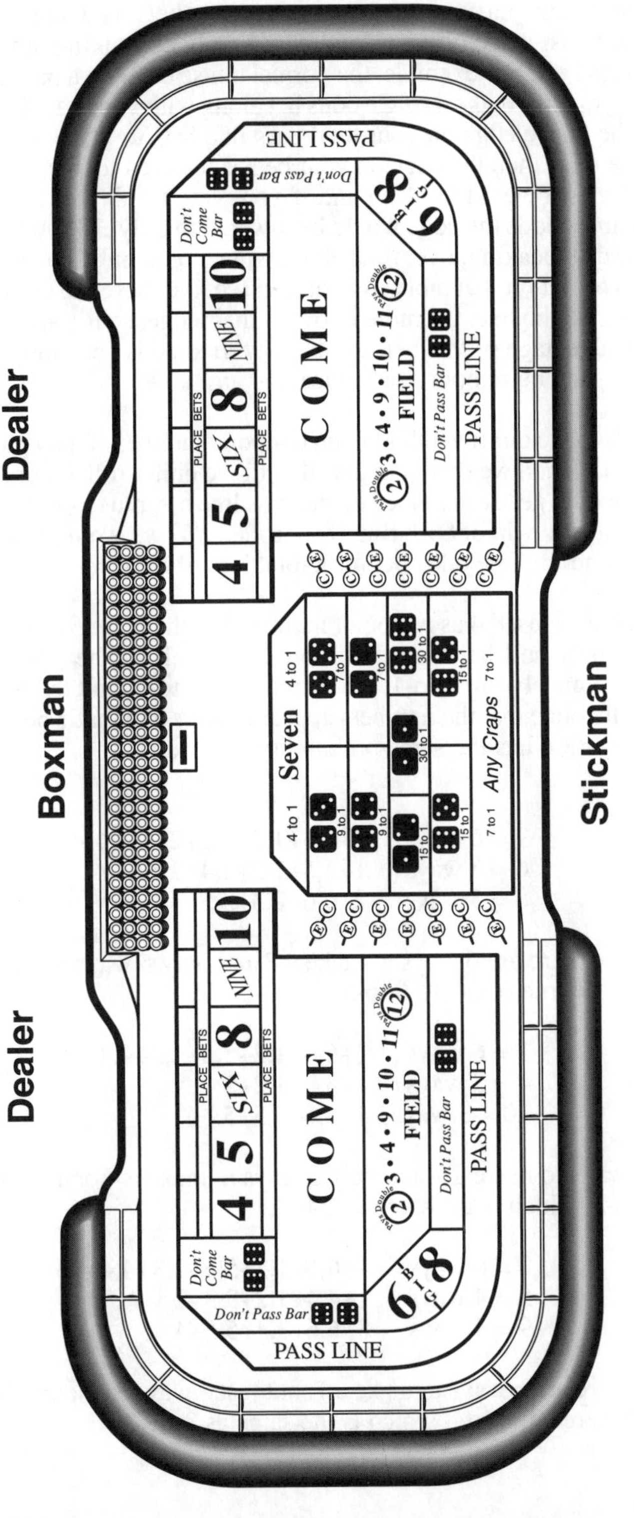

Dealer

Boxman

Dealer

Stickman

Typical craps table layout

Because the casino has no advantage on these bets you are effectively lowering the house edge on your total pass line bet by taking advantage of these free odds bets. For example, the normal house edge on a pass line bet is 1.41% but if you also make a single odds bet along with your pass line bet you will lower the house edge on your total pass line bets to .85%. If the casino offers double odds then the edge on your bets is lowered to .61% With triple odds the edge is lowered to .47% and if you were to play in a casino that allowed 10 times odds the edge would be lowered to only .18% which means that, statistically speaking, over time, that casino would only make 18¢ out of every $100 you bet on that table. As you can see, the more the casino allows you to bet behind the line, the more it lowers their edge, so it's always a good idea to take advantage of this bet. By the way, free odds bets, unlike regular pass line bets, can be removed or reduced, at any time.

All right, let's make our free odds bet on our point number of 4 by putting $20 behind the line. Then we continue to roll until we either roll a 4 or a 7. If a 4 came up we would get even money on the pass line bet, plus 2-to-1 on the free odds bet, for a total win of $50. But, if we rolled a 7, we would lose both the pass line bet and the free odds bet for a total loss of $30.

In this example we used 4 as our point number, but there are 5 other numbers that could appear and here are the true odds for all of the possible point numbers: the 4 and 10 are 2-to-1; the 5 and 9 are 3-to-2; and the 6 and 8 are 6-to-5. You'll notice that the numbers appear in pairs and that's because each paired combination has the same probability of occurring.

$$7 = 6 \text{ ways} \quad 1+6,6+1,2+5,5+2,3+4,4+3$$
$$6 = 5 \text{ ways} \quad 1+5,5+1,2+4,4+2,3+3$$
$$8 = 5 \text{ ways} \quad 2+6,6+2,3+5,5+3,4+4$$

As you can see there are 6 ways to make a 7 and only 5 ways to make a 6 or 8. Therefore, the true odds are 6-to-5.

$$7 = 6 \text{ ways} \quad 1+6,6+1,2+5,5+2,3+4,4+3$$
$$4 = 3 \text{ ways} \quad 1+3,3+1,2+2$$
$$10 = 3 \text{ ways} \quad 4+6,6+4,5+5$$

There are 6 ways to make a 7 and only 3 ways to make a 4 or 10, so the true odds are 6-to-3, which is the same as 2-to-1;

$$7 = 6 \text{ ways} \quad 1+6,6+1,2+5,5+2,3+4,4+3$$
$$5 = 4 \text{ ways} \quad 1+4,4+1,2+3,3+2$$
$$9 = 4 \text{ ways} \quad 3+6,6+3,4+5,5+4$$

and finally, there are 6 ways to make a 7, but just 4 ways to make a 5 or 9, so the true odds here are 6-to-4 which is the same as 3-to-2.

It's important that you remember these numbers, because 1.- you want to make sure that you're paid the right amount when you do win and 2.- you want to make sure that when you make your odds bets you make them in amounts that are paid off evenly.

As an example, if your point is 5 and you have $5 on the pass line, you wouldn't want to bet $5 behind the line because at 3-to-2 odds the casino would have to pay you $7.50 and they don't deal in change. When making the odds bet on the 5 or 9 you should always bet in even amounts and in the situation just mentioned most casinos would allow you to add an extra $1 so you would have $6 out and they could pay you $9, if you won. The only other situation where this occurs is on the 6 and 8 where the payoff is 6-to-5. So, in that instance you want to make your bets in multiples of $5. Also, if your pass line bet is $15, most casinos will allow you to bet $25 behind the line because, if you win, it's quicker for them to pay you $30, rather than dealing in $1 chips to give you $18 for $15. When situations like this exist, it's good to take advantage of them and bet the full amount you're allowed because that helps to lower the casino edge even more.

We've spent all this time talking about pass line betting, so what about don't pass betting? Well, everything applied to pass line betting works pretty much just the opposite for don't pass betting. If you put $10 on don't pass you would win on the come out roll if the shooter rolled a 2 or 3, you would tie if the shooter rolled a 12, and you would lose if the shooter rolled a 7 or 11. If any other number comes up then that becomes the shooter's point number and if he rolls a 7 before he rolls that same point number, you will win. If he rolls his point number before he rolls a 7, you will lose.

Don't pass bettors are also allowed to make free odds bets to back up their original bets, however, because the odds are in their favor they must lay odds rather than take odds. This means that if the point is 4 or 10, the don't pass bettor must lay 2-to-1, or bet $10 to win $5; on 5 or 9 he must lay 3-to-2, or bet $6 to win $4; and on 6 or 8 he must lay 6-to-5, or bet $6 to win $5. By taking advantage of these free odds bets the casino advantage is slightly lowered on the total don't pass bets to .68% with single odds; .46% with double odds; .34% with triple odds and .12% with 10 times odds. If you want to you can remove, or reduce the amount of your free odds, bet at any time. To make a free odds bet on don't pass you should place your odds bet right next to your original bet and then put a chip on top to connect the two bets. Keep in mind that when you make a free odds bet on don't pass the casino will allow you to make your bet based on the payoff, rather than the original amount of your don't pass bet. In other words, if the casino offered double odds, the point was 4 and you had $10 on don't pass, you would be allowed to bet $40 because you would only win $20 which was double the amount of your original $10 bet. Since you have to put out more money than you'll be getting back, laying odds is not very popular at the craps table and you'll find that the vast majority of craps players would rather bet with the shooter and take the odds. Statistically speaking, it makes no difference whether you are laying or taking the odds because they both have a zero advantage for the house.

One last point about don't pass betting is that once the point is established, the casino will allow you to remove your don't pass bet if you want to - but don't do it! As noted before, on the come out roll the pass line bettor has the advantage because there are 8 rolls that can win and only 4 that can lose, but once the point is established, there are more ways the shooter can lose than win, so at that point the don't pass bettor has the advantage and it would be foolish to remove your bet.

Now, let's take a look at the area marked come and don't come. Since you already know how to bet pass and don't pass, you should easily understand come and don't come because they're the exact same bets as pass and don't pass, except for the fact that you bet them after the point has already been established.

Let's say that the shooter's point is 6 and you make a come bet by putting a $5 chip anywhere in the come box. Well, that's just like making a pass line bet, except that the shooter's next roll becomes the come-out roll for your bet. If the shooter rolls a 7 or 11, you win. If a 2,3, or 12 is rolled you lose, and if anything else comes up then that becomes your point and the shooter must roll that number again before rolling a 7 in order for you to win. In this example if the shooter rolled a 4 the dealer would move your $5 come bet up into the center of the 4 box and it would stay there until either a 4 was rolled, which would make you a winner, or a 7 was rolled which would make you a loser. The house edge on a come bet is the same 1.41% as on a pass line bet. You are allowed free odds on your come bet and you make that bet by giving your chips to the dealer and telling him you want to take the odds. The dealer will then place those chips slightly off center on top of your come bet to show that it's a free odds bet. By the way, if you win, the dealer will put your winnings back in the come bet area so be sure to pick them up off the table or else it will be considered a new come bet.

One other point to note here is that when you make a come bet your bet is always working on every roll, even a come-out roll. However, when you take the odds on your come bets they are never working on the come-out roll. That may sound a little confusing, but here's what it means. In our example the shooter's initial point was 6 and then we made a $5 come bet. The shooter then rolled a 4 which became the point for our come bet. The dealer then moved our $5 come bet to the middle of the 4 box at the top of the table. We then gave $10 to the dealer and said we wanted to take the odds on the 4. On the next roll the shooter rolls a 6 which means he made a pass by rolling his original point number. The next roll will then become the shooter's come-out roll and the odds bet on our 4 will not be working. If the shooter rolls a 7 the pass line bettors will win and we will lose our $5 come bet because he rolled a 7 before rolling a 4. The dealer will then return our $10 odds bet because it wasn't working on the come-out roll. Now, if you want to, you can request that your odds bet be working on the come-out roll by telling the dealer. Then he'll put a marker on top of your bet to show that your odds bet is in effect on the come-out roll.

Naturally, don't come betting is the same as don't pass betting, except again for the fact that the bet isn't made until after the point is established. In this case let's say the point is 5 and you make a don't come bet by placing a $5 chip in the don't come box. Well, once again, that's just like making a don't pass bet except that the shooter's next roll becomes the come-out roll for your bet. If the shooter rolls a 2 or 3, you win. If a 7 or 11 is rolled, you lose. If a 12 is rolled it's a standoff and if anything else comes up then that becomes your point and the shooter must seven-out, or roll a 7, before rolling that point number again in order for you to win. In this example if the shooter rolled a 10 the dealer would move your $5 don't come bet into the upper part of the 10 box and it would stay there until either a 7 was rolled, which would make you a winner, or a 10 was rolled which would make you a loser. The house edge on a don't come bet is the same 1.40% as on a don't pass bet and you can make a free odds bet on your don't come bet by giving your chips to the dealer and telling him you want to lay the odds. The dealer will then place those chips next to and on top of your don't come bet to show that it's a free odds bet. The final point to note here is that don't come bets, as well as the free odds bets on them, are always working - even on the come-out roll.

Now let's talk about place betting and that refers to the 6 numbers you see in the area at the top of the table: 4,5,6,8,9 and 10. Anytime during a roll you can make a bet that one of those numbers will appear before a 7 and if it does you will receive a payoff that is slightly less than the true odds. For example: the true odds are 2-to-1 that a 4 or 10 will appear before a 7. However, if you make a place bet on the 4 or 10 you will only be paid off at 9-to-5 and that works out to a casino advantage of 6.67%

The true odds of a 5 or 9 appearing before a 7 are 3-to-2, but on a place bet you would only receive a payoff of 7-to-5 which works out to a casino edge of 4.0%. Finally, on the 6 and 8 the true odds are 6-to-5 that one of those numbers will appear before a 7, but on a place bet you would only be paid off at 7-to-6 which means the casino would have an edge of 1.52% on this bet.

As you can see, making a place bet on the 6 or 8 gives the casino its lowest edge and this means that a place bet on the 6 or 8 is one of the best bets you will find on the craps table.

When you want to make a place bet you aren't allowed to put the bet down yourself, you have to let the dealer do it for you. To do this you would just drop your chips down onto the table and tell the dealer what bet you wanted to make. For example you could put three $5 chips down and say "Place the 4,5 and 9." The dealer would then put $5 on the edge of the 4 box, $5 on the edge of the 5 box and $5 on the edge of the 9 box. You'll notice that when the dealer puts your bets on the edge of the boxes they will always be placed in an area that corresponds to where you're standing at the table and this helps the dealer to remember who placed that bet.

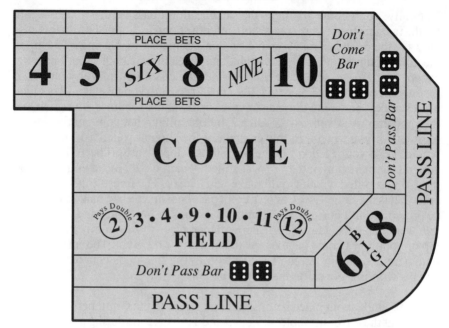

Enlargement of right side of craps layout

When making a place bet you don't have to bet more than one number and you don't have to bet the same amount on each number. You should, however, make sure that you always bet in multiples of $5 whenever you bet on the 4,5,9 or 10 and in multiples of $6 whenever you bet the 6 and 8. This will allow you to always get the full payoff on your bet. If, for example, you bet $3 on the 6 and you won you would only get back even-money, or $3, rather than the $3.50 which your bet should have paid and this results in an even bigger advantage for the casino. Another thing about place bets is that, unlike pass line bets, you can remove your place bets at any time and you do that by telling the dealer you want your bet down and he will take your chips off the table and return them to you. You could also tell the dealer that you didn't want your bet to be working on any particular roll or rolls and you do this by saying for example "off on the 5." The dealer would then put a little button on top of your bet that said "off" and he would remove it when you told him you wanted that number working again.

When we spoke about come bets before I mentioned that come bets are always working on every roll, but that's not the case with place bets because place bets are never working on the come-out roll. If you wanted to, however, you could ask for your place bet to be working on the come out roll by telling the dealer you wanted it working and he would place a button on top of your bet that said "on" to show that your bet was working on the come-out roll.

One last point about place bets is that when you win the dealer will want to know what you want to do for your next bet and you have three choices: if you want to make the same bet just say "same bet" and the dealer will give you your winning chips and leave your original place bet on the table. If you don't want to bet again, just say "take it down" and the dealer will return your place bet along with your winnings. And if you want to double your bet just say "press it" and the dealer will add your winning chips to your other place bet and return any extra chips to you. For example, if you won a $10 place bet on the 5 the dealer would have to give you back $14 in winning chips. If you said "press it" the dealer would add $10 to your place bet and return the remaining $4 in chips to you.

Besides, place betting there is also another way to bet that one of the point numbers will show up before a 7 does and that's called buying a number. A buy bet is basically the same as a place bet except you have to pay a commission of 5% of the amount of your bet and then if you win, the casino will pay you at the true odds. When making a buy bet you should always remember to bet at least $20 because 5% of $20 is $1 and that's the minimum amount the casino will charge you. The reason for the $1 minimum is because that's the smallest denomination chip they have at the craps table and they won't make change for anything under $1. The casino edge on any buy bet for $20 works out to 4.76% so let's take a look at a chart that shows the difference between buying and placing the point numbers.

Point Number	Casino Edge Buy Bet	Casino Edge Place Bet
4 or 10	4.76%	6.67%
5 or 9	4.76%	4.00%
6 or 8	4.76%	1.52%

As you can see the only numbers that you would want to buy rather than place are the 4 and 10 because the 4.76% edge on a buy bet is lower than the 6.67% edge on a place bet. For 5 and 9 the 4.76% edge on a buy bet is slightly worse than the 4.00% edge on a place bet and for the 6 and 8 the 4.76% is a hefty three times higher than the 1.52% edge on the place bet.

To buy the 4 or 10 you would just put your chips down on the layout and tell the dealer what bet you wanted to make. For example, if you put down $21 and said "buy the 10." The dealer will then keep the $1 chip for the house and put your $20 in the same area as the place bets but he'll put a button on top that says "buy" to let him know that you bought the number rather than placed it. Buy bets, just like place bets, can be removed at any time and are always off on the come-out roll. Also, if you do remove your buy bet you will get your 5% commission back.

Besides buy bets where you're betting with the shooter and hoping that a point number will appear before a 7 does, there are also lay bets where you're doing just the opposite - you're betting against the shooter and hoping that a 7 will appear before a point number does.

Lay bets are also paid at the true odds and you have to pay a 5% a commission of the amount you will win rather than the amount you're betting. Once again, when making a lay bet you should always remember to make them based on a minimum payoff of $20 because 5% of $20 is $1 and that's the minimum amount the casino will charge you.

Lay Number	Payoff	Casino Edge
4 or 10	$40 for $20	2.44%
5 or 9	$30 for $20	3.23%
6 or 8	$24 for $20	4.00%

For 4 and 10 you'll have to lay $40 to win $20 and the casino edge is 2.44%; for the 5 and 9 you'll have to lay $30 to win $20 and the casino edge is 3.23%; and for the 6 and 8 you'll have to lay $24 to win $20. The casino edge on that bet is 4.00%.

To make a lay bet you would just put your chips down on the layout and tell the dealer what you wanted to bet. For example, if you put down $41 and said "lay the 10." The dealer would then keep the $1 chip for the house and put your $40 in the same area as the don't come bets but he'll put a button on top that says "buy" to let him know that it's a lay bet. Lay bets, unlike buy bets, are always working on come-out rolls. Lay bets are, however, similar to buy bets in that they can be removed at any time and if you do remove your lay bet you will also receive your 5% commission back.

There are only a few other bets left located on the ends of the table to discuss and two of them are the big 6 and the big 8 which are both very bad bets. To bet the big 6 you place a chip in the big 6 box and then if the shooter rolls a 6 before rolling a 7 you win even money, or $1 for every $1 you bet. To bet the big 8 the same rules would apply: you put your bet in the box and then hope that the shooter rolls an 8 before rolling a 7 so you could win even money on your bet. The big 6 and big 8 can both be bet at any time and both are always working, even on the come-out roll. The casino edge on both the big 6 and the big 8 is 9.1%, which is the biggest edge we've seen so far. But, if you think back about some of the other bets we discussed doesn't this bet sound familiar? It should. This bet is the exact same as a place bet on the 6 or 8, but instead of getting paid off at 7-to-6 we're only getting paid off at even-money! Why would you want to bet the big 6 or big 8 at a house edge of more than 9% instead of making a place bet on the 6 or 8 at a house edge of only 1.5%? The answer is you wouldn't - so don't ever make this bet because it's a sucker bet that's only for people who don't know what they're doing.

The last bet we have to discuss on the player's side of the table is the field bet which is a one-roll bet that will pay even money if a 3,4,9,10 or 11 is rolled and 2-to-1 if a 2 or 12 is rolled. To make a field bet you would just place your chip anywhere in the field box and at first glance it doesn't seem like a bad bet.

After all, there are 7 numbers you can win on and only 4 numbers you can lose on! The only problem is that there are 20 ways to roll the 4 losing numbers and only 16 ways to roll the 7 winning numbers and even after factoring in the double payoff for the 2 and 12 the casino winds up with a hefty 5.6% advantage. In some casinos they pay 3-to-1 on the 2 (or the 12) which cuts the casino edge in half to a more manageable 2.8%, but as you've seen there are still much better bets you can make. By the way, if you win on a field bet the dealer will put your winning chips right next to your bet so it's your responsibility to pick them up, or else they'll be considered a new bet!

Now, let's take a look at some of the long-shots, or proposition bets in the center of the table. When you look at these bets one of the first things you'll notice is that, unlike the bets on the other side of the table, the winning payoffs are clearly labeled. The reason they do that is so you can see those big payoffs and want to bet them, but as you'll see, although the payoffs are high, so are the casino advantages.

All of the proposition bets are controlled by the stickman and he is the person who must make those bets for you. So, if you wanted to make a $1 bet on "any craps" you would throw a $1 chip to the center of the table and say "$1 any craps" and the stickmen would place that bet in the proper area for you. Then if you won, the stickman would tell the dealer at your end of the table to pay you. You should also be aware that they will only pay you your winnings and keep your original bet in place. If you don't want to make the same bet again, you should tell the stickman that you want your bet down and it will be returned to you.

There are only four proposition bets that are not one-roll bets and they are known as the "hardways." They are the hard 4, hard 6, hard 8 and hard 10. To roll a number the hardway means that the number must be rolled as doubles. For example 3 and 3 is a hard 6, but a roll of 4-2, or 5-1 are both called an easy 6, because they are easier to roll than double 3's.

To win a bet on hard 10 the shooter has to roll two 5's before rolling a 7 or an easy 10 such as 6-4 or 4-6. To win a bet on hard 4 the shooter has to roll two 2's before rolling a 7 or an easy 4 such as 3-1 or 1-3. The true odds of rolling a hard 4 or hard 10 are 8-to-1, but the casino will only pay you 7-to-1 which works out to a casino advantage of 11.1% on both of these bets.

To win a bet on hard 6 the shooter must roll two 3's before rolling a 7 or an easy 6 such as 5-1, 1-5; or 4-2, 2-4. To win a bet on hard 8 the shooter must roll two 4's before rolling a 7 or an easy 8 such as 6-2, 2-6 or 5-3, 3-5. The true odds of rolling a hard 6 or hard 8 are 10-to-1, but the casino will only pay you 9-to-1 which works out to a casino advantage of 9.1% on both of these bets.

As noted before, all of the other proposition bets are one-roll bets which means that the next roll of the dice will decide whether you win or lose. As you'll see, the house edge on all of these bets is very high and they should all be avoided.

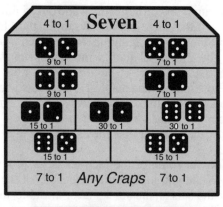

Two different types of proposition bets layouts

For the any craps bet you will win if a 2,3,or 12 is thrown on the next roll and lose if any other number comes up. The true odds are 8-to-1 but the casino will only pay you at 7-to-1 which gives them an edge of 11.1% on this bet and you'll notice that the stickman can put your bet either in the any craps box or, more likely, he'll put it on the circled marked "C" which stands for craps. The reason your bet will be placed in the "C" circle is that it's put in the circle that corresponds to where you're standing at the table and it makes it easier for the stickman to know who that bet belongs to.

For a craps 2 bet you win if the next roll is a 2 and lose if any other number shows up. The true odds are 35-to-1 but the casino will only pay you 30-to-1 which means that the edge on this bet is 13.9% In some casinos the odds for this bet will be shown as 30-for-1 which is actually the same as 29-to-1 and this results in an even bigger edge of 16.7% for the casino

A craps 12 bet works the same as a craps 2 bet, except that now you will only win if a 12 is thrown. Again, the true odds are 35-to-1 but you will only be paid at 30-to-1 which means the casino edge on this bet is the same 13.9% as in the last craps 2 bet. Also if the bet is shown on the layout as 30-for-1 the casino edge is raised to 16.7%

For a craps 3 bet you will only win if the next throw is a 3. The true odds are 17-to-1, but the casino will only pay you 15-to-1 which results in a casino advantage of 11.1% Once again, in some casinos the payoff will be shown as 15-for-1 which is the same as 14-to-1 and the house edge in that casino is an even higher 16.7%

The 11 bet is similar to the craps 3 bet, except that now the only number you can win on is 11. The true odds of rolling an 11 are 17-to-1, but the casino will only pay you 15-to-1 which gives them an 11.1% advantage. Additionally, if the payoff is shown on the layout as 15-for-1 rather than 15-to-1 the casino edge will be even higher at 16.7% By the way, because 11 sounds so much like 7 you will always hear 11 referred to at the table as "yo" or "yo-leven" to eliminate any confusion as to what number you are referring to. So, if you wanted to bet $5 on 11 you would throw a $5 chip to the stickman and say "$5 yo" and then he will either place it in the 11 box or place it on top of the "E" circle that corresponds to where you're standing at the table.

With a horn bet you are betting on the 2,3,11 and 12 all at once. A horn bet has to be made in multiples of $4 because you're making 4 bets at one time and you'll win if any one of those 4 numbers shows up on the next roll. You'll be paid off at the odds for the number that came in and you'll lose the rest of your chips. For example, if you make an $8 horn bet, this is the same as betting $2 on the 2, $2 on the 3, $2 on the 11 and $2 on the 12. If the number 2 came in you would get paid off at 30-to-1 so you would get back $60 in winnings and the casino would keep the $6 that you lost for the three $2 bets on the 3,11 and 12. The only advantage of a horn bet is that it allows you to make 4 bad bets at once rather than one at a time.

The last proposition bet we have to look at is also the worst bet on the craps table and it's the any 7 bet. With this bet you win if a 7 is rolled and lose if any other number comes up. The true odds are 5-to-1, but the casino will only pay you at 4-to-1 which gives them an edge of 16.7%

So there you have it! We've gone over all the possible bets you can make and now it's time to tell you how to win at the game of craps. Unfortunately, as you've seen, craps is a negative expectation game which means that every bet you make has a built-in advantage for the house. Actually, there is one bet that the casino has no advantage on and do you remember the name of that one? That's right it's the free odds bet and it's great that the casino has no advantage on that bet but the only way you're allowed to make that bet is to first make a negative expectation bet on pass/don't pass or come/don't come, so in essence, there are no bets you can make where you have an advantage over the house and in the long run the game of craps is unbeatable.

So, if that's the case then how do you win? Well, in reality there is only one way to win in craps and that way is to get lucky! Of course, this is easier said than done, but you will find it much easier to come out a winner if you only stick to the bets that offer the casino its lowest edge and those are the only bets you should ever make.

If you want to bet with the shooter I suggest you make a pass line bet, back it up with the free odds and then make a maximum of two come bets that are also both backed up with free odds. For example if double odds are allowed, you could start with a $5 pass line bet and say a 4 is rolled. You would then put $10 behind the line on your 4 and make a $5 come bet. If the shooter then rolled an 8 you would take $10 in odds on your come bet on the 8 and make another $5 come bet. If the shooter then rolled a 5 you would take $10 in odds on your come bet on the 5 and then stop betting. The idea here is that you always want to have a maximum of three numbers working and once you do, you shouldn't make anymore bets until one of your come numbers hits, in which case you would make another come bet, or if your pass line bet wins and then you would follow that up with another pass line bet. The important thing to remember is not to make more than two come bets because you don't want to have too much out on the table if the shooter rolls a 7. By using this betting system you'll only be giving the casino an edge of around .60% on all of your bets and with just a little bit of luck you can easily walk away a winner.

If you wanted to be a little more aggressive with this betting system there are some modifications you could make such as making a maximum of three come bets rather than two, or you could add place bets on the 6 and 8. Remember that a place bet on either the 6 or 8 only gives the casino a 1.52% advantage and that makes them both the next best bets after pass/don't pass and come/don't come. To add the place bets you would start off the same as before, but after you've made your second come bet you would look at the 6 and 8 and if they weren't covered you would then make a $6 place bet on whichever one was open or on both. By adding the place bets on the 6 and 8 you would always have at least three numbers in action and you could have as many as five covered at one time.

One final option with this system is to gradually increase the amount of your pass line and come bets by 50%, or by doubling them, and then backing them up with full odds, but I would only suggest you do this if you've been winning for awhile because it could get very expensive if the table was cold and no one was rolling many numbers. Of course, if the table got real cold you could always change your strategy by betting against the shooter and the strategy for that is basically just the opposite of the one I just told you about.

To bet against the shooter you would start with a $5 don't pass bet which you would back up with single free odds and then bet a maximum of two don't come bets that are both backed up with single odds. The reason you don't want to back up your bets with double odds is because when you're betting against the shooter you have to lay the odds which means you're putting up more money than you'll be getting back and, once again, it could get very expensive if a shooter got on a hot roll and made quite a few passes.

For an example of this system let's say you start with a $5 don't pass bet and a 4 is rolled. You would then lay the odds by putting $10 next to your $5 don't pass bet and then make a $5 don't come bet. If the shooter then rolled an 8 you would lay $6 in odds on your don't come bet on the 8 and make another $5 don't come bet. If the shooter then rolled a 5 you would lay $9 in odds on your come bet on the 5 and then stop betting. The idea here is that you always want to have a maximum of three numbers working and once you do, you shouldn't make anymore bets until one of your don't come numbers wins, in which case you would make another don't come bet, or if your don't pass bet wins and then you would follow that up with another don't pass bet. Once again, the important thing to remember is not to make more than two don't come bets because you don't want to have too much out on the table if the shooter gets hot and starts to roll a lot of numbers. With this system you'll always have a maximum of three numbers in action and you'll only be giving the casino an edge of about .80% on all of your bets. Some options to bet more aggressively with this system are to increase your free odds bets to double odds rather than single odds and also to make three don't come bets, rather than stopping at two. The choice is up to you but remember that because you must lay the odds and put out more money than you'll be getting back you could lose a substantial amount rather quickly if the roller got hot and made a lot of point numbers.

Now, one last point I want to make about betting craps is that the bankroll you'll need is going to be much bigger than the bankroll you'll need for playing any other casino game. If you're betting with the shooter you'll have one $5 pass line bet with double odds and two come bets with double odds which means that you could have as much as $45 on the table that could be wiped out with the roll of a 7. If you're betting against the shooter you'll have $5 on don't pass with single odds and two don't come bets with single odds which means you could have as much as $44 on the table that could be wiped out if the shooter got on a "hot" roll and made a lot of numbers. As I said before, you need to have an adequate bankroll to be able to ride out the losing streaks that can happen and you need to be able to hold on until things turn around and you start to win.

So how much of a bankroll is enough? Well, I would say about 7 times the maximum amount of money you'll have out on the table is adequate and 10 times would be even better. In both of our examples then you should have a bankroll of at least $300. If you don't have that much money to put out on the table then you might want to consider having lees money out on the table by making only one come or don't come bet rather than two or maybe even just limiting your bets to pass and don't pass along with the free odds.

Just remember that it doesn't matter whether you want to bet with the shooter or against the shooter - both of these systems will give you the best chance of winning because they allow the casino only the slightest edge and with a little bit of luck you can easily come out a winner. Good luck!

Controlling The Dice In Craps

by Larry Edell

A subject of controversy among craps players is the idea that a shooter can "control" the dice. In this story craps expert Larry Edell gives his thoughts on how he thinks a shooter can control the dice and what it takes to achieve it. We don't know if it works or not but we do kow that it can't possibly hurt your game if you want to give it a try!

You CAN control the dice. I have seen many people do it, both male and female, but it isn't easy. It will take a while to perfect your craft, because that's what it is - an expert craft. In fact, you actually must perfect three separate crafts - (1) Setting The Dice, (2) Establishing a good grip, and (3) Developing an expert throw.

Setting The Dice - It is possible for you to arrange the dice in a fashion so the sevens are minimized, and turn the game of craps from a negative expectation one into a positive expectation game. In order to this properly it takes a little practice, but it's worth it. By becoming a proficient dice-setter you can practice your trade anywhere in the world!

First, you need to imagine the two dice are rotating on a horizontal axis at the same time. If they stay straight and continue rotating, the right and left side faces on which the axle sits will not appear. The numbers on the right and left sides of each die would never show. There are only six different dice sets available and we'll look at all six. If you get a pair of regulation dice right now it will be easier to follow along

The 2354 set - Set both dice identically so when you rotate them toward you, all you see are the 2, 3, 5 and 4. The totals showing would be all hard ways - the hard four, hard six, hard ten and hard eight. This is called the "hard way set" and is one of the most popular sets. Now if you look closely you will see that the ones and sixes have been eliminated (on the horizontal axis) so in addition to fewer sevens, you would not be able to throw a two, three, eleven or twelve with this set. This set is great for hardways, place bets and 6's and 8's. You can set this quickly just by placing the 1's and 6's on both horizontal axis.

The 1364 set - Both dice should be set for 1, 3, 6 and 4. This set eliminates the 5's and 2's so it is impossible to roll a 3 or 11. It actually increases the frequency of sevens so it is used only for don't bettors and the come out. You can set this quickly just by placing the 5's and 2's on both horizontal axis.

The 1265 set - Another don't bettor set is the 1, 2, 6 and 5. You will have the fours and threes eliminated on the sides so these numbers will not roll. This set will produce more sevens but no fives or nines so if you see someone laying the fives and nines, he's probably using this set! You can set this quickly just by placing the 4's and 3's on both horizontal axis.

The 1265/2354 set - When you set the dice, both die can be set differently. For example, you set the first die as 1, 2, 6, 5 and the second die as 2, 3, 5, 4. Although this may take a little longer to set, it has terrific advantages - only two sevens, and two each of the 4, 5, 6, 8, 9 and 10. This set would be really good for place bettors after the come-out! You can set this quickly just by placing the 4 and 3 on one die's horizontal axis and the 1 and 6 on the other.

The 1265/1364 set - You can also set the first die to 1, 2, 6, 5 and the second to 2, 3, 5, 4. On the first die you are eliminating 4 & 3. On the second you are eliminating 2 & 7. This combination gives you two of each of the 5, 6, 7 and 8. This is the famous "6-T" set, because if you place the two sixes together to form a "T" you have this set in one quick motion. You can set this quickly by placing the 4 and 3 on one die's horizontal axis and the 5 and 2 on the other.

The 1364/2354 set - Finally, we get to my favorite. Set the first die to 1, 3, 6, 4 and the second to 2, 3, 5, 4. This set will produce only two sevens, but three each of the six and eight! There are also no twos or twelves and one each of 3, 4, 10 and 11. You can set this quickly by placing the 5 and 2 on one die's horizontal axis and the 1 and 6 on the other.

When you use a set, it doesn't matter exactly where the numbers are located, as long as the proper ones are there. For example, in my favorite it is fine to set them 6, 4, 1, 3 on one die, thus having the 5 and 2 on the horizontal axis. On the other die you can set it 4, 2, 3, 5 thus having the 1 and 6 on the horizontal axis. As long as the numbers on the horizontal axis remain as specified, it really doesn't matter where the other numbers on the vertical axis end up.

The really good thing about dice setting is that it doesn't cost you anything to use, except for maybe a little practice. So, if you're going to shoot anyway, why not pre-set the dice! Speaking of shooting, once you have the correct set you need to grip the dice properly so they stay together throughout your controlled throw.

The Expert Grip - Your dice gripping procedure should begin as soon as the stickman begins to push the dice toward you. Look at them, see which numbers are facing up. Then imagine, in your mind, exactly what to do to the dice to turn them into the position you want them to be.

If you are tipping the dealers, you can ask if they will return them to you "all sixes," or some other easy to manipulate position. You should buy a pair of dice (regulation size) and practice with them at home, so you can set them (after watching their return from the stickman) in about two seconds, so you don't hold up the game. Most boxmen will complain if your set takes longer, and you really want to have the dealers on your side, not fighting you every inch of the way.

When the current shooter sevens out you should start watching what the stickman does. He will return the used dice to the bowl and choose five dice and push them towards you. If, for example, you are looking for a hard way set, you should look for two dice with 2, 4 or 6 showing so you can set them easier. After you establish a point you will have only one pair returned each time so you need to set them even quicker.

One easy method to set the dice quickly is to remember that opposite sides add up to seven. So if they are returned to you with 1's and 2's showing, you know that 6's and 5's are on the opposite sides. You also need to remember to use one hand only, and if your other hand even remotely hovers near the dice you will really invite heat from the boxman, and he might even take the dice away if he thinks you've touched them with both hands.

Once you flip the dice in a few seconds you are ready to grip the dice in order to toss them to the other side of the table. The dice must be gripped firmly to insure that they travel together in parallel paths, at the same time.

In order for this to occur, your finger pressure must be equalized all over so the force is symmetrical. Depending on the size of your fingers (and whether you are male or female) your grip might be different than mine, or another shooter's. There are many grips, and each has a name, like "3 finger top," "4 finger diagonal," "5 finger top," and several others. My own personal favorite is called the "3 finger front" grip.

After the dice are set, you place your 2nd, 3rd and 4th fingers along the upper ridge of the front dice, and your thumb on the upper ridge in between the two back sides. Your pinky is tucked away and not used. You would make sure the dice are perfectly symmetrical and then toss them with a slight back spin, so they land and bounce once around the pass line and, still spinning, just glance off the rubber backboard and come to rest the way you want them to.

This takes quite a bit of practice, and you need to practice before you play, perhaps on a low limit table or even in your hotel room. But it's worth it! Once you learn how, it becomes a skill you will never forget, and will always use whenever you play!

Spend some time perfecting your grip, it will really be worth it in the long run! You can practice your set and grip at home, and perfect them before you move on to practicing your throw.

The Throw - In order to perfect your throw, you should establish yourself to be at the exact same table position whenever you play. There are two positions that will reduce the length of your throw to an absolute minimum - just to the left of the stickman or just to the right of the stickman. You should try both positions and choose the one that works the best for you.

After the dice have been set and you are gripping them properly, you should visualize your throw in your mind. See the dice leaving your hands, traveling together in a straight line and not wobbling, and landing around the pass line. Then they would bounce together, lightly glance off the backboard, and end up showing your desired results. You MUST visualize this happening before it actually happens, so it may be a second or two before you actually toss the dice.

When they are tossed they should be at an angle to minimize any energy that would be gathered by their descent. Try to toss them low, not more than 45 degrees from the table. When they leave your hands they should match your visualization perfectly, and you should be seeing the dice travel now a second time, just as they did in your mind.

The dice will leave you hand at the same time, and not wobble or change course. They should fly through the air together, side by side, spinning forward as they move. They should bounce once around the pass line, and still spinning, will glance off the backboard and come to rest without bouncing or hitting any chips. If there are chips present on the passline, you could ask the bettors to move them to the side, and they certainly will, as they want to make money on your roll as much as you do.

I have found that your throw will achieve more consistent results if you put your whole body into it, rather than just your wrist and arm. Shooting dice is very much like playing golf - you need have your entire body participate in the experience. When the dice leave your hand it is your hip and upper body that is contributing to the velocity of the dice, not just your arm. Your body should move around with the dice as they are released.

After the dice are set and gripped you should turn to face the stickman, as you did when you imagined your throw and its result. Turn your body and the dice back a bit to increase their spin, and turn your body and the dice towards and past the stickman to release them. So you should go through three positions in your mind - Before the throw, during the throw, and after the throw. After practice, this will become one fluid motion, and should become almost second nature to you after you've done it a few times.

Here is a trick that I use that may work for you also. When I shoot, I always imagine a cereal bowl sitting on the passline. It is my job to toss the dice lightly so they land in the cereal bowl. For some reason it is easier for me to imagine this happening than it is aiming for the pass line. You might try some different things you are more familiar with, like a shoebox, a small hat box, or even a cigar box. Do whatever it takes for you to succeed!

Conclusion - In order for you to become proficient at controlling the dice, you must master three crafts - (1) Setting The Dice, (2) Establishing your grip, and (3) Developing an expert throw. Remember to tip the dealers so they help you and return the dice to you partly set. When you have gripped the dice you must imagine the perfect throw in your mind before you actually do it. And when you throw, move the dice back to gather momentum, have them pass in front of the stickman, and release them gently, like you were throwing them into a small bowl.

And finally, have fun. Talk to the dealers and other players. Craps is the only game where you can make money and have fun at the same time!

Larry Edell is the publisher of "The Crapshooter," the only newsletter devoted to the game of craps. For a free copy of Larry's newsletter see the coupon section in the back of this book.

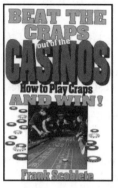

Roulette

by Steve Bourie

Virtually all American casinos use a double-zero roulette wheel which has pockets numbered from 1 to 36, plus 0 and 00 for a total of 38 pockets. This is in contrast to Europe where a single-zero wheel is used and the game has always been the most popular in the casino.

There are usually six seats at the roulette table and to help the dealer differentiate what each player is betting every player is assigned a different color chip which they purchase right at the table. Each table has its own minimum chip values and that information is usually posted on a sign at the table. As an example let's say a table has a $1 minimum chip value. This means that when you give the dealer your money the colored chips he gives you in return must have a minimum value of $1 each. So, if you gave the dealer $50 he would ask what value you wanted on the chips and if you said $1 he would give you 50 colored chips.

If you prefer, you could say you wanted the chips valued at $2 each and he would just give you 25 chips rather than 50. You can make the value of your colored chips anything you want and you'll notice that when the dealer gives you your chips he'll put one of your chips on the railing near the wheel with a marker on top to let him know the value of your chips. Later on when you're done playing at that table you must exchange your colored chips for regular chips before leaving. The colored chips have no value anywhere else in the casino so don't leave the table with them.

Besides the minimum chip value, there is also a minimum amount that must be bet on each spin of the wheel. Once again, the minimums are probably posted on a sign at the table and if it says $2 minimum inside and $5 minimum outside this means that if you are betting on any of the 38 numbers that pay 35-to-1 the total of all your bets must be $2. You could make two different $1 bets or one $2 bet, it doesn't matter except that the total of all your bets on the numbers must be at least $2. The $5 minimum outside means that any of the outside bets that pay 2-to-1, or even money, require that you bet $5 each time. On the outside bets you can't make a $3 bet and a $2 bet to meet the minimums - you have to bet at least $5 every time. After you've exchanged your cash for colored chips you're ready to place your first bet so, let's see what your options are:

You can make a *straight* bet where you only bet on one number and if it comes in you'll be paid 35-to-1. The casino advantage on this bet is 5.26% and by the time you're done with this roulette section I'm sure you'll be very familiar with that number.

Another choice you have is to do a *split*. This is where you put a chip on the line that separates two numbers. If either number comes up you'll be paid at 17-to-1. The casino advantage on this bet is 5.26%.

If you put a chip in an area that splits 4 numbers this is called a *corner* bet and if any one of those 4 numbers comes in you will be paid off at 8-to-1. The casino advantage on this bet is 5.26%.

If you put a chip at the beginning of a row of 3 numbers, this is called a *street* bet and if any one of those 3 numbers shows up you will be paid off at 11-to-1. The casino advantage on this bet is 5.26%.

You can also put a chip on the line between two streets so that you have a *double street* covered and if any one of those 6 numbers come in you'll be paid off at 5-to-1. The casino advantage on this bet is?... you guessed it...5.26%.

The only other bet you can make on the inside numbers is the *5- number* bet where you place one chip in the upper left corner of the number 1 box. If any one of those 5 numbers comes in you'll be paid off at 6-to-1 and what do you think the casino advantage is on this bet? Nope, I gotcha... it's 7.89%. Actually, this is the worst possible bet on the roulette table and the only bet you'll come across that doesn't have a 5.26% house edge on the double-zero roulette wheel. You should never make this bet.

One quick word here about "to" and "for" when discussing odds. Whenever the odds are stated as "to" this means that in addition to the stated payoff you also receive your original bet back. In other words, if you won your single number bet in roulette you would receive 35-to-1, which is a 35-chip payoff, plus you'd still keep your original one-chip bet, so you end up with 36 chips. Now if the odds are stated as "for" that means you do not receive back your original bet. If the odds in your single number bet were 35-*for*-1 you would still receive a 35-chip payoff but the casino would keep your original one-chip bet so you would only end up with 35 chips. The only place in a casino where the odds are always stated as "for" is in video poker. You might also come across it on a couple of craps bets where the odds are stated as "for-one" rather than "to-one" in order to give the casino a slightly better edge.

Now, getting back to our roulette examples, let's look at all of the outside bets that you can make and keep in mind that the house edge on all of these outside bets is...do you remember the number?...that's right...5.26%.

There are three bets you can make that will pay you even money, or 1-to-1, which means that if you win, you will get back one dollar for every dollar you bet:

Red or black - If you put a chip on red then a red number must come up in order for you to win. If the ball lands on a black number, 0 or 00 - you lose. The same thing goes for black - you lose if it comes in red, 0 or 00 and you win if the ball lands on a black number.

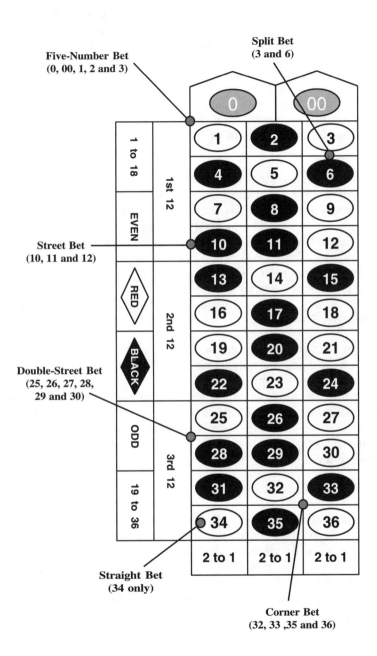

Typical felt layout for placing bets on American double-zero roulette wheel

Odd or even - If you put a chip on odd then the ball must land on an odd number in order for you to win. If it lands on 0, 00, or an even number - you lose. If you bet on even, you win if an even number shows up and lose if the ball lands on 0, 00 or an odd number.

1 through 18 and 19 through 36 - If you bet on 1 through 18, then you win if a number from 1 through 18 comes in and you lose if the ball lands on 0, 00 or a number higher than 18. Similarly, if you bet on 19 through 36, you win if one of those numbers comes in and you lose on 0, 00 or any number lower than 19.

The only other bets left are the *dozens* and columns bets. If you look at the roulette betting layout you can see three areas that each correspond to 12-number sections on the table. The one marked 1st 12 covers the numbers from 1 to 12, the one marked 2nd 12 covers the numbers from 13 to 24 and the other one that's marked 3rd 12 covers the last section of numbers from 25 to 36. If you bet on the 1st 12 you would win if a number from 1 to 12 came in and you would lose if anything else came in, including 0 or 00. The same principle holds true for each of the other dozen bets where you would win if a number in that section came in and you would lose if anything else showed up. All dozens bets pay 2-to-1.

The last bet to look at is the *column* bet and that is also a bet that pays 2-to-1. There are three possible column bets you can make and you'll notice that each area corresponds to the numbers in the column directly above it. So, if you put a chip under the first column you will win if any of the numbers in that column come in and you will lose if any other number, including 0 or 00 shows up. Once again, the same rule is in effect for each of the other columns where you would win if the number appears in the column above your bet and you would lose if it doesn't.

All right, now you know all the possible bets and you know how to make them at the table. So, the next question is "How do you win?" and the answer to that is very simple - You have to get lucky! And that's the ONLY way you can win at roulette. As you found out earlier, every bet, except for the 5-number bet, which I'm sure you'll never make, has a house edge of?...that's right...5.26%. So, feel free to put your chips all over the table and then just hope that you're lucky enough to have one of your numbers come up. You see, it just doesn't matter what you do because you'll always have that same house edge of 5.26% working against you on every bet you make.

Now, you may have heard of a system for roulette where you should place your bets only on the numbers that are evenly spaced out around the wheel. For example, if you wanted to play only four numbers, you could bet on 1,2,31 and 32 because when you looked at a roulette wheel, you would notice that if you divided it into four equal parts, you would have a number that appears in each of the four sections. So, is this a good system? Well, actually it's no better and no worse than any other roulette system. The fact is that it's purely a matter of chance where the ball happens to land and it makes no difference whether the numbers you choose are right next to each other or evenly spaced out on the wheel. Each number has an equal chance to occur on every spin of the wheel and the house edge always remains at 5.26%.

You can probably tell that I wouldn't recommend roulette as a good game to play because there are other games that offer much better odds, but if you really insist on playing the game I have three good suggestions for you. #1 - Go to Atlantic City! In Atlantic City if you make an even-money outside bet, like red or black, odd or even, 1 through 18 or 19 through 36 and if 0 or 00 come up, the state gaming regulations allow the casino to take only half of your bet. Because you only lose half of your bet this also lowers the casino edge on these outside bets in half to 2.63%. This rule is only in effect for even-money bets so keep in mind that on all other bets the house edge still remains at that very high 5.26%.

The second suggestion I have for you also involves some travel and here it is: Go to Europe! The game of roulette began in Europe and many casinos over there use a single-zero wheel which makes it a much better game because the house edge on a single-zero roulette wheel is only 2.70%. To make it even better, they have a rule called "en prison" which is similar to the Atlantic City casino rule. If you make an even-money outside bet and the ball lands on 0 you don't lose right away. Instead, your bet is "imprisoned" and you have to let it ride on the next spin. Then, if your bet wins, you can remove it from the table. Because of this rule, the casino edge on this bet is cut in half to 1.35% which makes it one of the best bets in the casino and almost four times better than the same bet when it's made on a standard double-zero roulette wheel in the United States.

Now, if you're not into traveling and you don't think you can make it to Atlantic City or Europe, then you'll just have to settle for suggestion #3 which is: Win quickly! Naturally, this is easier said than done, but in reality, if you want to win at roulette the best suggestion I can give you is that you try to win quickly and then walk away from the table because the longer you continue to bet the longer that big 5.26% house edge will keep eating away at your bankroll. One major principle of gambling is that in order to win you must only play the games that have the lowest casino edge and, unfortunately, roulette is not one of them.

Before closing out this look at roulette, let's take a minute to examine one of the most famous betting systems of all time and the one that many people frequently like to use on roulette. It's called the Martingale system and it is basically a simple system of doubling your bet whenever you lose. The theory behind it is that sooner or later you'll have to win and thus, you will always come out ahead. As an example, let's say you're playing roulette and you bet $1 on red, if you lose you double your next bet to $2 and if you lose that then you double your next bet to $4 and if you lose that you double your next bet to $8 and so forth until you eventually win. Now, when you finally do win you will end up with a profit equal to your original bet, which in this case is $1. If you started the same system with a $5 bet, you would have to bet $10 after your first loss, $20 after your second loss and so forth, but whenever you won you would end up with a $5 profit.

In theory, this sounds like a good idea but in reality it's a terrible system because eventually you will be forced to risk a great amount of money for a very small profit. Let's face it, even if you only wanted to make a $1 profit on each spin of the wheel, sooner or later you will hit a major losing streak where you will have to bet an awful lot of money just to make that $1 profit. For example, if you go eight spins without a winner, you would have to bet $256 on the next spin and if that lost then you'd have to bet $512. Would you really want to risk that kind of money just to make $1? I don't think so. You may think that the odds are highly unlikely that you would lose that many bets in a row, but eventually it will happen and when it does you will suffer some astronomical losses. One other problem with this system is that eventually you won't be able to double your bet because you will have reached the casino maximum, which in most casinos is $500 on roulette. Just keep in mind that the Martingale system works best when it's played for fun on paper and not for real money in a casino. If it was truly a winning system it would have bankrupted the world's casinos years ago.

Baccarat

by Steve Bourie

When you think of Baccarat you probably think of a game that's played by the casino's wealthiest players who sit at a private table and can afford to bet tens of thousands of dollars on the flip of a card and you know what? You're right! The game of Baccarat has always had a reputation as being for the richest gamblers and that usually scared off the average player, but nowadays more and more people are discovering that Baccarat is really a good game for the small stakes player because 1.-it has a relatively small advantage for the casino and 2.-it's very simple to play.

The mini-Baccarat table is the kind of Baccarat table you're most likely to find in the standard American casino and the game is played pretty much the same as regular Baccarat except that in the mini version all of the hands are dealt out by the dealer and the players never touch the cards. Other than that, the rules are virtually the same. Oh yes, one other difference you'll find is that the betting minimums will always be lower on mini-Baccarat and it's usually pretty easy to find a table with a $5 minimum.

Now, as I said before the game of Baccarat is very simple to play and that's because the only decision you have to make is what bet you want to make from the three that are available: player, banker or tie. After the players make their bets the game begins and two 2-card hands are dealt from a shoe that contains 8 decks of cards. One hand is dealt for the banker and another hand is dealt for the player. The values of the two cards in each hand are added together and the object of the game is to have a total as close to 9 as possible. After the values of the first two cards in each hand are totaled, a third card can be drawn by either the player, the banker or both. But, the decision as to whether or not a third card should be drawn is not decided by the dealer or the players - it is only decided by the rules of the game.

Actually the name Baccarat comes from the Italian word for zero and as you'll see there are lots of zeros in this game because when you add the cards together all of the 10's and all of the face cards are counted as zeros, while all of the other cards from ace though 9 are counted at their face value. So, a hand of Jack, 6 has a total of 6; 10,4 has a total of 4; king, 7 has a total of 7; and ace, queen which would be a great hand in blackjack, only has a total of 1. The other thing about adding the cards together is that no total can be higher than 9. So, if a total is 10 or higher you have to subtract 10 to determine its value. For example, 8,8 totals 16 but you subtract 10 and your total is 6; 9,5 has a total of 4; 8,3 has a total of 1; and 5,5 has a total of 0.

Once again, the object of the game of Baccarat is to have a total as close to 9 as possible, so after the first two cards are dealt if either the player or banker hand has a total of 9 then that's called a "natural" and that hand is the winner. If neither hand has a total of 9 then the next best possible hand is a total of 8 (which is also called a "natural") and that hand would be the winner. If both the player and the banker end up with the same total then it's a tie and neither hand wins.

Now, if neither hand has an 8 or a 9 then the rules of the game have to be consulted to decide whether or not a third card is drawn. Once that's done, the values of the cards are added together again and whichever hand is closest to a total of 9 is the winner. If both hands end up with the same total then it's a tie and neither hand wins.

If you want to bet on the player hand just put your money in the area marked "player" and if you win you'll be paid off at even-money, or $1 for every $1 you bet. The casino advantage on the player bet is 1.36%. If you want to bet on the banker hand you would place your bet in the area marked "banker" and if you win, you'll also be paid off at even-money, but you'll have to pay a 5% commission on the amount you win. So, if you won $10 on your bet, you would owe a 50¢ commission to the house. The 5% commission is only required if you win and not if you lose. The dealer will keep track of the amount you owe by putting an equal amount in a small area on the table that corresponds to your seat number at the table. So, if you're sitting at seat #3 and won $10 on the bank hand the dealer would pay you $10 and then put 50¢ in the #3 box. This lets him know how much you owe the casino in commissions and when you get up to leave the table you'll have to pay the dealer whatever amount is in that box. After adjusting for that 5% commission the casino advantage on the banker bet is 1.17%

Finally, if you want to bet on a tie you would place your bet in the area marked "tie" and if you win you'll be paid off at 8-to-1, or $8 for every $1 you bet. The big payoff sounds nice but actually this is a terrible bet because the casino advantage is a very high 14.1% and this bet should never be made.

As you've seen, the casino advantage in Baccarat is very low (except for the tie bet) and the rules are set in advance so no decisions are made by either the players or the dealer about how to play the cards. This means that, unlike blackjack where you have to decide whether or not you want another card, you have no decisions to make and no skill is involved. This also means that Baccarat is purely a guessing game, so even if you've never played the game before you can sit at a table and play just as well as anyone who's played the game for 20 years! This is the only game in the casino where this can happen and that's why I tell people that Baccarat is an especially good game for the beginning player because you need no special knowledge to take advantage of those low casino edge bets.

The only part of Baccarat that gets a little confusing is trying to understand the rules concerning the draw of a third card, but remember, the rules are always the same at every table and they'll usually have a printed copy of the rules at

A Sample Mini-Baccarat Table Layout

the table and will give you a copy if you ask for it. After playing the game for awhile you'll start to remember the rules on your own, but until then here's a rundown on how it works:

As noted before, if the first two cards in either hand total 8 or 9, then the game is over and the highest total wins. If the totals are both 8 or both 9 then it's a tie and neither hand wins. For any other total the rules have to be consulted and it's always the player hand that goes first. If the player hand has a total of 6 or 7, it must stand. The only other totals it can possibly have are 0,1,2,3,4 or 5 and for all of those totals it must draw a card.

PLAYER HAND RULES

8,9	STANDS (Natural)
6,7	STANDS
0,1,2,3,4,5	DRAWS

There, that wasn't too hard to understand was it? If the player hand has a total of 6 or 7 it stands and for anything else it has to draw a card. Well, that was the easy part because now it gets a little complicated.

After the player hand is finished the banker hand must take its turn and if its first 2 cards total 0,1 or 2 it must draw a card. If its two cards total 7 it must stand and if the total is 6 it will stand, but only if the player hand did not take a card.

BANK HAND RULES

8,9	STANDS (Natural)
0,1,2	DRAWS
6	STANDS (If player took no card)
7	STANDS

The only other possible totals the bank can have are 3,4,5 or 6 and the decision as to whether or not a 3rd card is drawn depends on the 3rd card that was drawn by the player hand.

When the banker hand has a total of 3 it must stand if the player's 3rd card was an 8 and it must draw if the player's 3rd card was any other card.

IF BANK HAS 3 and
Player's third card is 8 - BANK STANDS
Player's third card is 1,2,3,4,5,6,7,9,10 - BANK DRAWS

When the banker hand has a total of 4 it must stand if the player's 3rd card was a 1,8,9, or 10 and it must draw if the player's 3rd card was any other card.

IF BANK HAS 4 and
Player's third card is 1,8,9,10 - BANK STANDS
Player's third card is 2,3,4,5,6,7 - BANK DRAWS

When the banker hand has a total of 5 it must stand if the player's 3rd card was a 4,5,6 or 7 and it must draw if the player's 3rd card was any other card.

IF BANK HAS 5 and
Player's third card is 1,2,3,8,9,10 - BANK STANDS
Player's third card is 4,5,6,7 - BANK DRAWS

When the banker hand has a total of 6 it must stand if the player's 3rd card was a 6 or 7 and it must draw if the player's 3rd card was any other card.

IF BANK HAS 6 and
Player's third card is 1,2,3,4,5,8,9,10 - BANK STANDS
Player's third card is 6 or 7 - BANK DRAWS

There you have it - those are the rules of Baccarat concerning the draw of a third card. As you saw they were a little complicated, but remember that you don't have to memorize the rules yourself because the dealer will know them and play each hand by those rules, but you can always ask for a copy of the rules at the table to follow along.

Now let's try some sample hands: The player hand has queen,9 for a total of 9 and the banker hand has 4,4 for a total of 8. Which hand wins? Both hands are naturals, but the player hand total of 9 is higher than the banker hand total of 8, so the player hand is the winner.

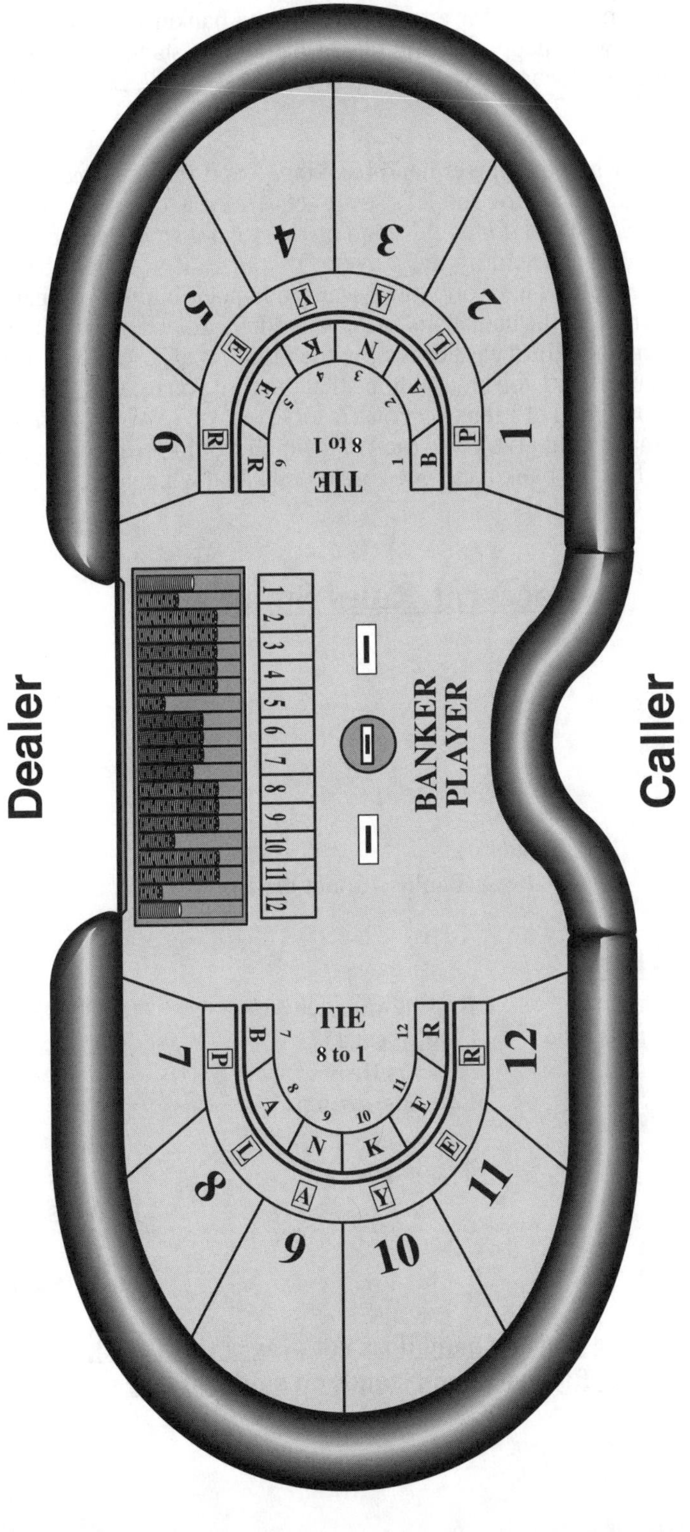

Dealer

Caller

BANKER
PLAYER

TIE
8 to 1

TIE
8 to 1

A 12-Seat Baccarat Table Layout

If the player hand has 4,2 for a total of 6 and the banker hand has ace, jack which totals 1, what happens? The player hand must stand on its 6 and the banker hand must always draw when it has a total of 0,1 or 2. Let's say the bank draws a 7 and wins 7 to 6.

What happens when the player hand has king, 5 and the bank hand has 2,4? The player hand must draw and let's say it gets a 7 for a total of 2. The banker hand has a total of 6 and if it could stand on that total it would win because its 6 is higher than the 2 held by the player. Of course, if you were betting on banker that's exactly what you would want to happen but, unfortunately for you, the rules require the bank hand to draw another card whenever its first two cards total 6 and the third card drawn by the player is a 7. So now, instead of having a winning hand you have to hope that the card you draw isn't a 5, which would give you a total of 1 making you a loser. You also wouldn't want to draw a 6 because that would give you a total of 2 which would give you a tie. In this case let's say that the bank hand goes on to draw an 8 which gives it a total of 3 and it wins 3 to 2.

Baccarat Rules Summary

Player Hand

When the first
two cards total

0-1-2-3-4-5	**Draws**
6-7	**Stands**
8-9	**Natural (Banker cannot draw)**

Banker Hand

When the first player's two cards total	DRAWS when player's third card is	STANDS when third card is
0-1-2	Always Draws	
3	1-2-3-4-5-6-7-9-0	8
4	2-3-4-5-6-7	1-8-9-0
5	4-5-6-7	1-2-3-8-9-0
6	6-7	1-2-3-4-5-8-9-0
7		Stands
8-9		Stands (Natural)

If the Player's hand does not draw a third card,
then the Banker's hand stands on a total of 6 or more.

If the player hand has 3,ace for a total of 4 and the banker hand has 8,7 for a total of 5, what happens? The player hand must draw and say it gets a 9 for a total of 3. Once again, the banker hand would like to stand on its total because it would win, but the rules have to be consulted first and in this case when the banker's first 2 cards total 5 and the player's third card drawn is a 9 the banker hand must stand, so the banker hand wins 5 to 3.

Finally, let's say the player hand has 4,3 for a total of 7 and the banker hand has 6,10 for a total of 6. The player hand must always stand on totals of 6 or 7 and the banker hand must also stand on its total of 6 because the player hand didn't take a third card. The player hand wins this one 7 to 6.

All right, now that you know how to play Baccarat we come to the important question which is - how do you win? Well, as I said before, if you bet on player you'll only be giving the casino a 1.36% edge and if you bet on banker you'll be giving the casino an even more modest edge of just 1.17%. While both of these are pretty low edges to give the casino you're still stuck with the fact that the casino will always have an edge over you and in the long run the game of Baccarat is unbeatable. So, if that's the case then how do you win? Well, the answer to that is very simple - You have to get lucky! And that's the ONLY way you can win at Baccarat. Of course, this is easier said than done, but fortunately, in the game of Baccarat, you have the option of making two bets that require no skill and both offer the casino a very low edge especially when you compare them to roulette where the house has a 5.26% advantage on a double-zero wheel and slot machines where the edge is about 8% to 10% I always stress the point that when you gamble in a casino you have to play the games that have the lowest casino edge in order to have the best chance of winning and with that in mind you can see that Baccarat is not that bad a game to play for the recreational gambler.

Now let's take a quick look at one of the most common systems for betting on Baccarat. One thing that many Baccarat players seem to have in common is a belief in streaks and the casinos accommodate these players by providing scorecards at the table that can be used to track the results of each hand. Many players like to bet on whatever won the last hand in the belief that it will continue to come in and they hope for a long streak.

The thinking for these players is that since Baccarat is purely a guessing game it's just like guessing the outcome of a coin toss and chances are that a coin won't alternately come up heads, tails, heads, tails, heads, tails but rather that there will be streaks where the same result will come in for awhile. So, is this a good system? Well, actually, it's no better and no worse than any other system because no matter what you do you'll still have the same casino edge going against you on every bet you make: 1.36% on the player and 1.17% on the banker. The one good thing about a system like this though is that you don't have to sit there and guess what you want to play each time. Instead, you go into the game knowing how you're going to play and you don't have to blame yourself if your guess is wrong, instead you get to blame it on your system!

How Good Are Those "Other" Games?

by Frank Scoblete

When I was a kid I had a friend, Billy, who came from a very large family on his mother's side. I never saw any of his relatives from his father's side. One day I asked him about it. "Oh, I never see those people from the 'other' side. I don't even know most of the people from the 'other' side." He emphasized the word "other" every time he spoke of them. Finally, I caught a glimpse of one of them one day and, you know what, she looked kind of "otherly."

I guess we all have our "others" in this life and the casinos are no different. You have the machines, you have poker, blackjack, craps, and roulette -- those are the standard fares from casino-gambling-times primordial; but then you have all those "other" games. Most "other" games are mutated versions of the traditional games; some evolved naturally, but most have been genetically engineered to look somewhat similar to their forebears with one major difference - they can usually take your money faster either because the house edge is higher or the game is speedier or some combination of both.

In the years that I have been writing about casino gambling, I have seen many "other" games such as Two Up, a coin flipping game; Casino War, the kid's game where high card wins; Russian Roulette, not the gun kind, the card version; Pokette, a combination of roulette and poker; Sic Bo, which is a dice game like Chuck-A-Luck which is a dice game like Mini-Just Dice which is a dice game like Heads and Tails which is a dice game like Sic Bo. I have played countless versions of blackjack: Red and Black, Multiple Action, Jackpot Blackjack, Bonus Blackjack, Over-Under 13 Blackjack, Royal Match and Double Exposure Blackjack. I have also played Red Dog, the casino version of acey-deucy; CrapJack, a combination of blackjack and craps; BacCraps, a combination of baccarat and craps; Pai Gow, tiles and poker version; Super Pan Nine, the gambling game, not the Chinese combinationdinner platter; Hickok's Six Card, a deadly poker variant named after a guy who died playing poker (is it any wonder this game expired?); Double Down Stud, the table game, not the porno movie; Fast Action Hold'em, a poker mutant; Bahamian Baccarat, that's mini-bac without the commission on the Bank bet, and the ubiquitous Big Wheel.

With the exception of the Pai Gow tiles or its poker variation, none of the above games have really caught the fancy of the casino gaming public. Many don't even exist anymore. They are dinosaur dead. However, some games have indeed hung/caught on, establishing niches in many, if not most, casinos and casino venues; and these few survivors have become the official "other" games in the casino pantheon. They are Let It Ride, Caribbean Stud, Three Card Poker, Spanish 21 and the aforementioned Pai Gow poker.

All are mutants of older games but not one has evolved naturally over time, rather each was deliberately created in the laboratory of mad-gambling scientists with one view in mind -- to take our money in as pleasant a way as possible. In fact, all of these "other" games range from decent to very good based on their respective house edges and speeds. So how good are these "other" games? If we judge based on a combination of speed and house edge, we can determine how many average bets we will lose in an hour of playing these games in the long run.

SPANISH 21 - Spanish 21 is the newest table game to generate some heat in casino circles. No wonder. Played with the correct basic strategy, called the Armada Strategy, players can face a house edge of around .8 percent -- which means for every $100 wagered at this game, you can expect to lose a mere 80 cents. Not bad. Of course, Spanish 21 earns much more for the casinos owing to the fact that most players do not know that a completely different basic strategy is called for. Instead, the Spanish 21 players use the basic strategy for regular blackjack, with some homespun variations on occasion, and wind up giving the casinos edges of two, three, four or more percent. Such edges, coupled with the relatively fast speed of the game (anywhere from 60 to 100 hands an hour) can cause players to wind up like the Spanish Armada, in the drink.

Spanish 21 is played exactly like regular blackjack with this difference -- all the 10-spot cards have been removed. The Kings, Queens and Jacks remain. To make up for the reduction in total blackjacks because of the removal of the 10-spots, the casino gives many exciting bonus hands such as:

    a. Five-card 21 pays 3 to 2.
    b. Six-card 21 pays 2 to 1.
    c. Seven (or more)-card 21 pays 3 to 1.
    d. A three-card hand of 6-7-8 composed of mixed suits pays 3 to 2.
    e. A three-card hand of 6-7-8 composed of the same suit pays 2 to 1.
    f. A three-card hand of 6-7-8 composed of all spades pays 3 to 1.
    g. A 7-7-7 hand composed of mixed suits pays 3 to 2.
    h. A 7-7-7 hand composed of the same suit pays 2 to 1.
    i. A 7-7-7 hand composed of all spades pays 3 to 1.
    j. A player may surrender the original bet but save the double-down bet. This rule does not apply if the hand is busted. This rule is called the Double-Down Rescue.
    k. There is a Jackpot bonus of $1,000 paid to any player who has 7-7-7 of the same suit if the dealer is also showing a 7 (of any suit). When

this occurs, all other players at the table receive a bonus of $50. Some casinos make the jackpot $1,000 per five dollars wagered up to a maximum of $5,000 for a $25 or higher bet. This option will appeal to those players who like the idea that a bad run can be dramatically turned around with a quick hit of luck.

Summary: Very Good Game
Loss Per Hour: Approximately one-half average bets.
Qualifier: Must play Armada Strategy.
Playing Tip: Slow the pace whenever possible.

CARIBBEAN STUD - Caribbean Stud sailed to the mainland from the islands, circa the 1980s, and has gotten a very strong foothold on the casino beach fronts. It is a game with a relatively high house edge of 5.3 percent, but as I wrote in *Bold Card Play: Best Strategies for Caribbean Stud, Let It Ride and Three Card Poker* (see ad on page 156), there is another way to figure the house edge at Caribbean Stud that brings it down to 2.6 percent because it includes the total amount bet and not just the initial wager. Caribbean Stud is a moderately paced game of between 45 and 55 decisions per hour.

There are two main wagers in Caribbean Stud -- the "ante" and the "bet." The "bet" area looks like a treasure chest just bursting with gold coins. The "ante" is the rectangular area. Atop the "ante" on the layout is a side bet - the jackpot - that is made by dropping a one-dollar chip in the jackpot slot. When a player opts to place a jackpot bet, he becomes eligible to hit the progressive jackpot (or a percentage thereof) that increases with each hand played. The side jackpot bet is strictly optional and does not influence the winning and losing of hands. To open, the players put a bet in the "ante" square and, if they wish, they can make the one-dollar jackpot bet. The dealer deals five cards face down to each player. The dealer then deals himself five cards, the last one face up. The players now have two choices to make: 1. they can play out their hands, or 2. they can surrender their hands and lose their "antes."

If they decide to play out their hands, they must place a bet that is "double" their "ante" in the "bet" square. Once the players have made their respective decisions, they put all their cards face down on the table. The dealer will now scoop up the "ante" bets from all the players who dropped out. This done, the dealer turns over his remaining four cards and makes the best poker hand possible out of them.

The dealer must "qualify" with an Ace-King hand for the game to be fully decided. If he fails to have a hand that is A-K or better, he pays off the "antes" and pushes on the "bets." The player then takes back the "bet" wager. If the dealer qualifies with a hand of Ace-King (or better), then all the players' hands are judged against it. If the player cannot beat the dealer's hand, the player loses both his "ante" and his "bet." If the player beats the dealer, the "ante" is paid off at even money, while the "bet" is usually paid off at the following house odds:

Winning Hand	Bonus Payout Table
Ace-King	1 to 1
One Pair	1 to 1
Two Pair	2 to 1
Three-of-a-kind	3 to 1
Straight	4 to 1
Flush	5 to 1
Full House	7 to 1
Four-of-a-kind	20 to 1
Straight Flush	50 to 1
Royal Flush	100 to 1

If the dealer fails to qualify, you don't win the bet bonus -- no matter how good your hand is. You also can't win a bonus if the dealer beats your hand.

The jackpot side bet is paid off independently, so you can lose to the dealer and still collect on the jackpot bet. The following is a typical jackpot pay scale:

Hand	Progressive Bonus
one pair	none
two pair	none
three of a kind	none
straight	none
flush	$50
full house	$75
four of a kind	$100
straight flush	10 percent of the progressive jackpot
royal flush	100 percent of the progressive jackpot

Summary: Good Game
Loss per hour: Approximately one average bet.
Qualifier: Raise on Ace-King-Jack-8-3 or better.
Playing Hint: Don't make jackpot side bet.

LET IT RIDE - A game that started fast out of the starting gates and seems to have just gotten more and more popular in the few short years it has existed is Shuffle Master's Let It Ride, another poker variant. The house edge is approximately 2.8 percent with the proper basic strategy (see ad on page 156 for my book *Bold Card Play Strategy: Best Strategies for Caribbean Stud, Let It Ride and Three Card Poker*) .

In front of each player are three betting squares labeled "1" and "2" and "$." The player places a bet in each square. The object of the game is to make the best poker hand that is a pair of 10s or better with your three cards and two community cards. You are "not" playing to beat the dealer as in Caribbean Stud, merely to get a good hand that pays a bonus according to a set payoff schedule. This bonus schedule applies to all hands. If, at the end of play, you have three bets working, you will receive the bonus on all three bets. If you only have one bet working, you will only receive the bonus on that one bet.

The dealer gives each player three cards and puts two cards face down as "community" cards. The players now look at their three-card hands. The players can now decide to withdraw their number "1" bet or let it ride. To let a bet ride, a player must put his three cards face down under his wager or behind his number "1" bet. To withdraw the number "1" bet, the player must scratch the felt to indicate to the dealer that the bet is to be returned. Players are not allowed to touch their chips once they are on the layout so the players cannot take back their bets themselves. The dealer will push the bet back if the player so desires.

Once the players have decided what to do with bet number "1" and the dealer has returned all withdrawals from play, the dealer now turns over the first of the two community cards. Again the players can decide whether to take off their number "2" bet or let that bet ride.

An important point to note is that the player who allows his number "1" bet to ride does not have to let his number "2" bet ride. Each bet is handled separately and there is a distinct strategy for each round of play. The "$" bet cannot be taken down.

Finally, the dealer turns over the second community card and the players are paid off according to the payoff schedule, or their losing bets are collected as the case may be. Some casinos have begun to offer a "Bonus" jackpot for an additional side bet, as is done with Caribbean Stud. You place this bet at the beginning of the round and it is not returnable as are bets number "1" and number "2."

Payoff Schedule For Let It Ride

Hand	Payoff
Pair of Tens	1 to 1
Pair of Jacks	1 to 1
Pair of Queens	1 to 1
Pair of Kings	1 to 1
Pair of Aces	1 to 1
Two Pair	2 to 1
Three-of-a-kind	3 to 1
Straight	5 to 1
Flush	8 to 1
Full House	11 to 1
Four-of-a-kind	50 to 1
Straight Flush	200 to 1
Royal Flush	1,000 to 1

Summary: Fair/Good Game
Loss per hour: Approximately one and a half average bets.
Qualifier: Must use proper Bold Card Play basic strategy.
Playing Tip: Only bet pair of 10s or better.

PAI GOW POKER - In negative expectation games, slow is good. Pai Gow Poker is deliciously slow, sometimes no more than 40 hands in an hour are actually played to completion. If you play according to the house way of setting the cards, you will face an approximately 2.5 percent casino edge.

Pai Gow Poker is a poker variation of the Chinese tile game. The game begins when one player is designated as the "dealer/banker." He must bank the bets of the other players. If no player wants to assume this role, the casino will bank the game. It is played with a standard deck of 52 cards with one joker added that can be used as an ace.

Before the deal, three dice are shaken and displayed to determine the order of the deal. Each player is then dealt seven cards with which he must make two hands based on poker rankings -- a back hand of five cards and a front hand of two cards. The five-card hand must outrank the two-card hand.

To win, you have to defeat the banker on both your front and back hands. To lose, the banker must defeat you on both as well. A "copy" or push goes to the banker. The house takes a five percent commission on all winning player hands and, since you win approximately 50 percent of the time, the house edge is a 2.5 percent.

Summary: Good Game
Loss Per Hour: Approximately one average bet.
Qualifier: You must play correct hand-making strategy. (You can find this in my book "Guerrilla Gambling: How to Beat the Casinos at Their Own Games!")
Playing Tip: When in doubt, let the house set your hand.

THREE CARD POKER - Another relatively new game that is gaining adherents throughout the country is Three-Card Poker, developed by poker pro Derek Webb. It is a very simple poker variant that has a very simple basic strategy, the objective of which is to beat the dealer's three-card hand. There is also an added incentive in attempting to win bonuses for certain premium hands.

The player can bet on three propositions called "Ante", "Play" and the independent "Pair Plus." The dealer deals the player three cards and himself three cards. If a player has opted to place an Ante bet, when he looks at his three cards he must decide whether to stay in the game or fold. To stay, he must place a bet equal to his Ante bet in the Play square. Now the dealer turns over his three cards. If the player beats the dealer's three-card hand, the player wins the Ante bet at even money. The Play bet pays a bonus for certain premium hands such as a straight flush, three of a kind, a straight and a flush. The Play pays even money for a pair.

The Pair Plus bet is a side bet that can be made without placing an Ante bet. If the player has a Pair Plus, which is two of a kind or better, he receives an additional payout. Many of these payouts are greater than one to one.

Unlike Caribbean Stud, where a dealer not qualifying for play cancels winning player hands, in Three Card Poker a non-qualifying dealer is a benefit to the players. What qualifies a dealer? Simply, if the dealer does not have at least a queen high or better hand, the players win on all their bets.

The house has a moderate edge on Three Card Poker when proper strategy is employed. The Ante and Play hands face a 2.14 percent house edge, while the Pair Plus bet comes in at 2.32 percent for the house (there is no strategy for Pair Plus). A conservative strategy would call for making only the Ante and Play wagers until one had a comfortable win before making several exploratory Pair Plus bets. If luck kept shinning on you when you did so, then continue to play all three propositions. For truly small bankrolls, you could play the Pair Plus without placing the Ante or Play wagers.

Three Card Poker Bonus Payout Schedule

Hand	Ante Bonus Payout	Pair Plus Payout
Straight Flush	5 to 1	40 to 1
Three of a Kind	4 to 1	30 to 1
Straight	1 to 1	6 to 1
Flush	0	4 to 1
Pair	0	1 to 1
High Card	0	Player loses

Winning Ante wagers are paid 1 to 1.
Winning Play wagers are paid 1 to 1.

Summary: Fair Game
Loss Per Hour: Approximately two average bets.
Qualifier: Best to avoid Pair Plus unless you're way ahead.
Playing Tip: Bet Play on your queen or better, otherwise fold.

There are probably a few good reasons why these "other" games have caught on. They offer the players choices to make that do affect their expectation, while simultaneously offering the players an opportunity to win big bonuses if Lady Luck smiles on them. Unlike my friend Billy's family, some of these "others" might be worth getting to know.

Award-winning author Frank Scoblete's books, videos and audio cassettes on casinogambling have sold over a million copies. He also publishes his own quarterly magazine, "The New Chance and Circumtance," and has his own website at www.scoblete.com.in association with RGT Online. See ads for his books on pages 84, 98, 134, 140 and below.

A Few Last Words

by Steve Bourie

When I sit down to put this book together each year I try to make sure that everything in here will help to make you a better and more knowledgeable gambler when you go to a casino.

I try to include stories that will help you understand how casinos operate, how to choose the best casino games and also how to play those games in the best way possible.

My philosophy with this book is that gambling in a casino is fun and for about 99% of the people who visit casinos that statement is true. The vast majority of people who gamble in casinos are recreational players who enjoy the fun and excitement of gambling. They know that they won't always win and they also realize that over the long term they will most likely have more losing sessions than winning ones. They also understand that any losses they incur will be the price they pay for their fun and they only gamble with money they can afford to lose. In other words, they realize that casino gambling is a form of entertainment, just like going to a movie or an amusement park, and they are willing to pay a price for that entertainment. Unfortunately, there are also some people who go to casinos and become problem gamblers.

According to Gamblers Anonymous you may be a problem gambler if you answer yes to at least seven of the following 20 questions:

1. Do you lose time from work due to gambling?
2. Does gambling make your home life unhappy?
3. Does gambling affect your reputation?
4. Do you ever feel remorse after gambling?
5. Do you ever gamble to get money with which to pay debts or to otherwise solve financial difficulties?
6. Does gambling cause a decrease in your ambition or efficiency?
7. After losing, do you feel you must return as soon as possible and win back your losses?
8. After a win, do you have a strong urge to return and win more?
9. Do you often gamble until your last dollar is gone?
10. Do you ever borrow to finance your gambling?
11. Do you ever sell anything to finance your gambling?

12. Are you reluctant to use your "gambling money" for other expenses?
13. Does gambling make you careless about the welfare of your family?
14. Do you ever gamble longer than you planned?
15. Do you ever gamble to escape worry or trouble?
16. Do you ever commit, or consider committing, an illegal act to finance your gambling?
17. Does gambling cause you to have difficulty sleeping?
18. Do arguments, disappointments, or frustrations create within you an urge to gamble?
19. Do you have an urge to celebrate good fortune by a few hours of gambling?
20. Do you ever consider self-destruction as a result of your gambling?

If you believe you might have a gambling problem you should be aware that help is available from The National Council on Problem Gaming, Inc. It is the foremost advocacy organization in the country for problem gamblers and is headquartered in Washington, D.C. It was formed in 1972 as a non-profit agency to promote public education and awareness about gambling problems and operates a 24-hour nationwide help line at 1-800-522-4700. Anyone calling that number will be provided with the appropriate referral resources for help with their gambling problem.

I sincerely hope that none of you reading this book will ever have a need to call that number but it was an issue that I felt should be addressed.

ARIZONA

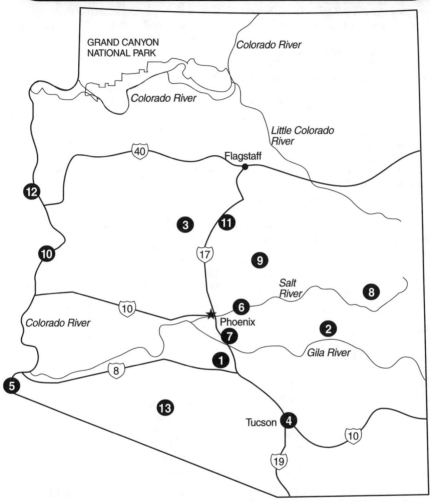

GRAND CANYON
NATIONAL PARK

Colorado River

Colorado River

*Little Colorado
River*

Flagstaff

*Salt
River*

Colorado River

Phoenix

Gila River

Tucson

In mid-1993 Arizona's Governor Symington signed a compact with the state's tribes that allowed them to offer slot machines on their reservations.

The compact doesn't allow for any table games but some casinos offer video versions of blackjack, craps and roulette. The Arizona tribes aren't required to release information on their slot machine percentage paybacks, however, according to the Arizona Department of Gaming, the terms of the compact require each tribes' machines to return the following minimum and maximum paybacks: video poker and video blackjack - 83% to 100%, slot ma-

chines - 80% to 100%, keno - 75% to 100%. Each tribe is free to set its machines to pay back anywhere within those limits.

All Arizona casinos have slots, video poker and video keno. Optional games include: video blackjack (VBJ), video craps (VC), video roulette (VR), poker (P), live keno (K), bingo (BG) and simulcasting (S). The minimum gambling age is 18 (21 if liquor is served) and all casinos are open 24 hours.

For more information on Arizona call the state's Office of Tourism at (800) 842-8257.

Apache Gold Casino Resort
P.O. Box 1210
San Carlos, Arizona 85550
(520) 475-7800
Map Location: **#2** (90 miles E. of Phoenix)
Website: www.apachegoldcasinoresort.com

Toll-Free Number: (800) APACHE-8
Rooms: 147 Price Range: $55-$95
Suites: 10   Price Range: $75-$150
Restaurants: 1 Liquor: Yes
Buffets: B-$6.95 (Sat/Sun) L-$7.95 D-$9.95/
        $13.95 (Fri)/$11.95 (Sat)/$10.95 (Sun)
Casino Size: 10,000 Square Feet
Other Games: P, K, BG, S, VR
Casino Marketing: (800) APACHE-8
Senior Discount: 10% room discount for AAA
AARP members. 15% for Club members.
Fun Book: Available through local motels, RV
        parks and the chamber of commerce
Special Features: Hotel is off-property and is
Best Western. Stay and Play Packages (Sun-
Thu) include room, drink and meal. Lounge
serves beer and wine. 18-hole golf course.
Driving range. Pro shop. Convenience store.
RV Park w/full hookups and dump station.

Blue Water Casino
119 W. Riverside Drive
Parker, Arizona 85344
(520) 669-7777
Website: www.bluewaterfun.com
Map Location: **#10** (160 miles W. of Phoenix)

Toll-Free Number: (888) 243-3366
Rooms: 200 Price Range: $49-$120
Suites: 25 Price Range: $99-$229
Restaurants: 5 Liquor: Yes
Buffet: B- $4.95 L:$7.95 D: $8.95
Other Games: P, K, BG
Senior Discount: 10% room discount (except
   in summer) for AAA and AARP members.
Special Features: All rooms have blow dry-
ers, 25 in. color TV, cable, voice mail,
balconies,data ports and coffee makers

Bucky's Casino & Resort
530 E. Merritt
Prescott, Arizona 86301
(520) 776-1666
Website: www.buckyscasino.com
Map Location: **#3** (91 miles S.W. of Flagstaff,
Junction of Hwy. 69 & Hwy. 89)

Toll-Free Number: (800) SLOTS-44
Room Reservations: (800) 967-4637
Rooms: 81 Price Range: $59-$129
Suites: 80 Price Range: $99-$179
Restaurants: 2 Liquor: Yes
Other Games: VBJ, P
Casino Marketing: (520) 771-0580
Special Features: Located in Prescott Resort
Hotel. Free shuttle service. Room discount for
AAA and AARP members.

Casino Arizona - Salt River
524 N. 92nd Street
Scottsdale, Arizona 85256
(480) 850-7777
Website: www.casinoaz.com
Map Location: **#6** (15 miles N.E. of Phoenix)

Toll-Free Number: (877) 7-24-HOUR
Restaurants: 5 Liquor: Yes
Buffets: B-$6.50 (Sat-Sun) L-$7.50
        D-$9.95/$14.95 (Sat-Sun)
Other Games: VBJ, VR, P, K, BG, S

Casino Arizona - Indian Bend
9700 E. Indian Bend
Scottsdale, Arizona 85256
(480) 850-7777
Website: www.casinoaz.com
Map Location: **#6** (15 miles N.E. of Phoenix)

Toll-Free Number: (877) 7-24-HOUR
Restaurants: 1 Liquor: Yes
Buffet: L/D-$7.50
Other Games: P

Casino Del Sol
5655 W. Valencia
Tucson, Arizona 85746
(520) 883-1700
Website: www.casinodelsol.com
Map Location: **#4**

Toll-Free Number: (800) 344-9435
Restaurants: 1 Liquor: No
Other Games: VBJ, P

Casino of the Sun

7406 S. Camino De Oeste
Tucson, Arizona 85746
(520) 883-1700
Website: www.casinosun.com
Map Location: **#4**

Toll-Free Number: (800) 344-9435
Restaurants: 2 Liquor: No
Buffets: L-$6.25 D-$7.25
Other Games: VBJ, P, BG
Special Features: Smoke shop. Gift shop. 50% food discount on Tuesdays.

Cliff Castle Casino & Hotel Lodge

555 Middle Verde Road
Camp Verde, Arizona 86322
(520) 567-9031
Website: www.cliffcastle.com
Map Location: **#11** (50 miles S. of Flagstaff)

Toll-Free Number: (800) 381-SLOT
Room Reservation Number: (800) 524-6343
Rooms: 82 Price Range: $59-$89
Suites: 2 Price Range: $79-$119
Restaurants: 5 Liquor: Yes
Buffets: B-$6.00 (Sunday Only)
Other Games: VBJ, VC, VR, K, P, BG
Casino Size: 114,000 Square Feet
Special Features: Casino is in Cliff Castle Lodge. Bowling alley. Kid's Quest childcare facility. Arcade. 3,500-seat amphitheater.

Cocopah Casino & Bingo

15136 S. Avenue B
Somerton, Arizona 85350
(520) 726-8066
Map Location: **#5** (13 miles S.W. of Yuma)
Website: www.wincocopahcasino.com

Toll-Free Number: (800) 23-SLOTS
Restaurants: 1 Snack Bar Liquor: No
Other Games: VBJ, BG
Special Features: RV park (800-537-7901). 18-hole golf course. $1 breakfast special from 3am-10am.

Desert Diamond Casino - I-19

1100 West Pima Mine Road
Sahuarita, Arizona 85629
(520) 294-7777
Website: www.desertdiamondcasino.net
Map Location: **#4**

Toll-Free Number: (866) 332-9467
Restaurants: 2 Liquor: Yes
Casino Size: 35,000 Square Feet
Other Games: VBJ, VR, P, K, BG

Desert Diamond Casino - Nogales

7350 S. Nogales Highway
Tucson, Arizona 85706
(520) 294-7777
Website: www.desertdiamondcasino.net
Map Location: **#4**

Toll-Free Number: (866) 332-9467
Restaurants: 2 Liquor: Yes
Casino Size: 15,000 Square Feet
Other Games: VBJ, VR, BG

Fort McDowell Casino

P.O. Box 18359
Fountain Hills, Arizona 85269
(602) 837-1424
Website: www.fortmcdowellcasino.com
Map Location: **#6** (25 miles N.E. of Phoenix)

Toll-Free Number: (800) THE-FORT
Restaurants: 3 (1 open 24 hours) Liquor: Yes
Buffets: B-$4.95/$7.95 (Sat-Sun)
    L-$6.95/$7.95 (Fri-Sat)
    D-$8.95 (Mon/Thu)/$11.95 (Sun/Wed)/
    $14.95 (Fri/Sat)/$13.95 (Tue)
Other Games: VBJ, P, K, BG, S,
Special Features: Free valley-wide transportation (reservations required). Gift shop.

Gila River Casino - Lone Butte

1200 S. 56th Street
Chandler, Arizona 85226
(520) 796-7777
Website: www.wingilariver.com
Map Location: **#7** (10 miles S.W. of Phoenix)

Toll-Free Number: (800) WIN-GILA
Restaurants: 1 Liquor: No
Casino Size: 30,000 Square Feet
Other Games: P

Gila River Casino - Vee Quiva
6443 N. Komatke Lane
Laveen, Arizona 85339
(520) 796-7777
Website: www.wingilariver.com
Map Location: **#7** (10 miles S.W. of Phoenix)

Toll-Free Number: (800) WIN-GILA
Restaurants: 2   Liquor: No
Casino Size: 30,000 Square Feet
Other Games: P, BG

Gila River Casino - Wild Horse
5512 W. Wild Horse Pass
Chandler, Arizona 85226
(520) 796-7727
Website: www.wingilariver.com
Map Location: **#7** (25 miles S.E. of Phoenix)

Toll-Free Number: (800) WIN-GILA
Restaurants: 1   Liquor: No
Casino Size: 60,000 Square Feet
Other Games: VC, VR, P, K, BG

Golden Hasan Casino
PO Box 10
Ajo, Arizona 85321
(520) 362-2746
Website: www.desertdiamondcasino.net
Map Location: **#13** (125 miles S.W. of Phoenix)

Restaurants: 1 Snack Bar
Hours: 12pm-12am/11am-1am (Fri-Sat)

Harrah's Ak Chin Casino Resort
15406 Maricopa Road
Maricopa, Arizona 85239
(480) 802-5000
Website: www.harrahs.com
Map Location: **#1** (25 miles S. of Phoenix)

Toll-Free Number: (800) HARRAHS
Rooms: 142 Price Range: $49-$150
Suites: 4   Price Range: $250
Restaurants: 4 (1 open 24 hours) Liquor: Yes
Buffets: S-$13.99 (Sun) L-$8.99
         D-$11.99-$13.99 (Fri/Sat)
Casino Size: 43,000 Square Feet
Other Games: VBJ, VC, VR, P, K, BG
Senior Discount: Various, if 50 or older
Special Features: Native-American crafts store and smoke shop. Pool with swim-up bar.

Hon-Dah Resort Casino
777 Highway 260
Pinetop, Arizona 85935
(928) 369-0299
Website: www.hon-dah.com
Map Location: **#8** (190 miles N.E. of Phoenix)

Toll-Free Number: (800) 929-8744
Rooms: 126 Price Range: $79-$99
Suites: 2 Price Range: $150-$180
Restaurants: 1   Liquor: Yes
Buffets: D-$13.95 (Fri-Sat)
Casino Size: 20,000 Square Feet
Other Games: VBJ, P, BG (Sun/Mon)
Special Features: 200-space RV park. Waterfall wildlife attraction in hotel lobby. Convenience store. Gas station. Cigar bar. Gift shop.

Mazatzal Casino
P.O. Box 1820
Hwy. 87, Milemarker 251
Payson, Arizona 85547
(520) 474-6044
Website: www.777play.com
Map Location: **#9** (90 miles N.E. of Phoenix)

Toll-Free Number: (800) 777-7529
Restaurants: 2   Liquor: Yes
Casino Size: 35,000 Square Feet
Other Games: VBJ, P, K, BG
Senior Discount: 10% off food, if 55 or older
Special Features: Offers Stay & Play packages (Sun-Thurs) with local motels that include: discounted room price, Fun Books, breakfast for two in restaurant, plus free shuttle to and from motel. Sports bar. Video arcade. Gift shop.

Paradise Casino
450 Quechan Drive
Yuma, Arizona 85364
(760) 572-7777
Website: www.paradisecasinoyuma.com
Map Location: **#5** (244 miles W. of Tucson)

Toll-Free Number: (888) 777-4946
Restaurants: 1 Liquor: Yes
Buffets: L/D-$4.25
Casino Marketing: (760) 572-2463
Other Games: P, K, BG
Senior Discount: 10% off food, if 65, or older
Special Features: $1.50 breakfast specials. Cappuccino bar.

Spirit Mountain Casino
8555 South Highway 95
Mohave Valley, Arizona 86440
(520) 346-2000
Map Location: **#12** (15 miles S. of Bullhead City)

Restaurants: 1 Snack Bar Liquor: Yes
Casino Size: 12,000 Square Feet
Special Features: Adjacent to 120-space full-service RV park. Convenience store. Gas station.

Yavapai Casino
1501 E. Highway 69
Prescott, Arizona 86301
(520) 445-5767
Website: www.buckyscasino.com
Map Location: **#3** (91 miles S.W. of Flagstaff)

Toll-Free Number: (800) SLOTS-44
Restaurants: 1 Snack Bar Liquor: No
Other Games: BG (Wed-Sun)
Special Features: Located across the street from Bucky's Casino. Free shuttle service.

CALIFORNIA

On March 7,2000 California voters approved a state-wide referendum that legally allowed the state's Indian tribes to begin offering electronic gaming machines, blackjack, and other house-banked card games. The games of craps and roulette are not permitted.

Most California card rooms also offer some form of player-banked blackjack but, because they are prohibited by law from playing blackjack, the game is played to 22 rather than 21. Additionally, players must pay a commission to the house on every hand they play. The amount will vary depending on the rules of the house but, generally, it's about two to five percent of the total amount bet. You can see a listing of California card rooms at the *americancasinoguide.com* web site.

There are also a few Indian casinos that charge players a commission on their blackjack games. The casinos that charge players a commission are noted in the special features section under each casino's listing.

California's tribes aren't required to release information on their slot machine percentage paybacks and, as of July, 2002 the state of California did not require any minimum returns on gaming machines.

Unless otherwise noted, all California casinos are open 24 hours and offer: slots, video poker, and video keno. Optional games offered include: blackjack (BJ), mini-baccarat (MB), poker (P), pai gow poker (PGP), Caribbean stud poker (CSP), let it ride (LIR), three card poker (TCP), bingo (BG), casino war (CW) and simulcasting (S). The minimum gambling age is 18 (21 if alcohol is served).

Although most of the casinos have toll-free numbers be aware that many of those numbers will only work for calls made within California. Also, many of the casinos are in out-of-the-way locations, so it is advisable to call ahead for directions.

For more information on visiting California call the state's department of tourism at (800) 862-2543.

Agua Caliente Casino
32250 Bob Hope Dr
Ranch Mirage, California 92270
(760) 321-2000
Website: www.hotwatercasino.com
Map Location: **#3** (115 miles E. of Los Angeles)

Restaurants: 3 Liquor: Yes
Buffets: B-$6.95 L-$9.95 D-$14.95
Other Games: BJ, MB, CSP, TCP,
        P, PGP, BG (Sun-Thu)
Special Features: Food Court, $1 off buffet with slot card. Associated with Spa Casino.

Alturas Casino
901 County Rd 56
Alturas, California 96101
(530) 233-3141
Map Location: **#27** (250 miles N.E. of Sacramento)

Restaurants: 1 Snack Bar Liquor: No
Hours: 9am-Midnight/1am (Fri-Sat)
Other Games: Slots Only, BG (Mon/Thu/Fri/Sun)

Augustine Casino
84001 Avenue 54
Coachella, California 92236
(760)391-9500
Map Location: **#8** (125 miles E. of Los Angeles)

Restaurants: 2 Liquor: Yes
Other Games: BJ, TCP

Black Bart Casino
P.O. Box 1177
Willits, California 95490
(707) 459-7330
Map Location: **#11** (160 miles N.W. of Sacramento)

Restaurants: 1 Deli Liquor: No
Hours: 8am-2am/24 hours (Fri/Sat)
Casino Size: 3,000 Square Feet
Other Games: Slots Only

Black Oak Casino
19400 Tuolumne Road North
Tuolumne, California 95379
(209) 928-9300
Website: www.blackoakcasino.com
Map Location: **#5** (100 miles S.E. of Sacramento)

Toll-Free Number: (877) 747-8777
Restaurants: 1 Liquor: Yes
Casino Size: 22,000 Square Feet
Other Games: BJ, TCP

Cache Creek Indian Bingo & Casino
14455 Highway 16
Brooks, California 95606
(530) 796-3118
Website: www.cachecreek.com
Map Location: **#2** (35 miles N.W. of Sacramento)

Toll-Free Number: (800) 452-8181
Restaurants: 4 Liquor: No
Buffets: L-$8.00 D-$10.00/$15.00 (Fri-Sun)
Casino Size: 18,000 Square Feet
Other Games: BJ, P, PGP, BG (Sun-Thu)

Cahuilla Creek Casino
PO Box 390845
Anza, California 92539
(909) 763-1200
Website: www.cahuillacreekcasino.net
Map Location: **#19** (30 miles S. of Palm Springs)

Restaurants: 1 Liquor: Yes
Buffets: Brunch-$8.95 (Thu/Sun)
Other Games: BJ, P, BG (Fri-Mon)
Special Features: Free supervised children's play area.

Casino Morongo
49750 Seminole Drive
Cabazon, California 92230
(909) 849-3080
Website: www.casinomorongo.com
Map Location: **#3** (90 miles E. of Los Angeles)

Toll-Free Number: (800) 252-4499
Restaurants: 2 Liquor: Yes
Casino Size: 100,000 Square Feet
Other Games: BJ, P, CSP, TCP, LIR, MB
            PGP, BG (Wed-Sun)
Special Features: Charges players a commission on their blackjack games. Slot club memebrs get food and gas discounts.

Casino Pauma
777 Pauma Reservation Road
Pauma Valley, California 92061
(760) 742-2177
Website: www.casinopauma.com
Map Location: **#20** (35 miles N.E. of San Diego)

Toll-Free Number: (877) 687-2862
Restaurants: 1 Liquor: Yes
Casino Size: 35,000 Square Feet
Other Games: P, TCP, PGP
Senior Discount: 2-for-1 lunch buffet, if 55+
Special Features: Offers card versions of craps and roulette. 95-cent breakfast special. 2-for-1 prime rib (Sun-Thu).

Cherae Heights Casino
P.O. Box 635
Trinidad, California 95570
(707) 677-3611
Website: www.cher-ae-heights-casino.com
Map Location: **#4** (25 miles N. of Eureka)

Toll-Free Number: (800) 684-BINGO
Restaurants: 1 Snack Bar Liquor: No
Other Games: BJ, P, BG (Wed-Sun)

Chicken Ranch Bingo
16929 Chicken Ranch Road
Jamestown, California 95327
(209) 984-3000
Map Location: **#5** (100 miles S.E. of Sacramento)

Toll-Free Number: (800) 752-4646
Restaurants: 1 Snack Bar Liquor: No
Hours: 9am-1am Daily
Casino Size: 35,000 Square Feet
Other Games: Slots only, BG

Chumash Casino
3400 East Highway 246
Santa Ynez, California 93460
(805) 686-0855
Website: www.chumashcasino.com
Map Location: **#13** (40 miles N.W. of Santa Barbara)

Toll-Free Number: (800) 728-9997
Restaurants: 1 Liquor: No
Buffets: L/D-$5.50
Other Games: BJ, P, PGP, BG, LIR, TCP

Colusa Casino & Bingo
P.O. Box 1267
Colusa, California 95932
(530) 458-8844
Website: www.colusacasino.com
Map Location: **#6** (75 miles N. of Sacramento)

Toll-Free Number: (800) 655-U-WIN
Restaurants: 1 Liquor: Yes
Buffets: L-$7.99 D-$9.99
Senior Discount: Various on Tue/Sun, if 55+
Other Games: BJ, P, BG (Fri-Tue)
Fun Book: Need coupon from local businesses

Eagle Mountain Casino
P.O. Box 1659
Porterville, California 93258
(559) 788-6220
Website: www.eaglemtncasino.com
Map Location: **#21** (60 miles S.E. of Fresno)

Toll-Free Number: (800) 903-3353
Restaurants: 2 Liquor: No
Buffets: B-$3.99 L/D-$4.99
Casino Size: 9,600 Square Feet
Other Games: BJ, BG

Elk Valley Casino
2500 Howland Hill Road
Crescent City, California 95531
(707) 464-1020
Website: www.elkvalleycasino.com
Map Location: **#7** (84 miles N. of Eureka)

Toll-Free Number: (888) 574-2744
Restaurants: 1 Liquor: No
Casino Size: 23,000 Square Feet
Other Games: BJ, P, BG (Fri-Mon)
Senior Discount: Lunch discount Tue, if 55+
Special Features: Weekly poker tournaments.

Fantasy Springs Casino
82-245 Indio Springs Drive
Indio, California 92203
(760) 342-5000
Website: www.fantasyspringsresort.com
Map Location: **#8** (125 miles E. of Los Angeles)

Toll-Free Number: (800) 827-2WIN
Restaurants: 4 (1 open 24 hours) Liquor: Yes
Buffets: Brunch-$14.95 (Sun)
Casino Size: 95,000 Square Feet
Other Games: BJ, MB, P, CSP, TCP, BG, S
Fun Book: Go to Fan Club desk
Senior Discount: Bingo discount, if 55+
Special Features: Nightly free entertainment

Feather Falls Casino
3 Alverda Drive
Oroville, California 95966
(530) 533-3885
Website: www.featherfallscasino.com
Map Location: **#22** (100 miles N. of Sacramento)

Toll-Free Number: (877) OK-BINGO
Restaurants: 1 Liquor: Yes
Buffets: B-$7.95 (Sun) D-$9.95 (Sun)/$10.95 (Mon/Wed/Thu)/$13.95 (Sat)/$15.95(Tue/Fri)
Casino Size: 38,000 Square Feet
Other Games: BJ
Senior Discount: Various, if 55, or older
Special Features: Charges players a commission on their blackjack games.

Gold Country Casino
4020 Olive Highway
Oroville, California 95966
(530) 538-4560
Website: www.gold-country-casino.com
Map Location: **#22** (100 miles N. of Sacramento)

Toll-Free Number: (800) 334-9400
Restaurants: 1 Snack Bar Liquor: No
Other Games: BJ, PGP, TCP, BG (Sun-Wed)
Senior Discount: Free continental breakfast, $5 gaming token, prize drawings, on Tue/Thu from 7am-11am, if 55, or older

Golden Acorn Casino and Travel Center
1800 Golden Acorn Way
Campo, CA 91906
619-478-5729
Website: www.goldenacorncasino.com
Map Location: **#33** (40 miles S.E. of San Diego)

Restaurants: 2 Liquor: Yes
Other Games: BJ, TCP, CW
Fun Book: Given with slot club sign-up
Special Features: 33-acre travel center with auto & truck stop services. Convenience store.

Harrah's Rincon Casino & Resort
33750 Valley Center Road
Valley Center, California 92082
(760) 760-751-3100
Website: www.harrahs.com
Map Location: **#20** (35 miles N.E. of San Diego)

Toll-Free Number: (877) 777-2457
Rooms: 183 Prices: $99-$159
Suites: 17 Prices: Casino Use Only
Restaurants: 5 Liquor: Yes
Buffets: B-$13.99 (Sat-Sun) L-$9.99
            D-$14.99/$19.99 (Fri-Sat)
Other Games: BJ, PGP, MB
Casino Size: 45,000 Square Feet

Havasu Landing Casino & Resort
5 Main Street
Havasu Lake, California 92363
(760) 858-4593
Website: www.havasulanding.com
Map Location: **#18** (200 miles E. of Los Angeles)

Toll Free Number: (800) 307-3610
Restaurants: 1 Liquor: Yes
Hours: 9:30am-12:30am/2:30am (Fri/Sat)
Other Games: BJ
Casino Size: 6,000 Square Feet
Special Features: Marina, RV park and campground rentals. Mobile homes on lake available for daily rental, call (760) 858-5410.

Hopland Sho-Ka-Wah Casino
13101 Nakomis Road
Hopland, California 95449
(707) 744-1395
Website: www.shokawah.com
Map Location: **#23** (100 miles N. of San Francisco)

Restaurants: 1 Liquor: No
Other Games: BJ, BG

Jackson Rancheria Casino & Hotel
12222 New York Ranch Road
Jackson, California 95642
(209) 223-1677
Website: www.jacksoncasino.com
Map Location: **#9** (60 miles S.E. of Sacramento)

Toll-Free Number: (800) 822-WINN
Rooms: 99 Price Range: $59-$239
Suites: 4 Price Range: $149-$259
Restaurants: 2 Liquor: No
Buffets: D-$8.95/$10.95 (Sat/Sun)
Other Games: BJ, LIR, TCP, BG (Mon-Wed)
Senior Discount: 10% off buffet, if 55, or older

Konocti Vista Casino
2755 Mission Rancheria Road
Lakeport, California 95453
(707) 262-1900
Website: www.kvcasino.com
Map Location: **#23** (120 miles N. of San Francisco)

Toll-Free Number: (800) FUN-1950
Restaurants: 1 Liquor: No
Other Games: BJ, PGP, LIR, TCP
Senior Discount: $10 in matchplay on Sundays if 55, or older

Lucky Bear Casino
P.O. Box 1348
Hoopa, California 95546
(530) 625-5198
Map Location: **#24** (30 miles N.E. of Eureka)

Restaurants: 1 Snack Bar Liquor: No
Hours: 10am-Mid/2am (Fri/Sat)
Other Games: Slots only

Lucky 7 Casino
350 N. Indian Road
Smith River, California 95567
(707) 487-7777
Website: www.lucky7casino.com
Map Location: **#7** (100 miles N. of Eureka)

Toll-Free Number: (866) 777-7170
Restaurants: 1 Liquor: Yes
Buffets: D-$12.95 (Fri-Sun)
Other Games: BJ, BG
Casino Size: 24,000 Square Feet

Mono Wind Casino
37302 Rancheria Lane
Auberry, California 93602
(559) 855-4350
Map Location: **#25** (30 miles N.E. of Fresno)

Restaurants: 1 Liquor: Yes
Buffets: L-$5.95 (Tue-Sun)
Other Games: BJ, PGP, BG
Senior Discount: 10% off in restaurant, if 55+

Paiute Palace Casino
PO Box 1325
Bishop, California 93514
(760) 873-4150
Website: www.paiutepalace.com
Map Location: **#26** (130 miles N.E. of Fresno)

Toll-Free Number: (888) 3-PAIUTE
Restaurants: 1 Liquor: No
Buffets: Brunch-$5.99 (Sun)
Other Games: BJ, P, CSP
Fun Book: Ask at cashier cage
Senior Discount: 10% off in restaurant, if 55
or older

Pala Casino
11154 Highway 76
Pala, California 92054
(760) 510-5100
Website: www.palacasino.com
Map Location: **#20** (35 miles N.E. of San Diego)

Toll-Free Number: (877) 946-7252
Restaurants: 6 Liquor: Yes
Buffets: L-$8.99 D-$12.99/$18.99 (Fri)
Other Games: BJ,MB,TCP,PGP,CSP,LIR, CW

Palace Indian Gaming Center
17225 Jersey Avenue
Lemoore, California 93245
(559) 924-7751
Website: www.thepalace.net
Map Location: **#10** (50 miles S. of Fresno)

Toll-Free Number: (800) 942-6886
Restaurants: 4 Liquor: No
Buffets: L-$6.99 D-$10.99
Casino Size: 105,000 Square Feet
Other Games: BJ, P, PGP, LIR, BG
Special Features: Table game hours Noon-4am
(Sun-Thu)/6am (Fri/Sat).

Pechanga Resort and Casino
45000 Pala Road
Temecula, California 92592
(909) 693-1819
Website: www.pechanga.com
Map Location: **#28** (50 miles N. of San Diego)

Toll-Free Number: (888) PECHANGA
Rooms: 489 Price Range: $89-$159
Suites: 33 Price Range: $179-$279
Restaurants: 6 Liquor: No
Buffets: L-$8.49 D-$11.49
Other Games: BJ, P, CSP, TCP, BG
Special Features: 170-space RV park with full
hook-ups. Live entertainment and headliner
acts. 2am to 5am buffet for $3.95.

Pit River Casino
20265 Tamarack Avenue
Burney, California 96013
(530) 335-2334
Map Location: **#29** (190 miles N. of Sacramento)

Toll-Free Number: (888) 245-2992
Restaurants: 1 Snack Bar Liquor: No
Hours: 10am-Midnight Daily
Other Games: BJ, BG
Senior Discount: $5 match play given on
Sundays and Mondays, if 55 or older.

Red Fox Casino & Bingo
300 Cahto Drive
Laytonville, California 95454
(707) 984-6800
Map Location: **#30** (150 miles N.W. of Sacramento)

Toll-Free Number: (888) 4-RED-FOX
Restaurants: 1 Snack Bar Liquor: No
Hours: 8am-Mid/2am (Fri/Sat)
Other Games: BJ, BG

Robinson Rancheria Bingo & Casino
1545 E. Highway 20
Nice, California 95464
(707)275-9000
Map Location: **#11** (100 miles N.W. of Sacramento)

Toll-Free Number: (800) 809-3636
Restaurants: 2 Liquor: No
Buffets: B-$4.50 L-$6.95 D-$7.95
Casino Size: 37,500 Square Feet
Other Games: BJ, P, PGP, BG
Fun Book: Ask at cage on birthday
Senior Discount: Various on Mon 9am-Noon, if 55 or older and Free bingo on Thursday.

San Manuel Indian Bingo & Casino
5797 North Victoria Avenue
Highland, California 92346
(909) 864-5050
Website: www.sanmanuel.com
Map Location: **#12** (65 miles E. of Los Angeles)

Toll-Free Number: (800) 359-2464
Restaurants: 2 Snack Bars Liquor: No
Casino Size: 75,000 Square Feet
Other Games: BJ, P, BG, PGP
Senior Discount: $10 bingo buy-in Fri, if 55+
Special Features: Charges players a commission on their blackjack games.

Shodakai Casino
PO Box 320
Calpella, California 94581
(707) 485-0700
Map Location: **#23** (115 miles N. of San Francisco)

Toll-Free Number: (800) 332-9683
Restaurants: 1 Snack Bar Liquor: No
Other Games: BJ, P, BG (Fri-Mon)

Soboba Casino
23333 Soboba Road
San Jacinto, California 92583
(909) 654-2883
Website: www.soboba.net
Map Location: **#3** (90 miles E. of Los Angeles)

Toll-Free Number: (888) 772-SOBOBA
Restaurants: 3 Liquor: Yes
Buffets: L-$6.95
Casino Size: 52,000 Square Feet
Other Games: BJ, MB, PGP, LIR

Spa Casino
140 N. Indian Canyon Drive
Palm Springs, California 92262
(760) 323-5865
Website: www.sparesortcasino.com
Map Location: **#3** (115 miles E. of Los Angeles)

Toll-Free Number: (800) 258-2WIN
Room Reservations: (800) 854-1279
Rooms: 215 Price Range: $79-$239
Suites: 15 Price Range: $219-$279
Restaurants: 2 (1 open 24 hours) Liquor: Yes
Casino Size: 15,000 Square Feet
Other Games: BJ, P, PGP, LIR
Senior Discount: Various on Wed., if 55+
Special Features: Hotel offers hot mineral spa with massages and facials. 10% room discount for seniors (55+) and AAA members.

Susanville Casino
900 Skyline Drive
Susanville, California 96130
(530) 252-1100
Website: www.susanvillecasino.com
Map Location: **#31** (160 Miles N.E. of Sacramento)

Restaurants: 1 Snack Bar Liquor: Yes
Hours: 10am-3am Daily
Other Games: BJ, P, BG (Wed-Sun)
Senior Discount: 25% off in deli, if 55, or older

Sycuan Casino
5469 Dehesa Road
El Cajon, California 92019
(619) 445-6002
Website: www.sycuancasino.com
Map Location: **#14** (10 miles E. of San Diego)

Toll-Free Number: (800) 279-2826
Restaurants: 6 Liquor: No
Buffets: L-$8.95 D-$12.95
Casino Size: 73,000 Square Feet
Other Games: BJ, MB, P, PGP, BG, LIR, CSP, S
Senior Discount: $5 discount on bingo packs
for Mon-Fri matiness and Tue/Thu evenings.

Table Mountain Casino & Bingo
8184 Table Mountain Road
Friant, California 93626
(559) 822-2485
Website: www.tmcasino.com
Map Location: **#15** (15 miles N. of Fresno)

Toll-Free Number: (800) 541-3637
Restaurants: 4 Liquor: No
Buffets: L-$9.95 D-$12.95
Other Games: BJ, P, PGP, LIR, TCP, BG

Trump 29 Casino
46200 Harrison Place
Coachella, California 92236
(760) 775-5566
Website: www.spotlight29casino.com
Map Location: **#8** (130 miles E. of Los Angeles)

Toll-Free Number: (800) 841-6666
Restaurants: 1 Liquor: Yes
Buffets: L/D-$9.99
Other Games: BJ, MB, P, PGP, CSP, LIR

Twin Pine Casino
22223 Highway 29 at Rancheria Road
Middletown, California 95461
(707) 987-0197
Website: www.twinpine.com
Map Location: **#32** (70 miles W. of Sacramento)

Toll-Free Number: (800) 564-4872
Restaurants: 1 Liquor: No
Other Games: BJ, PGP, BG
Senior Discount: $10 video match play
    10am-7pm Wednesdays, if 55, or older
Special Features: Daycare facility.

Valley View Casino
16300 Nyemii Pass Road
Valley Center, California 92082
(760) 291-5500
Website: www.valleyviewcasino.com
Map Location: **#20** (35 miles N.E. of San Diego)

Toll-Free Number: (866) 726-7277
Restaurants: 2 Liquor: No
Buffets: L-$6.99
    D-$9.99 (Mon)/$11.99/$13.99 (Fri)
Other Games: BJ, TCP
Special Features: Slot club members receive
buffet dinner discount.

Viejas Casino
5000 Willows Road
Alpine, California 91901
(619) 445-5400
Website: www.viejas.com
Map Location: **#16** (25 miles E. of San Diego)

Toll-Free Number: (800) 84-POKER
Restaurants: 5 Liquor: Yes
Buffets: L-$7.99 D-$9.99/$10.99 (Tue/Wed)
Other Games: BJ, MB, P, CSP, LIR,
              PGP, BG, S
Special Features: Charges players a commission on some of their blackjack games. Factory outlet shopping center.

Win-River Casino
2100 Redding Rancheria Road
Redding, California 96001
(530) 243-3377
Website: www.win-river.com
Map Location: **#17** (163 miles N. of Sacramento)

Toll-Free Number: (800) 280-8946
Restaurants: 1 Snack Bar Liquor: Yes
Casino Size: 37,000 Square Feet
Other Games: BJ, TCP, LIR, BG (Sun-Thu)
Special Features: Comedy club, entertainment center.

COLORADO

Colorado casinos can be found in the mountain towns of Black Hawk, Central City and Cripple Creek. There are also two Indian casinos (which abide by Colorado's limited gaming rules) in Ignacio and Towaoc.

Gambling is limited in two aspects: one, only electronic games (including slots, video poker, video blackjack and video keno) and the table games of poker, blackjack, let it ride and three-card poker are allowed. Two, a single wager cannot exceed $5.

The rules for poker are such that a raise is considered a separate bet. Three raises per round are allowed. On the last round, two players may go "head-to-head" with an unlimited number of raises. Nine varieties of poker are approved for casino play. Texas Hold 'Em, 7-Card Stud and Omaha are the most popular.

Blackjack wagers are limited to a $5 maximum, with most casinos allowing a $2 or $3 minimum bet. However, doubles and splits are considered separate bets. Colorado casinos employ Vegas Strip rules and most allow doubling after splits. Since pairs may be split three times (to make up to four hands) it is theoretically possible to bet $40 on what began as a single $5 wager.

Multiple action blackjack is also available in Colorado. Multiple action allows a player to place up to three bets (of up to $5 each) on a single blackjack hand. This hand is then played for three rounds against the same dealer up-card. Several Colorado casinos offer multiple action blackjack.

Here's information, as supplied by Colorado's Division of Gaming, showing the slot machine payback percentages for each city's casinos for the one year period from July 1, 2001 through June 30, 2002:

	Black Hawk	Central City	Cripple Creek
5¢ Slots	93.08%	92.56%	**93.52%**
25¢ Slots	94.66%	**94.81%**	94.63%
$1 Slots	95.19%	**95.37%**	**95.37%**
$5 Slots	**96.11%**	94.23%	94.95%
All	94.32%	94.08%	**94.42%**

These numbers reflect the percentage of money returned on each denomination of machine and encompass all electronic machines including video poker and video keno. The best returns for each category are highlighted in bold print.

The maximum hours Colorado casinos can operate are from 8am until 2am and the minimum gambling age is 21.

The two major gaming-oriented magazines n Colorado are *The Gambler* and the *Rocky Mountain News Gaming Guide*. Both are free, and available in most casinos. Look in them for ads for casino coupons or fun books. The *Denver Post* Weekend section (published every Friday) also contains coupons and fun book offers for the casinos in Black Hawk and Central City.

For more information on visiting Black Hawk call (303) 582-5221, for Central City information call (800) 542-2999 and for Cripple Creek information call (877) 858-GOLD. For general information on Colorado call the state's tourism board at (800) 433-2656.

Black Hawk

Map Location: #1 (35 miles west of Denver. Take U.S. 6 through Golden to Hwy 119. Take Hwy 119 to Black Hawk. Another route is I-70 West to exit 244. Turn right onto Hwy. 6. Take Hwy 6 to 119 and into Black Hawk.)

The Lodge at Black Hawk and the Isle of Capri are the only two casinos with hotel rooms in that city. The next closest lodging is at Harvey's Wagon Wheel Casino, 3/4-mile up Gregory St. in Central City (see Central City listings for particulars). Another alternative is the Gold Dust Lodge, located on Hwy. 119 about 1.5 miles from the Black Hawk casinos. The Gold Dust features 23 remodeled rooms with private baths, TV and telephones.

The casinos in Black Hawk and Central City are located one mile apart. The Black Hawk Shuttle Service provides free transportation around Black Hawk and Harvey's runs a free shuttle service from Black Hawk to Central City.

There are a few bus tour programs operating between the metropolitan Denver area and Black Hawk/Central City. These programs are bargain priced ($10 or less) and usually affiliated with one or two casinos that will reimburse a portion of the tour charge and also provide coupons or fun books. Check the "Weekend" section of the Friday *Denver Post* and *Rocky Mountain News* for bus tour ads and for casino ads that feature coupons.

All casinos offer electronic games (slots, video poker, video blackjack and video keno). Some casinos also offer: blackjack (BJ), poker (P), let it ride (LIR) and three card poker (TCP).

Black Hawk Casino by Hyatt
111 Richman Street
Black Hawk, Colorado 80422
(303) 567-1234
Website: www.blackhawkcasinobyhyatt.com

Restaurants: 4
Buffets: B-$8.99 (Sun/Tue) L-8.99 D-$12.99
Casino Size: 28,629 Square Feet
Other Games: BJ, P, TCP
Senior Discount: Various Mon-Fri if 55+
Special Features: 25% off food (Mon-Fri) for slot club members.

Black Hawk Station
141 Gregory Street
(303) 582-5582

Restaurants: 1 (snack bar)
Casino Size: 2,055 Square Feet
Other Games: BJ

Bull Durham Saloon & Casino
110 Main Street
(303) 582-0810

Restaurants: 1 (snack bar)
Casino Size: 2,547 Square Feet
Other Games: BJ
Fun Book: Ask at cage
Senior Discount: Special Fun Book if 55+

Bullwhackers Casino
101 Gregory Street
(303) 764-1600
Website: www.bullwhackers.com

Toll-Free Number: (800) GAM-BULL
Restaurants: 1
Casino Size: 16,019 Square Feet
Senior Discount: Specials on Tue/Wed if 55+
Special Features: Includes **Bullpen Sports Casino.**

Canyon Casino
131 Main Street
(303) 777-1111
Website: www.canyoncasino.net

Restaurants: 1
Casino Size: 11,173 Square Feet
Special Features: Includes **Grand Plateau Casino.**

Colorado Central Station Casino
340 Main Street
(303) 582-3000
Website: www.coloradocentralstation.com

Restaurants: 2
Buffet: B-$4.95 L-$7.95 D-$9.95
Casino Size: 16,997 Square Feet
Other Games: BJ, P, TCP
Special Features: 50% buffet discount with slot club card.

Eureka! Casino
211 Gregory Street
(303) 582-1040

Restaurants: 1
Casino Size: 1,902 Square Feet
Special Features: 50¢ strawberry margarita.

Fitzgeralds Casino
101 Main Street
(303) 582-6162
Website: www.fitzgeralds.com/blackhawk

Toll-Free Number: (800) 538-5825
Restaurants: 1
Casino Size: 9,874 Square Feet
Other Games: BJ, TCP

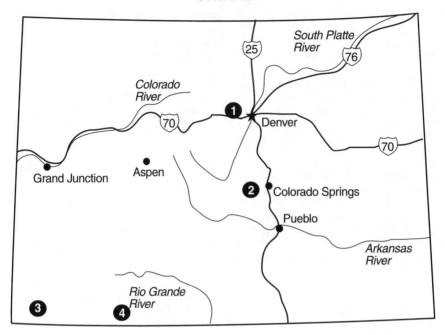

Gilpin Hotel Casino
111 Main Street
(303) 582-1133

Restaurants: 2
Buffets: B-$3.98 (Mon-Sat)/$9.98 (Sun)
Casino Size: 11,182 Square Feet
Special Features: $7.77 prime rib or lobster dinner for slot club members.

Golden Gates Casino
261 Main Street
(303) 277-1650
Website: www.goldengatescasino.com

Toll-Free Number (866) 343-1994
Casino Size: 4,373 Square Feet
Other Games: BJ, TCP
Special Features: Free sandwich and chips for players 11am-1:30pm and 5:00pm-7:30pm

Isle of Capri Casino - Black Hawk
401 Main Street
(303) 998-7777
Website: www.isleofcapricasino.com

Toll-Free Number (800) 843-4753
Rooms: 107 Price Range: $104-$130
Suites: 130 Price Range: $115-$175
Restaurants: 3 (1 open 24 hours)
Buffets: B-$5.99 L-$7.99 D-$12.99
Casino Size: 20,808 Square Feet
Other Games: BJ, LIR, TCP
Senior Discount: Specials Mon-Thu if 50+
Special Features: Parking garage.

The Lodge Casino at Black Hawk
240 Main Street
(303) 582-1771
Website: www.thelodgecasino.com

Toll-Free Number: (877) 711-1177
Rooms: 47 Price Range: $75-$140
Suites: 3 Price Range: $199-$350
Restaurants: 3
Buffets: B-$5.49 L-$7.49/$11.99 (Sun)
        D-$10.99/$19.95 (Fri)
Casino Size: 22,354 Square Feet
Other Games: BJ, P, LIR, TCP
Senior Discount: 50% off breakfast and lunch
        buffets Mon/Tue, if 50, or older
Special Features: 2-for-1 Fri. dinner and Sun.
brunch buffet with 250 slot club points. $10
off room with slot club card. $10 off room for
AAA/AARP members (Sun-Thu). Parking garage. Skybridge to Mardi Gras Casino.

Mardi Gras Casino
333 Main Street
(303) 582-5600
Website: www.mardigrasbh.com

Restaurants: 1
Casino Size: 14,196 Square Feet
Other Games: BJ, P, TCP
Special Features: Parking garage. Skybridge
to The Lodge Casino.

Red Dolly Casino
530 Gregory Street
(303) 582-1100

Restaurants: 1
Casino Size: 2,265 Square Feet
Special Features: 10-ounce steak dinner for
$4.95. 20-ounce steak dinner for $6.95.

Richman Casino
100 Richman Street
(303) 582-0400

Restaurants: 1 snack bar
Casino Size: 2,328 Square Feet
Other Games: BJ, TCP

Riviera Black Hawk Casino
444 Main Street
(303) 582-1000
Website: www.rivierablackhawk.com

Buffet: L-$7.99 D-$12.99
Casino Size: 23,879 Square Feet
Other Games: BJ, P
Special Features: Parking garage.

Silver Hawk
100 Chase Street
(303) 764-1400
Website: www.bullwhackers.com

Toll-Free Number: (800) GAM-BULL
Restaurants: 1
Casino Size: 3,696 Square Feet

Wild Card Saloon & Casino
112 Main Street
(303) 582-3412

Restaurants: 1 (snack bar)
Casino Size: 3,129 Square Feet

Central City

Map location: **#1** (same as Black Hawk). Central City is located one mile from Black Hawk. Turn left at the third stoplight on Hwy. 119 and proceed up Gregory Street.

Harvey's Wagon Wheel Hotel/Casino is the only hotel in Central City but there are also a few bed & breakfasts: the Gregory Inn (7 rooms, $55 to $155, 303-582-5561), Chateau L'acadienne (3 rooms, $60 to $94, 303-582-5209) and the High Street Inn (3 rooms, $75 to $85, 303-582-0622).

For Central City tourism information call (800) 542-2999.

Doc Holliday Casino
101 Main Street
Central City, CO 80427
(303) 582-1400

Restaurants: 1
Casino Size: 3,098 Square Feet

Dostal Alley Saloon & Gaming Emporium
1 Dostal Alley
Central City, CO 80427
(303) 582-1610

Restaurants: 1 Snack Bar
Casino Size: 741 Square Feet

Famous Bonanza/Easy Street
107 Main Street
(303) 582-5914
Central City, CO 80427
Website: www.famousbonanza.com

Restaurants: 1
Casino Size: 7,326 Square Feet
Other Games: BJ, TCP
Special Features: Restaurant features Mexican specialities.

Harvey's Wagon Wheel Hotel/Casino
321 Gregory Street
Central City, CO 80427
(303) 582-0800
Website: www.harrahs.com

Toll-Free Number: (800) 924-6646
Rooms: 118 Price Range $79-$139
Suites: 6 Price Range $140-$175
Restaurants: 2
Casino Size: 33,207 Square Feet
Other Games: BJ, P, TCP
Special Features: Tony Roma's restaurant. Covered parking garage.

Cripple Creek

Map Location: **#2** (47 miles west of Colorado Springs. Take exit 141 at Colorado Springs off I-25. Go west on Hwy. 24 to the town of Divide. Turn left onto Hwy. 67 and go 18 miles to Cripple Creek.)

Cripple Creek has several hotel/casinos the largest of which is the Double Eagle Hotel & Casino. There is also a 67-room motel, Gold King Mountain Inn, located 1/8-mile from the casinos, which offers rates of $49 (Winter) to $99 (Summer) per night. Free shuttle service is provided to and from the casinos. For hotel reservations, call 1-800-445-3607.

Many Cripple Creek casinos hand out coupons at their doors. Also check ads in the *Colorado Springs Gazette*, the *Pueblo Chieftain* and the free tourist magazines.

Some Cripple Creek parking lots charge a fee of $3 to $5 which is usually reimbursed by the casino. Check at the lot for each particular casino's parking rules. For Cripple Creek tourism information call (877) 858-GOLD.

All casinos offer electronic games (slots, video poker, video blackjack and video keno). Some casinos also offer: blackjack (BJ), poker (P), let it ride (LIR) and three card poker (TCP).

Black Diamond Casino
425 E. Bennett Avenue
Cripple Creek, Co 80813
(719) 689-2898

Restaurants: 1 (snack bar)
Casino Size: 1,478 Square Feet
Special Features: Free drink coupon handed out at door. Real gold vein in wall (upstairs). Free soup for players. Video arcade.

Brass Ass Casino
264 E. Bennett Avenue
Cripple Creek, Co 80813
(719) 689-2104
www.midnightrose.com/htmls/brassass.htm

Restaurants: 1 (snack bar)
Casino Size: 2,797 Square Feet
Special Features: Free hot dogs and popcorn. Connected to **Midnight Rose** and **J.P McGill's**.

Bronco Billy's Sports Bar & Casino
233 E. Bennett Avenue
Cripple Creek, Co 80813
(719) 689-2142
Website: www.broncobillyscasino.com

Toll Free Number: (877) 989-2142
Restaurants: 2
Other Games: BJ, TCP
Casino Size: 8,938 Square Feet
Fun Book: Ask at cashier's cage
Special Features: Includes **Buffalo Billy's** casino. Satellite tv's tuned to sports. 49¢ breakfast. $6.95 t-bone steak special. Double jackpots at top two minutes of every hour and 12am-1:30am every night.

Colorado Grande Gaming Parlor
300 E. Bennett Avenue
Cripple Creek, Co 80813
(719) 689-3517
Website: www.cripple-creek.co.us/grand.html

Restaurants: 1
Casino Size: 2,447 Square Feet
Senior Discount: Free lunch Tuesdays with
        AARP card and slot club card
Special Features: 50% off dining for slot club
members.

Creeker's Casino
274 E. Bennett Avenue
Cripple Creek, Co 80813
(719) 689-3239
Website: www.creekerscasino.com

Restaurants: 1
Buffets: L/D-$7.95/$14.95 (Sat)
Senior Discount: 50% off Thu buffet if 50+
Casino Size: 4,131 Square Feet
Special Features: Wedding chapel. $1 buffet
discount with slot club card. Video arcade.

Double Eagle Hotel & Casino
442 E. Bennett Avenue
Cripple Creek, Co 80813
(719) 689-5000
Website: www.decasino.com

Toll-Free Reservations: (800) 711-7234
Rooms: 146 Price Range: $60-$100
Suites: 12 Price Range: $120-$240
Restaurants: 2
Buffets: B-$6.95
        D-$8.95/$16.95 (Fri)/$14.95 (Sat)
Casino Size: 15,889 Square Feet
Other Games: BJ, P, TCP
Fun Book: Ask at the slot club
Special Features: Free self-parking. Video ar-
cade. AAA, AARP and slot club members get
10% room discount.

Gold Rush Hotel &
Casino/Gold Digger's Casino
209 E. Bennett Avenue
Cripple Creek, Co 80813
(719) 689-2646
Website: www.cripple-creek.co.us/grush.html

Toll-Free Number: (800) 235-8239
Rooms: 14 Price Range: $49-$79
Restaurants: 2
Casino Size: 5,395 Square Feet
Other Games: BJ, LIR
Special Features: **Gold Digger's** and **Gold
Rush** are interconnected. $3.99 steak special.
49-cent breakfast. 10% room discount to
miltary, AARP and AAA members.

Imperial Hotel & Casino
123 N. Third Street
Cripple Creek, Co 80813
(719) 689-2922
Website: www.imperialcasinohotel.com

Toll-Free Number: (800) 235-2922
Rooms: 29 Price Range: $45-$85
Suites: 2 Price Range: $100-$145
Restaurants: 2
Casino Size: 4,935 Square Feet

Johnny Nolon's Casino
301 E. Bennett Avenue
Cripple Creek, Co 80813
(719) 689-2080
Website: www.johnnynolons.com

Restaurants: 2
Casino Size: 5,815 Square Feet
Special Features: 50% off meals for slot club
members.

J.P. McGill's Hotel & Casino
232 E. Bennett Avenue
Cripple Creek, Co 80813
(719) 689-2497
www.midnightrose.com/htmls/jpmcgills.htm

Toll-Free Number: (888) 461-7529
Rooms: 36 Price Range: $40-$100
Suites: 3 Price Range: $155-$210
Restaurants: 1
Casino Size: 5,664 Square Feet
Special Features: Connected to **Midnight
Rose** and **Brass Ass**. 10% room discount for
slot club members.

Midnight Rose Hotel & Casino
256 E. Bennett Avenue
Cripple Creek, Co 80813
(719) 689-2865
Website: www.midnightrose.com

Toll-Free Number: (800) 635-5825
Rooms: 19 Price Range: $40-$95
Restaurants: 3
Casino Size: 8,602 Square Feet
Other Games: P
Special Features: Connected to **Brass Ass** and **J.P McGill's**. 10% room discount for slot club members.

Uncle Sam's Casino
251 E. Bennett Avenue
Cripple Creek, Co 80813
(719) 689-2222

Casino Size: 1,208 Square Feet
Special Features: Free hot dogs for players.

Virgin Mule
259 E. Bennett Avenue
Cripple Creek, Co 80813
(719) 689-2734

Restaurants: 1 snack bar
Casino Size: 582 Square Feet

Womacks/Legends Hotel & Casino
200-220 E. Bennett Avenue
Cripple Creek, Co 80813
(719) 689-0333
Website: www.womackscasino.com

Toll-Free Number: (888) 966-2257
Rooms: 21 Price Range: Casino Use Only
Suites: 2 Price Range: Casino Use Only
Restaurants: 1
Casino Size: 8,274 Square Feet
Other Games: BJ, TCP
Special Features: **Womacks** and **Legends** are interconnected. Rooms for club members only. Free parking.

Indian Casinos

Sky Ute Casino and Lodge
14826 Highway 172 N.
Ignacio, Colorado 81137
(970) 563-3000
Website: www.skyutecasino.com
Map Location: **#4** (345 miles S.W. of Denver, 20 miles S.E. of Durango)

Toll-Free Number: (888) 842-4180
Room Reservations: (800) 876-7017
Rooms: 36 Price Range: $45-$79
Restaurants: 2 Liquor: No
Buffets: B-$4.99 (Sat-Sun) L-$6.99
         D-$8.99/$13.99 (Fri-Sat)
Hours: 24 Hours Daily
Other Games: BJ, TCP, Bingo (Wed/Thu/Sun)
Senior Discount: 10% room and restaurant
                 discount, if 50 or older
Special Features: Southern Ute Cultural Center and Museum is located next to casino.

Ute Mountain Casino & RV Park
3 Weeminuche Drive/P.O. Drawer V
Towaoc, Colorado 81334
(970) 565-8800
Website: www.utemountaincasino.com
Map Location: **#3** (425 miles S.W. of Denver, 11 miles S. of Cortez on Hwys. 160/166)

Toll-Free Number: (800) 258-8007
Restaurants: 1 Liquor: No
Buffets: B-$4.50 (Sat-Sun) L-$5.95
         D-$7.75/$12.95 (Fri)
Casino Size: 32,000 Square Feet
Hours: 8am-4am Daily
Other Games: BJ, P, LIR, TCP,
             Keno, Bingo (Fri-Tue)
Fun Book: Given at local motels/RV parks
Senior Discount: 15% off food if 55, or older.
Special Features: 84-space RV Park. Ute Tribal Park tours available.

CONNECTICUT

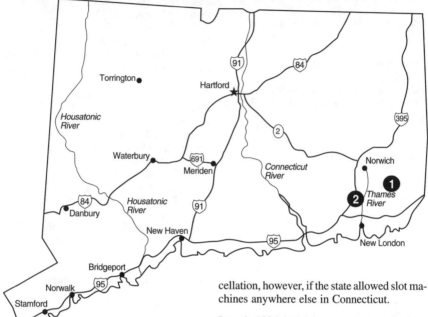

Foxwoods was New England's first casino. It is also the largest casino in the world and the world's most profitable casino.

The Mashantucket Pequot Tribe which operates Foxwoods had to sue the state to allow the casino to open. They argued that since the state legally permitted "Las Vegas Nights," where low-stakes casino games were operated to benefit charities, then the tribe should be entitled to do the same. Eventually, they won their case before the U.S. Supreme Court and began construction of their casino which was financed by a Malaysian conglomerate (after 22 U.S. lenders turned down their loan requests).

When the casino first opened in February 1992, slot machines were not permitted. In January 1993 a deal was made between Governor Weicker and the Pequots which gave the tribe the exclusive right to offer slot machines in return for a yearly payment of $100 million, or 25% of the gross slot revenue - whichever is greater. The agreement was subject to can-

cellation, however, if the state allowed slot machines anywhere else in Connecticut.

In early 1994 the Mohegan tribe signed a compact with the state that allows them to offer casino gambling at their reservation in Uncasville (map location #2). The Pequots gave permission for the Mohegans to have slot machines in their casino and in return the state lowered the Pequots yearly payment requirements to $80 million, or 25% of the gross revenue - whichever is greater. The same payment schedule also applies to the Mohegans. The payment schedules are subject to cancellation, however, if the state legalizes any other form of casino gambling. The Mohegan casino opened in October 1996.

The minimum gambling age at both properties is 18 for bingo and 21 for the casino. Both casinos are also open 24 hours. For information on visiting Connecticut call the state's Vacation Center at (800) 282-6863.

The games offered at Foxwoods are: blackjack, craps, roulette, baccarat, mini-baccarat, big six wheel, bingo, poker, pai gow poker, Caribbean stud poker, let it ride, keno, pull tabs, red dog, casino war and chuck-a-luck. There is also a simulcast facility with pari-mutuel betting.

Foxwoods is the world's largest casino with over 300,000 square feet of gaming space. The property features three hotels, 24 food outlets, three regular casinos, a smoke-free casino, a slots-only casino, a high-limts casino, a simulcast facility a 3,200-seat bingo and a total of more than 6,700 electronic gaming machines.

Foxwoods Resort Casino
Route 2
Ledyard, Connecticut 06339
(860) 312-3000
Website: www.foxwoods.com
Map Location: **#1** (45 miles S.E. of Hartford; 12 miles N. of I-95 at Mystic). From I-95 take exit 92 to Rt. 2-West, casino is 7 miles ahead. From I-395 take exit 79A to Rt. 2A follow to Rt. 2-East, casino is 2 miles ahead.

Toll-Free Number: (800) FOXWOODS
Hotel Reservations: (800) FOXWOODS
Rooms: 1,416 Price Range: $140-$325
Suites: 198 Price Range: $175-$1,500
Restaurants: 24 (3 open 24 hours)
Buffets: B-$7.95 L-$13.45 D-$13.45
Casino Size: 314,492 Square Feet
Casino Marketing: (800) 99-SLOTS
Special Features: Three hotels with pool, spa, beauty salon and golf. Turbo Ride: a 48-seat computer-controlled large-screen-movie adventure ride. Five nightclubs. Gift shops. *Wampum Card* members earn complimentaries at table games, slots, poker and race book. 10% room discount for AAA and AARP members.

The following information is from Connecticut's Division of Special Revenue regarding Foxwoods' slot payback percentages for the fiscal year ending June 30, 2002:

Denomination	Payback %
5¢	90.74
25¢	91.24
50¢	90.32
$1.00	92.36
$5.00	94.88
$10.00	94.92
$25.00	96.20
$100.00	96.60
Multi-Denom.	88.96
Average	**91.97**

These figures reflect the total percentages returned by each denomination of slot machine from July 1, 2001 through June 30, 2002. Foxwoods' total win on its slot machines during that year was slightly more than $796 million and of that amount 25%, or about $199 million, was paid to the state.

Keep in mind that the casino doesn't pay any tax on its table games and therefore it isn't required to report the profits on that part of its operation. A rough estimate of the table game wins, however, is possible. Since the average casino generates about 65% of its profits from its slot machines, it can be estimated that Foxwoods' total combined (slots and table games) win is about $1.22 billion. After subtracting the slot winnings of $796 million this leaves a table games win of about $424 million.

The games offered at Conecticut's other casino, Mohegan Sun, are: blackjack, craps, roulette, baccarat, mini-baccarat, pai gow, wheel of fortune, bingo, poker, pai gow poker, Caribbean stud poker, let it ride, Spanish 21, casino war, sic bo and keno. There is also a simulcast facility with pari-mutuel betting.

Mohegan Sun Casino
1 Mohegan Sun Boulevard
Uncasville, Connecticut 06382
(860) 862-8000
Website: www.mohegansun.com
Map Location: **#2** (Take I-95 Exit 76/I-395 North. Take Exit 79A (Route 2A) East. Less than 1 mile to Mohegan Sun Boulevard)

Toll-Free Number: (888) 226-7711
Room Reservations: (888) 777-7922
Rooms: 1,020 Price Range: $175-$400
Suites: 180 Price Range: $300-$1,000
Restaurants: 29 (3 open 24 hours)
Buffets: B-$7.95 L-$12.95 D-$12.95
Casino Size: 295,000 Square Feet
Casino Marketing: (888) 226-7711
Special Features: Food court with specialty food outlets. 6,000-square-foot Kid's Quest - supervised children's activity center. On-site gas station. Free nightly entertainment in the Wolf Den Showroom.

Here's information from Connecticut's Division of Special Revenue regarding Mohegan Sun's slot payback percentages for the fiscal year ending June 30, 2002:

Denomination	Payback %
25¢	90.89
50¢	90.67
$1.00	91.63
$5.00	94.41
$10.00	95.25
$25.00	96.12
$100.00	96.40
$500.00	99.27
Average	**91.78**

These figures reflect the total percentages returned by each denomination of slot machine from July 1, 2001 through June 30, 2002.

The total win on all of their slot machines during that period was slightly less than $680 million and of that amount 25%, or almost $170 million, was paid to the state.

DELAWARE

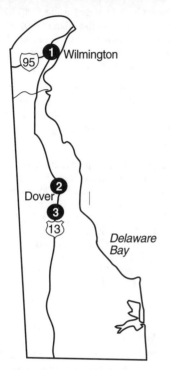

Delaware's three pari-mutuel facilities all feature slot machines. Technically, the machines are video lottery terminals (VLT's) because they are operated in conjunction with the Delaware Lottery. Unlike VLT's in other states, however, Delaware's machines pay out in cash. The VLT's also play other games including: video poker, video keno and video blackjack.

By law, all video lottery games must return between 87% and 95% of all wagers on an annual basis. According to figures from the Delaware Lottery for the six-month period from January 1 through June 30, 2002 the average VLT return at Delaware Park was 92.45%, at Dover Downs it was 91.57% and at Midway Slots & Simulcast it was 90.56%.

The hours of operation for all three facilities are 8am-2am (1pm-2am on Sunday). The minimum gambling age is 21 for slots and 18 for horse racing. For more information on visiting Delaware call the state's tourism office at (800) 441-8846.

Delaware Park Racetrack & Slots
777 Delaware Park Boulevard
Wilmington, Delaware 19804
(302) 994-2521
Website: www.delpark.com
Map Location: **#1**

Toll-Free Number: (800) 41-SLOTS
Restaurants: 8
Buffets: L/D-$10.95 (Thu-Fri)
Valet Parking: $3
Special Features: Live thoroughbred racing late April through mid-November. Daily simulcasting of horse racing.

Dover Downs Slots
1131 N. DuPont Highway
Dover, Delaware 19901
(302) 674-4600
Website: www.doverdowns.com
Map Location: **#2**

Toll-Free Number: (800) 711-5882
Rooms: 220 Price Range: $125-$145
Suites: 12 Price Range: $225-$745
Restaurants: 3
Buffets: B/L/D-$12.50
Valet Parking: $3
Casino Size: 80,000 Square Feet
Special Features: Live harness racing November through April. Daily simulcasting of horse racing.

Midway Slots & Simulcast
Delaware State Fairgrounds
U.S. 13 South
Harrington, Delaware 19952
(302) 398-4920
Website: www.midwayslots.com
Map Location: **#3** (20 miles S. of Dover)

Toll-Free Number: (888) 88-SLOTS
Restaurants: 2
Buffets: L/D-$10.99
Valet Parking: $2
Senior Discount: Various, if 50, or older
Special Features: Live harness racing September through November at Harrington Raceway. Daily simulcasting of horse racing.

FLORIDA

Florida does not have legalized casino gambling. It does, however, have a thriving day-cruise industry which allows gamblers to board ships that cruise offshore where casino gambling is legal. From the east coast the boats sail three miles out into the Atlantic Ocean and from the west coast the boats travel nine miles out into the Gulf of Mexico.

There are a variety of boats in operation ranging from Port Canaveral's 1,800-passenger cruise ship all the way down to the 149 passenger SunCruz boat in Key Largo.

Generally, you will find that the larger ships have more of a variety of things to do besides the gambling, but the cost will be a little higher because of added port/service charges. Most of the ships that sail from the major ports, such as Port Everglades and the Port of Palm Beach, will add port/service charges to the quoted cruise price. Usually, there is also a charge to park your car at those locations. Since late 1994 many smaller ships have begun operations and because they don't dock at the large ports they usually don't have port/service charges added to their cruise prices. Also, most of them offer free parking. You will find that almost all of the ships (especially in the Miami/Ft. Lauderdale area) are constantly running price specials so don't be surprised if you call and are quoted a price lower than the regular brochure rates listed here.

The nearest Caribbean casinos are in the Bahamas with one on Grand Bahama Island: The Royal Oasis Casino Resort (800) 223-1818.

The Royal Oasis Casino operates a 727 jet charter service which has two flights daily from the Fort Lauderdale airport. One flight leaves at 9am and returns at 5:15pm. The other flight leaves at 6:30pm and returns at 12:45am. Grand Bahama Island is 90 miles from Fort Lauderdale and the flight takes 30 minutes. The cost is $79 (plus taxes of $63) which includes round-trip taxi transportation between the airport and the casino. Look in the coupon section in the back of this book for a special free trip offer to the Royal Oasis Casino.

The other two casinos are in the Bahamian capital of Nassau which is on New Providence

Island: Crystal Palace Casino (800) 222-7466 and Atlantis, Paradise Island (800) 321-3000. Technically, Atlantis is on Paradise Island and not in Nassau because you have to cross a bridge in downtown Nassau to get there.

There is daily scheduled jet service on several airlines to the Nassau airport from both Miami and Fort Lauderdale. Nassau is 150 miles from Miami and the flying time is approximately 45 minutes.

Unless otherwise noted, all Florida casino boats offer: blackjack, craps, roulette, slots and video poker. Some casinos also offer: mini-baccarat (MB), poker (P), pai gow poker (PGP), three-card poker (TCP), Caribbean stud poker (CSP), let it ride (LIR), big 6 wheel (B6) and bingo (BG). Each boat sets its own minimum gambling age: on some boats it's 21 and on others it's 18. The minimum drinking age is 21.

For Florida visitor information call (904) 488-5607. For information on the Florida Keys or Key West call (800) 352-5397.

Daytona Beach

Map Location: **#12**

SunCruz Casino - Daytona
4880 Front Street
Ponce Inlet, Florida 32127
(904) 322-9000
Website: www.suncruzcasino.com

Reservation Number: (800) 474-DICE
Gambling Age: 18   Ship's Registry: U.S.A.
Food Service: A la Carte Menu
Schedule:
    11:00am - 4:00pm (Mon-Fri)
    12:00pm - 5:00pm (Sat/Sun)
    7:00pm - 12:00am/12:30am (Fri/Sat)
Price: $10
Port Charges: Included   Parking: Free
Casino Size: 18,000 Square Feet
Other Games: MB, P, LIR, CSP, TCP
Senior Discount: Sail free if 60 or older
Special Features: 560-passenger *SunCruz III* departs from Ponce Inlet near Down the Hatch restaurant. Must be 18, or older, to board.

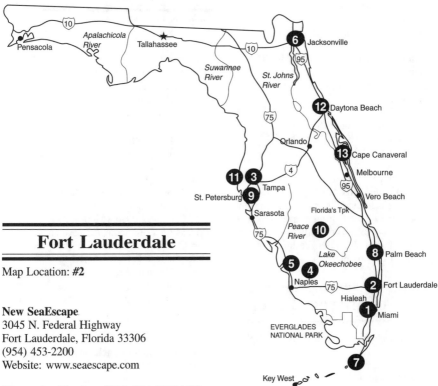

Fort Lauderdale

Map Location: **#2**

New SeaEscape
3045 N. Federal Highway
Fort Lauderdale, Florida 33306
(954) 453-2200
Website: www.seaescape.com

Reservation Number: (877) SEA-ESCAPE
Gambling Age: 18 Ship's Registry: Bahamas
Food Service: Buffet Included
Schedule:
   11:00am - 4:30pm (Tue-Sun)
   7:30pm - 12:30am (Mon-Thu)
   7:30pm - 1:30am (Fri/Sat)
   6:30pm- 11:30pm (Sun)
Prices: Day- $29.95/$34.95 (Sun)
   Eve- $29.95 (Sun-Thu) /$39.95 (Fri/Sat)
Port Charges: $3   Security Charge: $3
Parking: $7
Other Games: MB, P, PGP, LIR, BG
Senior Discount: $5 off any cruise, if 55+
Special Features: 1,050-passenger *Island Adventure* sails from Port Everglades in Fort Lauderdale. All prices are for advance purchase tickets only - $10 surcharge on tickets purchased at pier. Showroom with live entertainment on each cruise. Full-service dinner upgrade available. Private cabin rentals available. Children's prices offered on all cruises. Call for reservation to poker room. Must be 21 or older on evening cruises unless accompanied by parent or legal guardian.

Royal Casino Entertainment
4000 S. Ocean Drive Suite-100
Hollywood, Florida 33019
(954) 458-9930

Toll-Free Number: (888) 721-2121
Gambling Age: 21 Ship's Registry: U.S.A.
Buffets: L/D-$7
Schedule:
   11:00am - 5:00pm (Tue-Sun)
   7:00pm - 1:00am/2am (Fri/Sat/holidays)
Price: $10
Port Charges: $3   Parking: $6
Other Games: MB, CSP, TCP
Special Features: 500-passenger, *Royal Casino* departs from Amabassador Hotel on A1A in Hollywood. Must be 21, or older to board.

SunCruz Casino - Hollywood
647 E. Dania Beach Boulevard
Dania, Florida 33004
(954) 929-3800
Website: www.suncruzcasino.com

Reservation Number: (800) 474-DICE
Gambling Age: 18   Ship's Registry: U.S.A.
Food Service: L-$5 D-$7
Schedule:
    11:00am - 4:15pm (Mon-Fri)
    12:00pm - 5:30pm (Sat-Sun)
    7:30pm - 12:30am (Sun-Thu)
    7:30pm - 1:15am (Fri/Sat/holidays)
Price: $10
Port Charges: Included   Parking: Free
Other Games: MB, P, LIR, CSP, TCP
Special Features: 600-passenger, twin-hulled, *SunCruz VI* departs from Martha's Restaurant on A1A in Hollywood. Must be 18, or older, to board. Slot club offers cashback. A la carte menu also available.

Fort Myers Beach

Map Location: **#5** (40 miles N. of Naples)

Big M Casino
450 Harbor Court
Fort Myers Beach, Florida 33931
(941) 765-7529
Website: www.bigmcasino.com

Toll-Free Number: (888) 373-3521
Gambling Age: 21   Ship's Registry: U.S.A.
Buffets: L-$8.95 D-$12.95
Schedule:
    11:00am - 4:30pm (Daily)
    6:00pm -11:30pm (Daily)
Prices: $10/$20 (Sat eve)
Port Charges: Included
Parking: Free (Valet also free)
Other Games: LIR
Special Features: 400-passenger *Big M* sails from Moss Marina next to Snug Harbor on Fort Myers Beach. Must be 21, or older, to board.

Jacksonville

Map Location: **#6**

La Cruise Casino
4738 Ocean Street
Atlantic Beach, Florida 32233
(904) 241-7200
Website: www.lacruise.com

Reservation Number: (800) 752-1778
Gambling Age: 18   Ship's Registry: Panama
Food Service: A la Carte
Schedule:
    11:00am - 4:00pm (Tue-Thu/Sat)
    1:00pm - 6:00pm (Sun)
    7:00pm -12:00am (Mon-Sat)
Price: Free (afternoons)/$5 (evenings)
Port Charges: Included   Parking: Free
Other Games: P, CSP, B6, BG
Senior Discount: Free sail Tue, if 55, or older
Special Features: 450-passenger *La Cruise* sails from Mayport Village. Must be 18, or older, to board.

SunCruz Casino - Jacksonville
4378 Ocean Street
Atlantic Beach, Florida 32233
(904) 249-9300
Website: www.suncruzcasino.com

Toll-Free Number: (800) 474-DICE
Gambling Age: 18   Ship's Registry: U.S.A.
Buffets: $8 (Fri-Sat eves/Sun afternoon)
Food Service: A la carte menu
Schedule
    11:00pm - 4:00pm (Mon-Sat)
    12:00pm - 5:00pm (Sun)
    7:00pm - 12:00am (Sun-Thu)
    7:00pm - 12:30am (Fri/Sat/Holidays)
Price: Free
Port Charges: Included   Parking: Free
Other Games: MB, P, CSP, LIR
Special Features: 495-passenger, *SunCruz X* departs from Mayport Village. Must be 18 or older to board.

The IGT Casino Chip Program

Because of the intense competition among South Florida's casino boats some of them are involved in a special promotional program that can provide some great savings to casino-goers. The program involves the *In Good Taste* (IGT) credit card which offers a 25% discount on gambling chips purchased with the card.

The IGT card has been around for more than 30 years and originally started as a discount credit card for use only at restaurants. You can still use the card for a 25% discount at restaurants but it now offers that same discount in other areas including: airline travel, hotel lodging, cruises, Las Vegas and Biloxi gambling vacations, florists, dry cleaners, magazine subscriptions and more.

Whenever you make a purchase with the IGT card you receive a 25% discount when you are billed. They do not, however, give a discount on the tax or tip. As an example, let's say you charge a $100 dinner on the card, plus $6 tax and a $15 tip for a total of $121. When you get your bill from IGT you will be charged $75 for the dinner ($100 less 25%), plus $6 tax and the $15 tip for a total of $96. Upon receipt of the bill you also have the option of paying it by check or charging it to your Visa, MasterCard or Discover card.

As of August 2002 there were five casino boats in South Florida participating in the IGT program. On the Casino Princesa or the SeaEscape in Fort Lauderdale, you can purchase up to $125 in special chips with the IGT card. You will only be billed $93.75 by IGT which means you are starting off $31.25 ahead. You can receive all $125 worth of chips in $5 or $25 denominations. These special chips can only be played on table games and cannot be cashed - they must be played. If you win your bet you will be paid with regular chips and the special IGT chips will continue to remain in play until your bet loses. You are allowed to participate in the IGT program once per week on the Princesa and twice per month on the SeaEscape.

The SunCruz boats in Hollywood and Key Largo participate in the IGT program and they will both allow you to buy up to $250 in chips. Those boats will also give you the choice of receiving $100 in $5 chips, or $250 in $25 chips. If you opt for the $5 chips you will be required to bet a minimum of $10 each time. The rest of the program is pretty much the same with IGT billing you $75 for the $100 in chips, or $187.50 for the $250 in chips, meaning you are starting off either $25 or $62.50 ahead. You are limited to one buy-in per month at both of these boats. The Royal Casino boat in Hollywood also participates in the IGT program with rules identical to the two Sun Cruz boats.

The IGT program is truly a powerful program because you are starting off with a major mathematical advantage over the house. Lest you forget, it is supposed to be the other way around! On rare occasions some Las Vegas casinos have special chip programs similar to this where you can get maybe a 5% edge at best - $1,050 in special chips for $1,000 - but never as high as 25% like this program offers; it's very advantageous for the players. How come it works in South Florida? Three probable reasons:

1 - Competition. There are quite a few boats to choose from so the boats have to offer something extra to get people in their casinos.

2 - Bad players. The average South Florida casino-goer is a recreational gambler and not very knowledgeable. The casino edge against these players is much higher than knowledgbale gamblers who know the proper playing strategies.

3 - Time. You're stuck on a boat for 3-1/2 hours with nowhere to go. It probably takes no more than 30 minutes to go through the IGT chips and end up with all regular chips. If you were in a land-based casino you could simply walk out and take your money home but on a casino boat you still have another three hours to go before it heads back to shore. With all that time on your hands you have nothing left to do but gamble and all of those bad blackjack players usually give it all back to the casinos.

Keep in mind that if you're a perfect basic strategy blackjack player the highest mathematical casino edge on any of these boats' blackjack games is about one-half of one percent, so you should have an excellent chance of coming out a long-term winner with the IGT program.

The usual cost for a one year IGT membership is $48 but they will give you a free 6-month membership if you live in certain metropolitan areas. Call them at 800-4-IGT-USA or visit their website at www.igtcard.com for more details.

Scouting Report - South Florida Casino Boats

SeaEscape - Six-deck blackjack: dealer stands soft 17, double down on any first two cards, resplit any pair (except aces), double after split allowed and late surrender offered. The casino edge against a perfect basic strategy player is .34%. The craps game offers a maximum of 2X odds.

Only 25¢ video poker machines. Jacks or Better with 6/5 (95% return) and 7/5 (96.15% return) pay tables. Surprisingly good 10/7 Double Bonus (100.17% return), plus some 7/5 Double Bonus (98.02% return) machines.

SunCruz, Hollywood - Six-deck ($25 minimum) and eight-deck ($5 minimum) games: dealer stands on soft 17, double down on any first two cards, resplit any pair (except aces), double after split allowed and late surrender offered. The casino edge in this game against a perfect basic strategy player is .34% against six decks and .36% with eight decks in play.

Craps game offers 5X odds. For video poker players there are some 25¢ Jacks or Better machines with 6/5 (95% return), 7/5 (96.15% return) and 8/5 (97.28% return) pay tables. At the $1 level there are 8/5 Jacks or Better (97.28% return) and also some 7/5 Bonus (98.02% return) games. The only casino boat with a cashback slot club (.05%).

Palm Beach Princess - Six-deck ($25 minimum) and eight-deck ($5 minimum) games: dealer stands on soft 17, double down on any first two cards, resplit any pair (except aces) and double after split allowed. No surrender. The casino edge against a perfect basic strategy player is .41% against six decks and .43% with eight decks in play. Buy in at the cage for $1,000 and receive $1,100 in non-negotiable $25 chips for use on $25 tables or higher.

Craps game has 2X odds. Dollar and 25¢ video poker with 7/5 Jacks or Better (96.15% return) or 7/5 Bonus (98.01% return).

Key Largo

Map Location: **#7** (50 miles S. of Miami)

SunCruz Casino - Key Largo
99701 Overseas Highway
Key Largo, Florida 33037
(305) 451-0000
Website: www.suncruzcasino.com

Reservation Number: (800) 474-DICE
Gambling Age: 18   Ship's Registry: U.S.A.
Food Service: A la Carte Snack Bar
Shuttle Schedule:
 Departs/Returns 2:00pm/2:30 (Wed/Sat/Sun)
 Departs/Returns 5:00pm/5:30 (daily)
 Departs/Returns 7:00pm/7:30 (daily)
 Departs/Returns 9:30pm/10:00 (Fri/Sat)
 Returns   12:45am (Sun-Thu)
 Returns   1:15am (Fri/Sat)
Prices: $10
Port Charges: Included   Parking: Free
Other Games: CSP, TCP
Special Features: 149-passenger *SunCruz I*
departs from the Holiday Inn docks in Key
Largo. The boat then stays offshore and a wa-
ter taxi shuttles passengers back and forth ac-
cording to the above schedule. Must be 18, or
older, to board.

Miami

Map Location: **#1**

Casino Princesa
100 S. Biscayne Boulevard
Miami, Florida 33131
(305) 379-LUCK
Website: www.casinoprincesa.com

Reservation Number: (305) 379-LUCK
Gambling Age: 21 Ship's Registry: U.S.A.
Food Service: A la Carte Menu
 12:30pm - 5:00pm (Daily)
 7:30pm -12:30am (Daily)
 1:00am - 6:00am (Sat)
Prices: $5.95
Port Charges: Included
Parking: $8 Valet Parking: $9/$12 (Fri-Sun)
Casino Size: 10,000 Square Feet
Other Games: MB, P, LIR
Special Features: 600-passenger *Casino
Princesa* sails from downstown's Bayside
Marketplace. Must be 21, or older to board.

Majesty Casino Cruises
1280 Fifth Street
Miami Beach, Florida 33139
 (305) 532-2111
Web Site: www.majestycasino.com

Reservation Number: (305) 532-2111
Gambling Age: 21   Ship's Registry: U.S.A.
Buffet: Included
Schedule:
 12:30 - 5:00pm Daily
 7:30pm - 12:00am/12:30am (Fri-Sat)
Price: $20/$5 (Local Residents)
Port Charges: Included   Parking: Free
Other Games: MB
Special Features: 450-passenger, *Majesty* de-
parts from Miami Beach Marina. Must be 21,
or older, to board.

Palm Beach

Map Location: **#8**

Horizon's Edge
200 E 13th Street
Riviera Beach, Florida 33404
Web Site: www.horizonsedge.com

Toll Free Number: (800) 582-5932
Gambling Age: 21   Ship's Registry: U.S.A.
Food Service: Buffet and A la carte
Schedule & Prices:
  11:00pm - 4:00pm $13
  6:00pm - 11:00pm (Sun-Thu) $13
  7:00pm - 12:00am (Fri/Sat) $18
Port Charges: Included   Parking: Free
Special Features: 850-passenger *Palm Beach
Princess* sails from dock near Port of Palm
Beach. Ship operates seasonally November-
April then returns to Lynn, Massachusetts.

Palm Beach Princess
One E. 11th Street
Riviera Beach, Florida 33404
(561) 845-2101
Website: www.pbcasino.com

Reservation Number: (800) 841-7447
Gambling Age: 21   Ship's Registry: Panama
Food Service: Buffet Included
Schedule & Prices:

11:30am - 5:00pm (Mon-Fri)	$30
11:30am- 5:00pm (Sat/Sun	$35
6:30pm - 11:30pm (Sun-Thu)	$30
6:30pm - 12:30am (Fri/Sat)	$35

Port Charges: Included   Parking: $5
Casino Size: 15,000 Square Feet
Other Games: SB, LIR, P, Oasis Stud Poker
Senior Discount: $5 or $10 discount, if 55+
Special Features: 850-passenger *Palm Beach Princess* sails from Port of Palm Beach. Rates subject to seasonal variations. Private cabin rentals. Swimming pool. Lounge with live entertainment, cabaret shows, games and dancing. Children only allowed on day cruises. Must be 21 or older to board on evening cruises.

Texas Treasure Casino Cruises
2001 Broadway Suite-500
Riviera Beach, Florida, 33404
(561) 863-7778
Website: www.txtreasure.com
Map Location: **#3** (10 miles N.E. of Corpus Christi)

Reservation Number: (866) TEXAS-11
Gambling Age: 21   Ship's Registry: Panama
Meal Service: Buffet Included
Schedule:
10:30pm - 3:30pm (Daily)
7:30pm - 12:30am/11:30 (Sun)/1:30 (Fri/Sat)
Price: $20 All Cruises
Port Charges: Included   Parking: Free
Other Games: MB, LIR, PGP, Casino War
Special Features: 800-passenger *Texas Treasure* sails from Port of Palm Beach. Must be 21, or older, to board.

Port Canaveral

Map Location: **#13** (60 miles S. of Daytona Beach)

SunCruz Casino - Port Canaveral
610 Glen Cheek Drive
Cape Canaveral, Florida 32920
(321) 799-3511
Website: www.suncruzcasino.com

Toll-Free Number: (800) 474-DICE
Gambling Age: 18   Ship's Registry: U.S.A.
Buffets: L-$5.00 D-$7.00
Schedule
11:00pm - 4:00pm (Mon-Sat)
1:00pm - 6:00pm (Sun)
7:00pm - 12:00am (Sun-Thu)
7:00pm - 12:30am (Fri/Sat/Holidays)
Price: Free
Port Charges: Included   Parking: Free
Other Games: MB, P, CSP, LIR, TCP
Special Features: 1,000-passenger, *SunCruz VIII* departs from Port Canaveral. Must be 18 or older to board. A la carte food menu also available.

Sterling Casino Lines
Terminal B
Cape Canaveral, Florida 32920
(407) 783-2212
Website: www.sterlingcasinolines.com

Reservation Number: (800) ROLL-7-11
Gambling Age: 21 Ship's Registry: Bahamas
Buffets: Included
Schedule:
11:00am - 4:00pm (Daily)
7:00pm - 12:00am (Daily)
Port Charges: Included   Parking: Free
Casino Size: 75,000 Square Feet
Other Games: B, MB, LIR
Special Features: 1,800-passenger, *Ambassador II* departs from terminal 2 at Port Canaveral. Free live entertainment in the lounge. Must be 21, or older, to board.

Port Richey

Map Location: **#11** (15 miles N.W. of Tampa)

Stardancer Casino - Port Richey
7847 Bayview Street
Port Richey, Florida 34668
Website: www.stardancercasino.com

Reservation Number: (800) 688-PLAY
Gambling Age: 21   Ship's Registry: U.S.A.
Food Service: Free
Daily Shuttle Schedule:
    Departs: 9:30am/11:30am/3pm/7pm
    Returns: 2:30pm/5pm/9pm/12am
Price: Free
Port Charges: Included   Parking: Free
Other Games: P, LIR, SB
Special Features: 250-passenger boat departs
from Port Richey waterfront next to Hooter's.
The boat then stays offshore and a water taxi
shuttles passengers back and forth according
to the above schedule. Must be 21, or older,
to board.

St. Petersburg

Map Location: **#9**

SunCruz Casino - John's Pass
12788 Kingfish Drive
Treasure Island, Florida 33706
(727) 895-3325
Website: www.suncruzcasino.com

Reservation Number: (800) 474-DICE
Gambling Age: 18   Ship's Registry: U.S.A.
Buffets: L-$5 D-$7
Schedule:
    11:30am - 5:00pm (Mon-Fri)
    11:30am - 5:30pm (Sat/Sun)
    7:00pm -12:30am (Sun-Thu)
    7:00pm - 1:00am (Fri/Sat)
Prices: $10
Port Charges: Included   Parking: Free
Other Games: MB, P, CSP, LIR
Special Features: 590-passenger *SunCruz V*
sails from Kingfish Wharf at John's Pass on
Treasure Island (next to Gator's). Must be 18
or older to sail. A la carte food menu also avail-
able.

Stardancer Casino - Madeira Beach
150 153rd Avenue
Madeira Beach, Florida 33708
(727) 393-5110
Website: www.stardancercasino.com

Reservation Number: (800) 688-PLAY
Gambling Age: 21   Ship's Registry: U.S.A.
Buffets: Included
Schedule & Prices:
    11:30am - 5:00pm (Daily) $17
    7:00pm -12:30am (Mon-Thu) $20
    7:00pm - 1:00am (Fri/Sat) $20
Port Charge: Included   Parking: Free
Other Games: P, SB
Special Features: 440-passenger *Stardancer*
sails from Hubbard's Marina at John's Pass Vil-
lage Boardwalk in Madeira Beach. Must be
21, or older, to board.

Tarpon Springs

Map Location: **#9**

Stardancer Casino - Tarpon Springs
Dodecanese Boulevard
Tarpon Springs, FL 34688
(727) 938-5727
Website: www.stardancercasino.com

OPERATES SEASONALLY - CALL FIRST
Reservation Number: 800-688-PLAY
Gambling Age: 21   Ship's Registry:USA
Food Service: Free
Shuttle Schedule:
    Departs: 9:30am/11:30am/3pm/7pm
    Returns: 2:30pm/5pm/9pm/12am
Prices: Free
Port Charge: Included   Parking: Free
Other Games: SB
Special Features: Water taxi shuttles passen-
gers back and forth to casino boat anchored
off Port Richey according to the above sched-
ule. Must be 21, or older, to board.

Indian Casinos

Florida has six Indian gaming locations. The Seminole Tribe has five and the sixth is on the Miccosukee's reservation.

There is no state-tribal compact in effect in Florida and the state has gone to court to shut down the Indian gaming operations. In turn, the Seminole tribe has made a formal appeal to the Secretary of the Interior's office to allow full-scale casino gambling on their reservations. Until the matter is fully resolved, federal officials have not allowed the state to shut down any tribal gambling operation.

All Indian casinos offer high-stakes bingo, video pull tabs and poker games with a maximum pot of $10. All are open 24 hours (except Brighton) and the minimum gambling age is 18.

Brighton Seminole Bingo and Casino
Route 6, Box 611
Okeechobee, Florida 34974
(863) 763-9268
Website: www.seminoletribe.com/enterprises/
brighton/casino.shtml
Map Location: **#10** (75 miles N.W. of West Palm Beach)

Toll-Free Number: (800) 360-9875
Hours: 10am-1am (Tue-Sun)
Restaurants: 1   Liquor: No
Casino Size: 27,000 Square Feet
Special Features: Poker starts at 3pm. No poker on Sunday.

Coconut Creek Seminole Bingo and Casino
5550 NW 40th Street
Coconut Creek, Florida 33073
(954) 977-6700
Website: www.seminoletribe.com/enterprises/
hollywood/coco.shtml
Map Location: **#2**

Toll-Free Number: (866) 2-CASINO
Restaurants: 1 snack bar (open 24 hrs)

Hollywood Seminole Gaming
4150 N. State Road 7
Hollywood, Florida 33021
(954) 961-3220
Website: www.seminoletribe.com/enterprises/
hollywood/casino.shtml
Map Location: **#2** (5 miles S. of Fort Lauderdale)

Toll-Free Number: (800) 323-5452
Restaurants: 2 Snack Bars   Liquor: Yes
Casino Size: 73,500 Square Feet

Miccosukee Indian Gaming
500 S.W. 177 Avenue
Miami, Florida 33194
(305) 222-4600
Website: www.miccosukee.com
Map Location: **#1**

Toll-Free Number: (800) 741-4600
Room Reservations: (877) 242-6464
Rooms: 256 Price Range: $69-$107
Suites: 46 Price Range: $125-$189
Restaurants: 2 (1 open 24 hours) Liquor: Yes
Buffets: B-$8.95 L/D-$11.95

Seminole Gaming Palace and Casino
5223 N. Orient Road
Tampa, Florida 33610
(813) 621-1302
Website: www.seminoletribe.com/enterprises/
tampa/gaming.shtml
Map Location: **#3**

Toll-Free Number: (800) 282-7016
Restaurants: 1 Cafeteria Liquor: Yes

Seminole Gaming Palace
506 South 1st Street
Immokalee, Florida 33934
(941) 658-1313
Map Location: **#4** (35 miles N.E. of Naples)

Toll-Free Number: (800) 218-0007
Restaurants: 2 (1 open 24 hours) Liquor: Yes
Casino Size: 43,000 Square Feet

GEORGIA

There is one casino boat in Georgia which sails three miles out into international waters where casino gambling is permitted.

For information on visiting Georgia call the state's tourism department at (800) 847-4842.

Emerald Princess Dinner Cruise & Casino
One St. Andrews Court
Brunswick, Georgia 31520
(912) 265-3558
Website: www.emeraldprincesscasino.com
Map Location: **#1** (75 miles S. of Savannah)

Reservation Number: (800) 842-0115
Gambling Age: 18
Ship's Registry: Panama
Buffets: Included

Schedule
11:00am - 4:00pm (Sat)
 1:00pm - 6:00pm (Sun)
 7:00pm - 12:00am (Mon-Thu)
 7:00pm - 1:00am (Fri-Sat)
Prices: Range from $10-$25
Port Charges: Included
Parking: Free
Games Offered: Blackjack, Craps,
          Roulette, Caribbean Stud Poker
Special Features: 400-passenger *Emerald Princess* sails from Brunswick Landing Marina in downtown Brunswick. Reservations are required for all cruises. Packages with hotel accommodations are available. No one under 18 permitted to board.

IDAHO

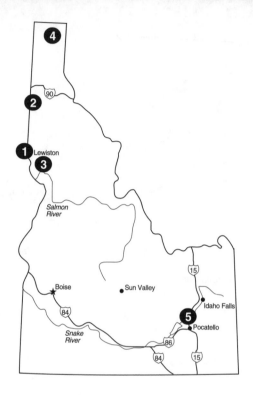

Idaho has five Indian casinos that offer electronic pull-tab machines and other video games. The machines don't pay out in cash. Instead they print out a receipt which must be cashed by a floor attendant or taken to the cashier's cage. Some casinos also offer bingo.

According to David High in the attorney general's office the terms of the compact between the tribes and the state do not require any minimum payback percentage that the gaming machines must return to the public.

The minimum gambling age at all casinos is 18 and they are all open 24 hours. For Idaho tourism information call (800) 635-7820

Clearwater River Casino
17500 Nez Perce Road
Lewiston, Idaho 83501
(208) 746-5733
Website: www.crcasino.com
Map Location: **#1** (250 miles N. of Boise)

Toll-Free Number: (877) 678-7423
Restaurants: 1 Snack Bar Liquor: No
Casino Size: 30,000 Square Feet
Other Games: Bingo (Thu-Sun)
Senior Discount: Sunday Bingo discount if 55+
Special Features: 33-space RV park.

Coeur D'Alene Casino Resort Hotel
U.S. Highway 95/P.O. Box 236
Worley, Idaho 83876
(208) 686-5106
Website: www.cdacasino.com
Map Location: **#2** (350 miles N. of Boise)

Toll-Free Number: (800) 523-2464
Rooms: 93 Price Range: $80
Suites: 3 Price Range $220-$350
Restaurants: 2 Liquor: Yes
Buffet: B-$4.99/$6.99 (Sat)/$11.99 (Sun)
    L-$6.99 D-$11.99/$13.99 (Sat)/
    $14.99(Wed)/$15.99(Fri)
Casino Size: 30,000 Square Feet
Other Games: Bingo (Fri-Sun), Simulcasting
Senior Discount: 10% off bingo, if 55, or older

Coyote Casino
404 Main Street
Kamiah, Idaho 83536
(208) 935-1638
Website: www.crcasino.com
Map Location: **#3** (225 miles N. of Boise)

Toll-Free Number: (877) 678-7423
Restaurants: 1 Liquor: No
Hours: 24 Hours Daily
Casino Size: 2,300 Square Feet
Other Games: Bingo (Thu-Sat)

Kootenai River Inn & Casino
Kootenai River Plaza
Bonners Ferry, Idaho 83805
(208 267 8511
Map Location: **#4** (450 miles N. of Boise)

Toll-Free Number: (800) 346-5668
Rooms: 47 Price Range: $75-$111
Suites: 4 Price Range $119-$124
Restaurants: 1 Liquor: Yes
Buffets: B-$9.95 (Sun)
Casino Size: 30,000 Square Feet
Other Games: Bingo (Wed/Fri/Sun)
Special Features: Hotel affiliated with Best
Western.

Shoshone-Bannock Gaming
P.O. Box 868
Fort Hall, Idaho 83203
(208) 237-8778
Website: www.sho-ban.com
Map Location: **#5** (5 miles N. of Pocatello)

Toll-Free Number: (800) 497-4231
Restaurants: 1 Snack Bar Liquor: No
Casino Size: 15,000 Square Feet
Other Games: Bingo (Fri-Sun/Tue)

ILLINOIS

Illinois was the second state to legalize riverboat casinos. Riverboat casinos began operating there in September 1991 with the launching of the first boat: the Alton Belle.

All Illinois riverboats offer dockside gambling. Unlike Mississippi, however, the casinos are not open 24 hours. State law limits the number of gaming licenses to 10. There are currently nine casinos open and the 10th license is being pursued by several different gaming companies.

Admission is free to all Illinois casinos and, unless otherwise noted, all casinos offer: slots, video poker, blackjack, craps, roulette and Caribbean stud poker. Some casinos also offer: let it ride (LIR), baccarat (B), mini-baccarat (MB), poker (P) and three-card poker (TCP). The minimum gambling age is 21.

Here's information from the Illinois Gaming Board showing each casino's average slot payback percentage for the one-year period from July 1, 2001 through June 30, 2002:

CASINO	PAYBACK %
Casino Queen	94.94
Alton Belle	94.53
Grand Victoria	94.20
Rock Island	93.84
Hollywood	93.69
Par-A-Dice	93.28
Empress	93.26
Harrah's Joliet	92.83
Harrah's Metropolis	92.59

These figures reflect the total percentages returned by each casino for all of their electronic machines. As you can see, the Casino Queen returned the most to its slot machine players, while Harrah's in Metropolis returned the least.

The Best Places To Play In The Chicago Area
by John Grochowski

The good word among casinos in the Chicago area is "dockside." Early August, 2002, brought the big change to Indiana gambling boats. In exchange for paying a higher gaming tax, Indiana gambling boats now may remain at the dock. No longer do customers have waits of up to an hour-and-a-half for boarding times.

With a couple of differences, that matches Illinois' move to dockside in 2000. For starters, Illinois casinos are permitted to build permanently moored barges, putting the gaming floor on a single level, while Indiana casinos must remain on boats, leaving customers with trips up and down the stairs or escalators to find their games of choice. On the other hand, Indiana casinos are much larger than those in Illinois, where law limits each license to 1,200 gaming positions. In the Chicago area, the typical Indiana casino has about one-and-a-half times as many slots machines and nearly twice as many tables as the typical Illinois operation.

One Illinois license remains inactive. The former Silver Eagle partners and their successors, holders of the license for the East Dubuque riverboat that closed in 1998, failed in their attempt to relocate in the northwest Chicago suburb of Rosemont. They are being permitted to sell the license to recoup losses, but with no financial gain. It's now up to the Illinois Gaming Board to review license applicants and decide where to place a new casino. Rosemont remains a candidate, along with south suburban locations including Calumet City and Harvey, and north suburbs including Waukegan, Zion and North Chicago.

For now, there are eight casinos within a 45-minute drive of Chicago — four in Illinois and four in Indiana. But this big-city market is not Las Vegas, or Atlantic City, or even Tunica County. With the exception of Trump and Majestic Star in Gary, Indiana, which share a land-based pavilion, there is no casino-hopping on foot. Casinos are not walking distance from each other. Some are more than an hour apart by car. What that means to a customer searching for a good game is that the pressure isn't as intense on casinos to provide one. There's no worry that you're going to walk out and try the game next door. You'll find no single-deck blackjack in the Chicago area, and 100-percent video poker machines are few and far between. Still, there are some opportunities to pick and choose among the games. Here are the ones to look for:

Roulette: Unfortunately, all roulette wheels in the Chicago-area casinos are standard American double-zero versions.

Craps: The face of Chicago-area craps changed in 1999 when Binion's Horseshoe Gaming entered the picture. Horseshoe in Hammond offers 100x odds, and 20x odds have become common among competitors. Horseshoe caters to the big players, and has the highest maximum bets — up to $10,000.

Blackjack: All games use either six or eight decks. For a basic strategy player, the best sets of rules are in force in Joliet, both at Empress aboard Empress I and Empress II and at Harrah's aboard Northern Star and Southern Star. Both use six decks. The dealer stands on all 17s, the player may double down on any first two cards, including after splits, and may resplit Aces. The house edge on the game is .33% against a basic strategy player. The ability to resplit aces sets the Joliet game apart from the rest of the area. Trump and Majestic Star, both in Gary, Ind., come close. They have six-deck games with the same basic rules with two exceptions: The player may not resplit aces, but late surrender is offered. That leaves a house edge of .35 percent.

Video Poker: The only 100 percent-plus game in the area is 10-7 Double Bonus Poker, and that's available only at the $1 level at Empress Joliet, both on Empress I and Empress II. Some machines add a progressive jackpot on the royal flush, enhancing the 100.17 percent payback to experts on the basic game. Empress also has a nice video poker room aboard the Empress I boat, featuring multigame Game King machines in both quarter and dollar denominations. The dollar games have the higher pay tables, including 8-5 Bonus Poker (99.2 percent with expert play); 8-5 ACES Bonus Poker (99.4) and Not So Ugly Deuces Wild (99.7 percent). It's not Las Vegas-style full-pay Deuces, but one of the best games near Chicago nonetheless. Four-of-a-kind paybacks are lowered to 4-for-1 while full houses are enhanced to 4-for-1 and flushes to 3-for-1, just as in the game known as Illinois Deuces. However, five-of-a-kind also is enhanced to 16-for-1 and straight flushes to 10-for-1.

Majestic Star, which had been the weakest video poker casino in the area, may now be the best overall video poker house in the area. It now has 9/6 Jacks or Better, a 99.5 percent game with expert play, on single-hand dollar and quarter IGT Game King machines. Even nickel players can play 9-6 Jacks or Better on Fifty Play Poker machines. On Fifty Play, you can select any number of hands to play at once up to 50. The result is that nickel players can play a single hand, betting just five nickels at a time and get the full 9-6 pay table. Majestic Star also has 9-7 Double Bonus, a 99.1 percent game, on all its quarter and dollar Game Kings.

The advent of Triple Play and Five Play Poker has brought many decent games to the area. It's easy to find Triple Play and Five Play games with 9/6 Jacks or Better and Not So Ugly Deuces. Players can find those games on Triple Play/Five Play quarter machines at Trump and on dollar machines at Harrah's Joliet and Empress Joliet.

There have been some downgrades. Grand Victoria in Elgin, Illinois, which for many years had 9/6 Jacks or Better for dollar players, along with a bank of $5 9/6 games, has dropped to 8/5 pay tables. Harrah's Joliet, which had $1 9/7 Double Bonus Poker with a fast-moving progressive jackpot on royal flushes that frequently took the theoretical return over the 100-percent mark, eliminated the game when it moved to its barge. Now the big dollar progressive game is 9-6 Double Double Bonus, a 98.9 percent game at the base value of $4,000 for a royal flush.

John Grochowski is the gaming columnist for the "Chicago Sun-Times" and a contributing writer to many gaming magzines. John is also the author of several books on casino gambling. For ordering information on John's books: "The Casino Answer Book," "The Slot Machine Answer Book" and "The Video Poker Answer Book" be sure to look for his ads in the front part of this book.

For more information on Illinois casinos contact the state's Bureau of Tourism at (800) 223-0121.

Alton Belle Riverboat Casino
219 Piasa Street
Alton, Illinois 62002
(618) 474-7500
Website: www.argosycasinos.com
Map Location: #1 (260 miles S.W. of Chicago. 25 miles N. of St. Louis, MO)

Reservation Number: (800) 336-SLOT
Restaurants: 3
Buffets: B-$4.95 (Fri-Sun)
L-$7.95 D-$11.95
Valet Parking: $5
Casino Hours: 8am-6am Daily
Casino Size: 23,000 Square Feet
Other Games: LIR, TCP
Casino Marketing: (800) 500-VIP1
Fun Book: Only given to groups
Senior Discount: 10% off buffets, if 50 or older
Special Features: Casino feature both a 1,200-passenger modern yacht and also a barge docked on the Mississippi River.

Casino Queen
200 S. Front Street
E. St. Louis, Illinois 62201
(618) 874-5000
Website: www.casinoqueen.com
Map Location: #6 (290 miles S.W. of Chicago)

Reservation Number: (800) 777-0777
Rooms: 150 Price Range: $89-$149
Suites: 7 Price Range: $300
Buffets: B-$5.95 L-$8.95/$10.95 (Sun)
D-$12.95
Valet Parking: $4
Casino Hours: 9am-6:30am
Casino Size: 27,500 Square Feet
Other Games: MB, LIR
Senior Discount: On Wed. get free danish, coffee, juice, 2-for-1 breakfast or lunch,35% off gift shop and free valet parking, if 50+
Special Features: 2,500-passenger, old-fashioned, paddlewheeler docked on the Mississippi river. 140-space RV park. Sports Bar with 27 tv's and live entertainment on weekends. MetroLink light-rail station at doorstep. 10% room discount to AAA members. $1 off buffets for slot club members.

Empress Casino Hotel Joliet
2300 Empress Drive
Joliet, Illinois 60436
(815) 744-9400
Website: www.empresscasino.com
Map Location: #2 (43 miles S.W. of Chicago)

Reservation Number: (888) 4-EMPRESS
Rooms: 85 Price Range: $59-$120
Suites: 17 Price Range: Only through casino
Restaurants: 3
Buffets: L-$8.95/$11.95 (Sun)
D-$13.95 (Sun/Tue/Wed)/$17.95/$19.95 (Fri)
Valet Parking: Free
Casino Hours: 8:30am-6:30am
Casino Size: 16,800 Square Feet - *Empress I*
Casino Size: 19,400 Square Feet - *Empress II*
Other Games: LIR, B, TCP
Special Features: 1,000-passenger *Empress I* and 1,500-passenger *Empress II* are modern yachts docked on the Des Plaines River. Rooms are at on-property Empress Hotel. 80-space RV park.

Grand Victoria Casino
250 S. Grove Avenue
Elgin, Illinois 60120
(847) 888-1000
Website: www.grandvictoria-elgin.com
Map Location: #4 (41 miles N.W. of Chicago)

Reservation Number: (847) 888-1000
Restaurants: 3
Buffets: L-$11.99 D-$20.99
Valet Parking: $5
Casino Hours: 8:30am-6:30am
Casino Size: 29,850 Square Feet
Other Games: B
Fun Book: Only given to groups
Senior Discount: 10% off buffet, if 65, or older
Special Features: 1,200-passenger paddle wheeler-replica docked on the Fox River.

Harrah's Joliet
150 N. Scott Street
Joliet, Illinois 60431
(815) 774-2610
Website: www.harrahs.com
Map Location: **#2** (43 miles S.W. of Chicago)

Reservation Number: (800) HARRAHS
Rooms: 200 Price Range: $69-$159
Suites: 4 Price Range: $325
Restaurants: 2
Buffets: L-$7.99/$15.99 (Sat-Sun) D-$9.99/
$14.99/$15.99 (Mon)/$18.99 Fri-Sun)
Casino Hours: 8:30am-6:30am Valet Parking: $5
Casino Size: 39,000
Other Games: MB, P, LIR
Special Features: Casino is on a barge docked on the Des Plaines River.

Harrahs Metropolis
203 S. Ferry Street
Metropolis, Illinois 62960
(618) 524-2628
Website: www.harrahs.com
Map Location: **#8** (Across from Paducah, KY. Take exit 37 on I-24)

Toll-Free Number: (800) 935-7700
Restaurants: 2
Buffets: B-$11.99 (Sat/Sun) L-$9.99
D-$13.99/$15.99 (Fri-Sun)
Casino Hours: 9am-7am Valet Parking: $5
Other Games: MB, LIR
Casino Size: 29,600 Square Feet
Casino Marketing: (800) 929-5905
Special Features: 1,300-passenger sidewheeler replica docked on Ohio River. 120-room Amerihost Inn across street (800-434-5800).

Hollywood Casino - Aurora
1 New York Street Bridge
Aurora, Illinois 60506
(630) 801-7000
Website: www.hollywoodcasino.com
Map Location: **#7** (41 miles W. of Chicago)

Toll Free Number: (800) 888-7777
Restaurants: 5
Buffets: B-$5.99/$9.99 (Sun) L-$8.99
D-$12.99/$15.99 (Fri)
Valet Parking: $2/$4 (Fri-Sat)/Free with Marquee Card
Casino I Hours: 8:30am-6:30am
Casino II Hours: 10:30am-2am
Casino Size: 37,954 Square Feet

Other Games: MB, LIR
Senior Discount: 2-for-1 breakfast or lunch buffet on Thu. if 55+ and slot club member
Special Features: Casino is on a barge docked on the Fox River.

Jumer's Casino Rock Island
1735 First Avenue
Rock Island, Illinois 61201
(309) 793-4200
Website: www.jumerscri.com
Map Location: **#3** (170 miles W. of Chicago)

Reservation Number: (800) 477-7747
Restaurants: 1 on boat adjacent to casino
Buffets: B-$6.95 (Sun) L-$6.95 D-$9.95
Valet Parking: Free
Casino Hours: 8am-3am Daily
Casino Size: 17,200 Square Feet
Casino Marketing: (800) 477-7747
Senior Discount: Free buffet (Mon-Thu) if you play a minimum of $50 in slots or buy in for at least $50 and play for a minimum of 50 minutes on table games, if 50, or older.
Special Features: 1,200-passenger old-fashioned paddlewheel boat on the Mississippi River. Free hors d'oeuvres, coffee, juice and soft drinks. $1 mixed drinks. Restaurant is on the *Effie Afton* which is another boat docked next to the casino.

Par-A-Dice Hotel Casino
21 Blackjack Boulevard
East Peoria, Illinois 61611
(309) 698-7711
Website: www.par-a-dice.com
Map Location: **#5** (170 miles S.W. of Chicago)

Toll-Free Number: (800) 727-2342
Toll-Free Number: (800) 332-5634
Room reservations: (800) 547-0711
Rooms: 208 Price Range: $83-$103
Suites 12 Price Range: $98-$250
Restaurants: 4
Buffets: B-$6.95 L-$8.95
D-$11.95/ $15.95 (Fri/Sat)
Valet Parking: $5
Casino Hours: 8:30am-4:30am
Casino Size: 26,116 Square Feet
Senior Discount: 25% off buffet, if 55, or older
Special Features: 1,600-passenger modern boat docked on the Illinois River. Rooms can only be booked through casino on weekends. Slot club members get 10% off buffet and $10 off room rates.

INDIANA

Although the governor vetoed riverboats for his state, the Indiana legislature voted to override him and in June 1993 Indiana became the sixth state to legalize riverboat gambling.

All riverboats offer dockside gambling but the casinos do not stay open 24 hours. The hours of operation are shown in the individual listings for each particular casino.

Admission is free to all Indiana casinos except for two: Argosy and Aztar. However, if you're a rated player from another casino you may get free admission to these casinos. Call ahead to ask them about their requirements.

Following is information from the Indiana Gaming Commission regarding average slot payout percentages for the one-year period from January 1 through December 31, 2001:

CASINO	PAYBACK %
Argosy	94.2
Blue Chip	93.5
Trump Casino	92.8
Caesars Indiana	93.2
Horseshoe Casino	93.3
Majestic Star	92.7
Grand Victoria	92.9
Harrah's	92.3
Belterra	93.3
Casino Aztar	92.0

These figures reflect the total percentages returned by each casino for all of their electronic machines including slot machines, video poker, video keno, etc.

Unless otherwise noted, all casinos offer: blackjack, craps, roulette, slots, video poker, video keno and Caribbean stud poker. Optional games include: baccarat (B), mini-baccarat (MB), poker (P), pai gow poker (PGP), three card poker (TCP), Spanish 21 (S21), big 6 wheel (B6) and let it ride (LIR). The minimum gambling age is 21.

For more information on visiting Indiana call (800) 289-6646.

Argosy Casino & Hotel - Lawrenceburg
777 Argosy Parkway
Lawrenceburg, Indiana 47025
(812) 539-8000
Website: www.argosycasinos.com
Map Location: **#3** (95 miles S.E. of Indianapolis)

Toll-Free Number: (888) ARGOSY-7
Rooms: 300 Price Range: $79-$139
Suites: 6 Price Range: $160-$310
Restaurants: 4
Buffets: B-$7.30 L-$9.40
         D-$13.50/$16.95 (Fri/Sat)
Valet Parking: $3
Hours 9am-5am Daily
Admission: $3/ $5 (Fri-Sat 7pm-11pm)
Casino Size: 74,300 Square Feet
Other Games: MB, B6, LIR, SP21, TCP
Casino Marketing: (888) ARGOSY-7
Senior Discount: $1 off admission Sun-Thu
         and Fri/Sat 9am-5pm, if 55, or older
Special Features: 4,000-passenger modern yacht docked on the Ohio River. Closest casino to Cincinnati. Reservations are recommended, especially for weekends and holidays.

Belterra Casino and Resort
777 Belterra Drive
Belterra, IN 47043-9402
(812) 427-4008
Website: www.belterracasino.com
Map Location: **#1** (35 miles S.W. of Cincinnati, Ohio)

Toll-Free Number: (888) BELTERRA
Rooms: 308 Price Range: $79-$149
Suites: Casino use only
Restaurants: 7
Buffets: B-$7.95$14.95 (Sun) L-$8.95
         D-$12.95
Valet Parking: Free
Hours: 8am-4am/5am (Fri-Sat)
Casino Size: 38,000 Square Feet
Other Games: MB, LIR, TCP
Special Features: 2,600-passenger sidewheeler docked on the Ohio River. Health club and spa. 18-hole golf course.

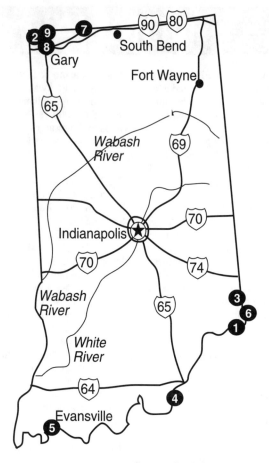

Blue Chip Casino
2 Easy Street
Michigan City, Indiana 46360
(219) 879-7711
Website: www.bluechip-casino.com
Map Location: **#7** (40 miles E. of Chicago)

Reservation Number: (888) 879-7711
Rooms: 180 Price Range: $79-$109
Suites: Casino use only
Restaurants: 3
Buffets: B-$6.95 L-$8.95
    D-$11.95/$13.95 (Tue)/$16.95 (Fri-Sat)
Valet Parking: Free
Hours: 8am-3am/5am (Fri-Sat)
Casino Size: 25,000 Square Feet
Other Games: MB, P, LIR, TCP
Senior Discount: 2-for-1 lunch buffet on
               Tuesdays if 55, or older
Special Features: 2,000-passenger modern
yacht docked in a man-made body of water.

Caesars Indiana
11999 Avenue of the Emperors
Elizabeth, Indiana 47117
(812) 969-6000
Website: www.caesars.com
Map Location: **#4** (20 miles S. of New Albany)

Rooms: 503 Prices: Price Range: $49-$149
Toll-Free Number: (888) ROMAN-4-U
Buffets: B-$7.95/$11.95 (Sat-Sun) L-$8.95
         D-$13.95/15.95 (Fri)
Valet Parking: Free
Hours: 9am-5am Daily
Casino Size: 25,000 Square Feet
Other Games: B, MB, LIR, P
Special Features: 5,000-passenger sidewheeler
docked on the Ohio River.

The 5,000-passenger *Glory of Rome* at Caesars Indiana is the world's largest riverboat casino.

Casino Aztar

421 N.W. Riverside Drive
Evansville, Indiana 47708
(812) 433-4000
Website: www.casinoaztar.com
Map Location: **#5** (168 miles S.W. of Indianapolis)

Toll-Free Number: (800) DIAL-FUN
Rooms: 240 Price Range: $69-$115
Suites: 10 Price Range: $139-$205
Restaurants: 5
Buffets: B-$5.95/$12.95 (Sun) L-$7.95
Valet Parking: Free
Hours: 8am-5am Daily
Admission: $3
Casino Size: 47,863 Square Feet
Other Games: MB, LIR, B6, P
Senior Discount: Coffee, donuts and 25% off all restaurants and gift shops on Mondays 8am-9am, plus 10% off rooms and food all other days if 55 or older
Special Features: 2,700-passenger old fashioned paddlewheeler docked on the Ohio River. 10% room discount for AAA members.

Grand Victoria Casino & Resort

600 Grand Victoria Drive
Rising Sun, Indiana 47040
(812) 438-1234
Map Location: **#6** (40 miles S.W. of Cincinatti)

Reservation Number: (800) GRAND-11
Rooms: 201 Price Range: $59-$139
Restaurants: 4
Buffets: B-$6.95 L-$8.95/$12.95 (Sun)
   D-$12.95/$14.95 (Fri)
Valet Parking: Free
Hours: 8am-4am/5am (Fri-Sat)
Casino Size: 40,000 Square Feet
Other Games: S21, LIR, P, TCP
Senior Discount: 50%off buffets and a chance to win prizes on Tuesdays and 10% off on selected amenities every day if 55+
Special Features: 3,000-passenger paddle wheeler docked on Ohio River. Hotel is Hyatt. Golf course. Thursdays ladies receive 50% off buffet if slot club member. Single-zero roulette

Harrah's East Chicago
One Showboat Place
East Chicago, Indiana 46312
(219) 378-3000
Website: www.harrahs.com
Map Location: **#9** (12 miles E. of Chicago)

Reservation Number: (877) 496-1777
Rooms: 286 Prices: $75-$195
Suites: 7 Prices: Casino Use Only
Restaurants: 5
Buffets: B-$9.99/$18.99 (Sat-Sun) L-$11.99
          D-$18.99/$24.99 (Fri-Sat)
Valet Parking: $5 but discounted for Total
          Rewards Card members
Hours: 8am-5am Daily
Casino Size: 53,000 Square Feet
Other Games: S21, MB, P, PGP, LIR, TCP
Special Features: 3,750-passenger modern
yacht docked on Lake Michigan.

Horseshoe Casino Hammond
777 Casino Center Drive
Hammond, Indiana 46320
(219) 473-7000
Website: www.horseshoe.com
Map Location: **#2** (10 miles E. of Chicago)

Reservation Number: (866) 711-7463
Restaurants: 3
Buffets: B-$7.99/$18.99 (Sun) L-$11.99
          D-$15.99/$24.99 (Fri-Sat)
Valet parking: $5/$3 with Winner's Circle
Card.
Hours: 8am-5am Daily
Casino Size: 43,000 Square Feet
Other Games: B, MB, LIR, P
Senior Discount: Free valet Mondays, if 55+
Special Features: 3,000-passenger modern
yacht docked on Lake Michigan. Slot club
members get 15% off food and in gift shop.

Majestic Star Casino
1 Buffington Harbor Drive
Gary, Indiana 46406
(219) 977-7777
Website: www.majesticstar.com
Map Location: **#8** (15 miles E. of Chicago)

Reservation Number: (888) 2B-LUCKY
Restaurants: 6
Buffets: L-$8.99 D-$13.99/$17.99 (Fri-Sat)
Valet Parking: Free
Hours: 8am-4am Daily
Casino Size: 25,000 Square Feet
Other Games: S21, MB, B, PGP, TCP, LIR, B6
Special Features: 1,300-passenger modern
yacht docked on Lake Michigan. Slot club
members get 25% discount at deli.

Trump Hotel Casino
1 Buffington Harbor Drive
Gary, Indiana 46406
(219) 977-8980
Website: www.trumpindiana.com
Map Location: **#8** (15 miles E. of Chicago)

Reservation Number: (888) 218-7867
Rooms: 300 Price Range: $69-$139
Restaurants: 3 (1 Deli on boat)
Buffets: B-$4.99 L-$8.99
          D-$13.99/$17.99 (Fri)
Valet Parking: Free
Hours: 9am-5am Daily
Casino Size: 37,000 Square Feet
Other Games: B, MB, PGP, B6
Special Features: 2,300-passenger modern
yacht docked on Lake Michigan.

IOWA

Iowa was the first state to legalize riverboat gambling. The boats began operating on April Fools Day in 1991 and passengers were originally limited to $5 per bet with a maximum loss of $200 per person, per cruise. Because of these restrictions several boats later moved to Mississippi which offered 24-hour, no-limit, dockside gambling.

In September 1991 the first riverboats began operating in the bordering state of Illinois and these boats didn't have Iowa's restrictive bet or loss limits. The increased competition from these boats cut deeply into the profitability of the Iowa boats and in early 1994 the Iowa legislature voted to eliminate the gambling restrictions. Additionally, a provision was added to allow slot machines (no video poker) to be placed at the state's four pari-mutuel facilities, subject to voter approval. The slot machine measure passed in referendums in three of the four affected counties.

Here's information, as supplied by the Iowa Racing and Gaming Commission, showing the electronic gaming machine payback percentages for all non-Indian locations for the 2002 fiscal year from July 1, 2001 through June 30, 2002:

LOCATION	PAYBACK %
Prairie Meadows	94.20
Bluffs Run	93.59
Harrah's	93.53
Belle of Sioux City	93.53
Dubuque Greyhound	93.60
Dubuque Diamond Jo	93.44
Isle of Capri - Bettendorf	93.42
Isle of Capri - Marquette	93.36
Ameristar	93.33
Lakeside	93.29
Rhythm City	93.25
Mississippi Belle II	93.10
Catfish Bend	92.73

These figures reflect the total percentages returned by each riverboat casino or pari-mutuel facility for all of its electronic machines including: slots, video poker, video keno, etc. As you can see, Prairie Meadows returned the most to their players, while Catfish Bend returned the least.

Admission to all Iowa riverboat casinos is free. Most boats cruise from June through October and remain dockside from November through May although there might be slight differences in those schedules among the various boats.

Iowa is also home to three Indian casinos. Unless otherwise noted, all riverboats and Indian casinos offer: blackjack, roulette, craps, slots and video poker. Some casinos also offer: mini-baccarat (MB), poker (P), pai gow poker (PGP), Caribbean stud poker (CSP), let it ride (LIR), big 6 (B6), bingo (BG), keno (K), three card poker (TCP) and Spanish 21 (S21). The minimum gambling age is 21. For more information on visiting Iowa call the state's tourism department at (800) 345-4692.

Ameristar Casino Council Bluffs
2200 River Road
Council Bluffs, Iowa 51501
(712) 328-8888
Website: www.ameristarcasinos.com
Map Location: **#8**

Toll-Free Number: (877) 462-7827
Rooms: 152 Price Range: $70-$189
Suites: 8 Price Range: $225-$275
Restaurants: 4 (1 open 24 hours)
Buffets: L-$5.99/$10.99 (Sun)
    D-$9.99/$11.99 (Fri)/$10.99 (Sat-Sun)
Casino Size: 38,040 Square Feet
Schedule: Cruises 7:30am-9:30am weekdays
    (Apr-Oct), then remains dockside 24 hours
Other Games: S21, PGP, CSP, LIR, TCP
Senior Discount: 15% off food and hotel gift
    shop, if 55, or older
Special Features: 2,700-passenger sidewheeler replica that cruises the Missouri River. Sports bar. Video arcade. Kids Quest supervised children's entertainment center.

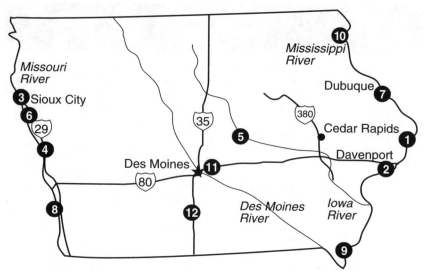

Argosy's Belle of Sioux City Casino
100 Larsen Park Road
Sioux City, Iowa 51101
(712) 294-5600
Website: www.argosycasinos.com
Map Location: **#3**

Toll-Free Number: (800) 424-0080
Restaurants: 2 (1 open 24 hours)
Buffets: B-$2.99/$9.95 (Sat/Sun) L-$6.95
    D-$9.95/$11.95 (Fri-Sat)
Casino Size: 8,430 Square Feet
Schedule: Cruises 7:30am-9:30am weekdays
  (Apr-Oct), then remains dockside 24 hours
Other Games: S21, PGP, CSP, TCP
Fun Book: Given at Iowa welcome centers
Special Features: 1,200-passenger old-fashioned stern wheeler that cruises the Missouri River.

Catfish Bend Casino
902 Riverview Drive
Fort Madison, Iowa 52627
(319) 372-2946
Website: www.catfishbendcasino.com
Map Location: **#9** (180 miles S.E. of Des Moines)

Toll Free Number: (800) 372-2946
Restaurants: 2
Buffets: L-$6.95/$9.95 (Sun) D-$5.95 (Thu)/
9.95 (Sun/Tue)/$8.95 (Mon/Wed)/$14.95 (Fri)
Schedule: Opens 6:30am, cruises May-Aug
    from 9am-11am (Mon-Sat), then
    remains dockside and stays open until
    2am/24 hours (Wed-Sun)

Casino Size: 14,572 Square Feet
Other Games: P, CSP, LIR
Special Features: 1,500-passenger paddle wheeler that cruises the Mississippi River. Docks in Burlington from November through April.

Dubuque Diamond Jo Casino
3rd Street Ice Harbor
Dubuque, IA 52004
(319) 583-7005
Website: www.diamondjo.com
Map Location: **#7**

Toll-Free Number: (800) LUCKY-JO
Restaurants: 2
Buffets: B-$4.95 (Sun) L-$6.95/$8.50 (Sun)
    D-$13.95 (Fri/Sat Only)
Valet Parking: $2
Schedule: Cruises 7:30am-9:30am (Mon-Fri),
    then remains dockside and stays open
    until 3am/24 hours (Fri/Sat)
Casino Size: 17,813 Square Feet
Other Games: P, CSP, LIR
Senior Discount: Players club members, 55 or
    older, get a 2-for-1 lunch buffet Fridays, free
    valet parking 9am-4pm daily and free deli
    breakfast 7:30-9:30am Monday-Friday
Special Features: 1,600-passenger old-fashioned steamboat replica that cruises the Mississippi River. Players club members get 20% buffet discount and 25% discount in gift shop.

Harrah's Casino - Council Bluffs
One Harrah's Boulevard
Council Bluffs, Iowa 51501
(712) 329-6000
Website: www.harrahs.com
Map Location: **#8**

Toll Free Number: (800) HARRAHS
Rooms: 240 Price Range: $59-$179
Suites: 11   Price Range $199
Restaurants: 3 (1 open 24 hours)
Buffets: B-$6.99 L-$8.99/$12.99 (Sun)
    D-$12.99/ $11.99 (Mon/Thu/Sat/Sun)
Schedule: Cruises 7:30 am to 9:30 am, then
   remains dockside and stays open 24 hours
Casino Size: 28,006 Square Feet
Other Games: P, PGP, CSP, LIR, B6, S21
Special Features: 2,365-passenger paddle
wheel-replica that cruises the Missouri River.

Isle of Capri Casino - Bettendorf
1821 State Street
Bettendorf, Iowa 52722
(319) 359-7280
Website: www.isleofcapricasino.com
Map Location: **#2**

Toll-Free Number: (800) 724-5825
Rooms: 256 Price Range: $74-$95
Restaurants: 3
Buffets: B-$4.95 L-$7.95 D-$12.95
Schedule: Cruises 7am-9am (Mon-Fri), then
   remains dockside and stays open 24 hours
Other Games: P, PGP, CSP, LIR
Casino Size: 26,744 Square Feet
Senior Discount: On Tue/Thu slot club
     members receive discounts if 50+
Special Features: 2,500-passenger old-fashioned paddle wheeler that cruises the Mississippi River.

Isle of Capri Casino - Marquette
P.O. Box 460
Marquette, Iowa 52158
(563) 873-3531
Website: www.isleofcapricasino.com
Map Location: **#10** (60 miles N. of Dubuque)

Toll-Free Number: (800) 4-YOU-BET
Rooms: 22 Price Range: $85
Suites: 3 Price Range: $125
Restaurants: 1
Buffets: B-$5.99/$8.99 (Sun) L-$6.99
    D-$9.99/$11.99 (Fri/Sat)
Schedule: Opens 9am, cruises 10:00am to
noon
    (Mon-Fri), then remains dockside and
    stays open until 3am/24 hours (Fri-Sat)
Casino Size: 18,747 Square Feet
Other Games: CSP, LIR, TCP
Fun Book: Distributed by local hotels
Senior Discount: On Tue/Thu slot club
    members receive discounts if 50+
Special Features: 1,200-passenger paddle
wheeler that cruises the Mississippi River.
Marina within walking distance.

Lakeside Casino Resort
777 Casino Drive
Osceola, Iowa 50213
(641) 342-9511
Website: www.lakesidecasino.net
Map Location: **#12**

Toll-Free Number: (877) 477-5253
Rooms: 60   Price: $69-$125
Suites: 3   Prices $145
Restaurants: 2
Buffets: B-$5.25 L-$6.25
    D-$9.50/$11.50(Fri-Sat)
Schedule: Cruises 7:30am-9:30am (Mon-Fri)
    and 7:00 am-9:00 am (Sat-Sun) then
    remains dockside stays open 24 hours
Casino Size: 25,000 Square Feet
Other Games: LIR, TCP
Senior Discount: Various on Mon if 55+
Special Features: 1,500-passenger old-fashioned paddle wheeler that cruises on West
Lake. 47-space RV park. Fishing/boating dock.
Free coffee, juice and muffins during cruises.

Mississippi Belle II
Showboat Landing
Clinton, Iowa 52733
(563) 243-9000
Map Location: **#1** (83 miles E. of Cedar Rapids)

Toll-Free Number: (800) 457-9975
Restaurants: 1
Buffets: B/L-$6.95 D-$9.95/$10.95 (Fri-Sat)
Schedule: Opens 9am, cruises 1pm-3pm
  (Mon-Fri,May-Oct), then remains dockside
  and stays open until 2am/4am (Fri/Sat)
Casino Size: 9,952 Square Feet
Other Games: S21, P, CSP, LIR , TCP
Special Features: 1,000-passenger old-fashioned paddle wheeler that cruises the Mississippi River.

Rhythm City Casino
130 West River Drive
Davenport, Iowa 52801
(319) 328-8000
Website: www.rhythmcitycasino.com
Map Location: **#2** (80 miles S.E. of Cedar Rapids)

Toll-Free Number: (800) BOAT-711
Rooms: 160 Price Range: $59-$95
Suites: 29 Price Range: $125
Restaurants: 2 (1 open 24 hours)
Buffets: B-$3.95 L-$6.95/$10.95 (Sun)
          D-$9.95/$11.95 (Fri-Sat)
Schedule: Cruises 7:30-9:30am (Mon-Fri),
  then stays dockside and is open 24 hours
Casino Size: 30,044 Square Feet
Other Games: S21, PGP, CSP, LIR
Senior Discount: Various on Tue/Wed if 50+
Special Features: 2,200-passenger riverboat
cruises the Mississippi River.

Indian Casinos

Casino Omaha
1 Blackbird Bend, Box 89
Onawa, Iowa 51040
(712) 423-3700
Map Location: **#4** (30 miles S. of Sioux City,
60 miles N. of Omaha, 4 miles W. of I-29 at
exit 112)

Toll-Free Number: (800) 858-U-BET
Restaurants: 1 Liquor: Yes
Buffets: L-$5.50 D-$7.50/$9.99 (Fri)
Hours: 8am-2am/24 Hours (Fri/Sat)
Other Games: P
Casino Size: 30,000 Square Feet
Fun Book: Coupons available at the slot club
booth on some weekdays.

Meskwaki Bingo & Casino
1504 305th Street
Tama, Iowa 52339
(641) 484-2108
Website: www.meskwaki.com
Map Location: **#5** (40 miles W. of Cedar Rapids)

Toll-Free Number: (800) 728-4263
Rooms: 204 Price Range: $39-$79
Suites: 4 Price Range: $175
Restaurants: 4 Liquor: No
Buffets: B-$5.25 L-$7.25 D-$8.25
Hours: 24 Hours Daily
Other Games: P, CSP, LIR, MB, TCP
            S21, K, BG, Simulcasting
Senior Discount: $1 off buffet if 55+
Special Features: 70-space RV park.

Winnavegas
1500 330th Street
Sloan, Iowa 51055
(712) 428-9466
Website: www.winnavegas-casino.com
Map Location: **#6** (20 miles S. of Sioux City)

Toll-Free Number: (800) 468-9466
Restaurants: 1 Liquor: Yes
Buffets: L-$4.95 D-$6.95
Hours: 24 Hours Daily
Other Games: MB, P, CSP, LIR, BG

Pari-Mutuels

Bluffs Run Casino
2701 23rd Avenue
Council Bluffs, Iowa 51501
(712) 323-2500
Website: www.harrahs.com
Map Location: **#8** (102 miles S. of Sioux City)

Toll-Free Number: (800) BET-2-WIN
Restaurants: 4 (1 open 24 hours)
Buffets: B-$4.99 L-$5.99/$8.99 (Sun)
        D-$8.99/$11.99 (Mon)
Hours: 24 Hours Daily
Casino Size: 35,200 Square Feet
Other Games: Only slots
Special Features: Owned by Harrah's. Live dog racing (Tue-Sun). Horse and dog race simulcasting. 120-space RV park. Free shuttle service from local hotels.

Dubuque Greyhound Park & Casino
1855 Greyhound Park Drive
Dubuque, Iowa 52001
(563) 582-3647
Website: www.dgpc.com
Map Location: **#7**

Toll-Free Number: (800) 373-3647
Restaurants: 1
Buffets: L-$7.95 D-$10.95
Hours: 9am-2am/24 hours (Fri/Sat)
Casino Size: 11,675 Square Feet
Other Games: Only slots
Senior Discount: $2 off buffet, if 55, or older
Special Features: Live dog racing (Wed-Sun) during season which runs from May through October. Greyhound and thoroughbred simulcasting all year. Free valet parking.

Prairie Meadows Racetrack & Casino
1 Prairie Meadows Drive
Altoona, Iowa 50009
(515) 967-1000
Website: www.prairiemeadows.com
Map Location: **#11** (5 miles E. of Des Moines)

Toll-Free Number: (800) 325-9015
Restaurants: 1
Buffets: B-$4.50 L-$5.50 D-$10.95
Hours: 24 Hours Daily
Casino Size: 39,324 Square Feet
Other Games: Only slots
Senior Discount: 15% restaurant and gift shop discount, if 55, or older
Special Features: Live thoroughbred and quarter-horse racing during season which runs from April through November. Simulcasting of dog and horse racing all year.

KANSAS

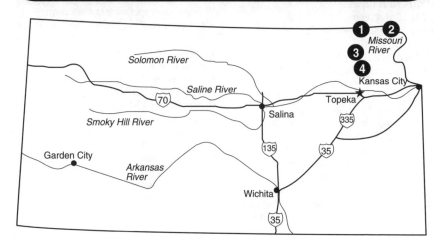

There are four Indian tribes in Kansas with casinos. According to officials at the Kansas State Gaming Agency the terms of the state's compacts with the tribes regarding the minimum payback amounts on their machines are not a matter of public record and no information can be released.

Unless otherwise noted, all Kansas casinos are open 24 hours and offer the following games: blackjack, craps, roulette, slots and video poker. Other games include: poker (P), Caribbean stud poker (CSP), let it ride (LIR), three card poker (TCP) and bingo (BG). The minimum gambling age is 21.

For more information on visiting Kansas call the state's tourism department at (800) 2-KANSAS.

Casino White Cloud
777 Jackpot Drive
White Cloud, Kansas 66094
(785) 595-3430
Map Location: **#2**

Toll-Free Number: (877) 652-6115
Restaurants: 1   Liquor: Only Beer
Buffets: L-$5.75   D-$8.75
Casino Size: 21,000 Square Feet
Casino Hours: 9am-1am/3am (Fri/Sat)
Other Games: TCP, P, BG, K, No Roulette
Special Features: No alcohol served on Sundays.

Golden Eagle Casino
1121 Goldfinch Road
Horton, Kansas 66439
(785) 486-6601
Map Location: **#3** (45 miles N. of Topeka)
Website: www.goldeneaglecasino.com

Toll-Free Number: (888) 464-5825
Restaurants: 2   Liquor: No
Buffets: B-$3.95 L-$5.95
        D-$7.95/$8.95(Thu-Sat)/$10.95 (Tue)
Other Games: P, LIR
Casino Marketing: (888) 464-5825, ext 251
Senior Discount: Free breakfast Friday if 55+

Harrah's Prairie Band Casino
12305 150th Road
Mayetta, Kansas 66509
(785) 966-7777
Website: www.harrahs.com
Map Location: **#4** (17 miles N. of Topeka)

Toll-Free Number: (800) HARRAHS
Rooms: 100 Price Range: $109-$129
Restaurants: 2 Liquor: Yes
Buffets: B-$6.99 L-$7.97/$9.99 (Sun)
        D-$11.99 (Sun-Thu)/$13.99 (Fri-Sat)
Casino Size: 63,000 Square Feet
Other Games: P, CSP, LIR, TCP
Senior Discount: $3 off buffet Mon/Wed if 55+
Special Features: Alcohol is only served in
Prairie Pub and membership card required to
enter (10 day waiting period for membership).
Buffet discount for senior slot club members.

Sac & Fox Casino
1322 U.S. Highway 75
Powhattan, Kansas 66527
(785)-467-8000
Map Location: **#1** (60 miles N. of Topeka)
Website: www.sacandfoxcasino.com

Toll-Free Number: (800) 990-2946
Restaurant: 3 Liquor: Yes
Buffets: B-$3.95 L-$6.95 D-$8.95
Casino Size: 40,000 Square Feet
Other Games: CSP, LIR
Senior Discount: AARP members get free
                breakfast buffet on Thursdays
Special Features: Membership card required
to be served alcohol in the Pub. 24-hour truck
stop. Golf driving range. RV hook-ups.

LOUISIANA

Video poker is permitted at Louisiana truck stops, racetracks/OTB's and bars/taverns in 31 of the state's 64 parishes (counties). There is no limit to the number of machines permitted at racetracks and off-track betting locations, however, truck stops are allowed no more than 50, while bars and taverns are permitted a maximum of three.

Louisiana was the fourth state to approve riverboat casino gambling and its 1991 gambling law allows a maximum of 15 boats statewide. In 1992 a provision was added for one land-based casino in New Orleans. The state also has three land-based Indian casinos and one gaming machines-only casino at a pari-mutuel facility.

As of August 2002 there were 14 riverboat casinos in operation in 12 different locations (the two Lake Charles locations each have two boats) and the state's Gaming Control Board had approved an application by Pinnacle Gaming (Boomtown/Casino Magic) to receive the 15th license. They are expected to open a new casino sometime in early 2004 in Lake Charles. All riverboat casinos remain dockside and are open 24 hours.

Louisiana's gaming regulations require that gaming machines in casinos be programmed to pay back no less than 80% and no more than 99.9%. For video gaming machines at locations other than casinos the law requires a minimum return of 80% and a maximum return of 94%.

Louisiana gaming statistics are not broken down by individual properties. Rather, they are classified by region: Baton Rouge (BR) , Lake Charles (LC), New Orleans (NO) and Shreveport/Bossier City (SB).

The Baton Rouge casinos consist of the Argosy and Casino Rouge. The Lake Charles casinos include Harrah's and Isle of Capri. New Orleans area casinos are: Bally's, Boomtown, Harrah's (landbased) and Treasure Chest. The Shreveport/Bossier city casinos include: Casino Magic, Hollywood, Isle of Capri, Harrah's and Horseshoe.

Here's information, as supplied by the Louisiana State Police - Riverboat Gaming Section, showing the average electronic machine payback percentages for each area's casinos for the six-month period from December, 2001 through May, 2002:

	BR	LC	NO	SB
5¢	92.1%	90.4%	90.7%	90.1%
25¢	93.2%	91.6%	92.3%	92.1%
$1	94.8%	93.0%	94.1%	93.8%
$5	96.2%	94.2%	95.5%	95.6%
All	93.6%	92.4%	92.6%	93.3%

These numbers reflect the percentage of money returned on each denomination of machine and encompass all electronic machines including video poker and video keno. The best returns for each category are highlighted in bold print and you can see that the Baton Rouge area casinos offered the best returns in every category.

The casino games offered are: blackjack, craps, roulette, slots and video poker. Optional games include: baccarat (B), mini-baccarat (MB), poker (P), Caribbean stud poker (CSP), pai gow poker (PGP), let it ride (LIR), casino war (CW), three-card poker (TCP), big 6 wheel (B6), keno (K) and bingo (BG). The minimum gambling age is 21.

For more information on visiting Louisiana call the state's tourism department at (800) 633-6970.

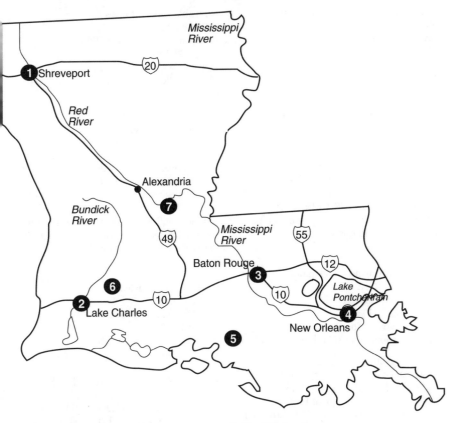

Bally's Casino Lakeshore Resort
1 Stars & Stripes Boulevard
New Orleans, Louisiana 70126
(504) 248-3200
Website: www.ballysno.com
Map Location: **#4**

Toll-Free Number: (800) 57-BALLY
Restaurants: 1 (Snack bar on boat)
Buffets: B-$5.95/ $12.95 (Sun) L-$8.95
 D-$12.95/$15.95 (Fri-Sat)
Casino Size: 30,000 Square Feet
Other Games: MB, P, CSP, PGP, LIR, TCP
Senior Discount: 15% discount on buffets &
 logo shop on Mon/Thu if 55 or older
Special Features: 1,200-passenger paddle
wheeler that remains dockside on Lake
Pontchartrain. Buffets, restaurant and sports
bar are located in land-based terminal.

Belle of Baton Rouge
103 France Street
Baton Rouge, Louisiana 70802
(225) 378-6000
Website: www.argosycasinos.com
Map Location: **#3**

Toll-Free Number: (800) 676-4847
Restaurants: 4 (1 on boat)
Casino Size: 29,000 Square Feet
Other Games: MB, CSP, LIR, TCP
Senior Discount: If 50, or older, join Belles
 and Beaus Senior Club for monthly offers
Special Features: 1,500-passenger paddle
wheeler on the Mississippi River. 300-room
Sheraton Hotel is adjacent to casino (call 800-
325-3535). 10% off food/drink for slot club
members.

Boomtown Casino - Bossier City
300 Riverside Drive
Bossier City, Louisiana 71171
(318) 746-0711
Website: www.boomtowncasinos.com
Map Location: **#1** (across the Red River From Shreveport)

Toll-Free Number: (866) 462-8696
Rooms: 100 Price Range: $85-$125
Suites: 88 Price Range: $105-$145
Restaurants: 3
Buffets: B-$8.99 L-$9.99
          D-$12.99/$14.99 (Fri-Sat)
Casino Size: 28,000 Square Feet
Other Games: MB, CSP, LIR, TCP
Special Features: 1,925-passenger paddle wheeler on the Red River.

Boomtown Casino - Westbank
4132 Peters Road
Harvey, Louisiana 70058
(504) 366-7711
Website: www.boomtowncasinos.com
Map Location: **#4** (a suburb of New Orleans)

Toll-Free Number: (800) 366-7711
Restaurants: 4 (1 snack bar on boat)
Buffets: B/L-$8.95 D-$14.95/$18.95 (Fri)
Casino Size: 30,000 Square Feet
Other Games: MB, P, PGP, CSP, LIR, TCP
Fun Book: Need coupon from local hotels
Senior Discount: $2 off buffets, if 55, or older
Special Features: 1,600-passenger paddle wheeler on the Harvey Canal.

Casino Rouge
1717 River Road North
Baton Rouge, Louisiana 70802
(225) 381-7777
Website: www.casinorouge.com
Map Location: **#3**

Toll-Free Number: (800) 44-ROUGE
Restaurants: 4 (1 snack bar on boat)
Buffets: L-$8.95/$16.95 (Sun)
          D-$11.95/$15.95 (Fri)/$13.95 (Sat)
Casino Size: 28,146 Square Feet
Other Games: MB, P, CSP, LIR, TCP, B6
Senior Discount: 50% off Mon. lunch if 50+
Special Features: 1,500-passenger paddle wheeler on the Mississippi River. Slot club members get 10% off in buffet (Tue-Thu) and gift shop.

Harrah's Lake Charles
800 Bilbo Street
Lake Charles, Louisiana 70601
(337) 437-1500
Website: www.harrahs.com
Map Location: **#2** (220 miles W. of New Orleans)

Toll-Free Number: (800) 977-PLAY
Restaurants: 5 (1 open 24 Hours)
Rooms: 132 Price Range: $79-$149
Buffets: B-$8.99 (Sat/Sun) L-$9.99 D-$15.99
Other Games: MB, P, PGP, CSP, LIR, TCP
Casino Marketing: (800) 625-BOAT
Special Features: Includes two paddlewheel boats: 1,700-passenger Pride of Lake Charles, and the 1,460-passenger Star Casino. Rooms also available at nearby Holiday Inn (800-367-1814). Buffet discounts for slot club members.

Harrah's New Orleans
4 Canal Street
New Orleans, Louisiana 70130
(504) 533-6000
Website: www.harrahs.com
Map Location: **#4**

Toll-Free Number: (800) HARRAHS
Restaurants: 2 (1 open 24 hours)
Buffet: B-$7.99 L-$11.99/$18.99 (Sun)
          D-$18.99/$21.99 (Fri-Sat)
Schedule: 24 hours daily
Casino Size: 100,000 Square Feet
Other Games: B, MB, CSP, LIR, P, PGP
Valet Parking: $5 every two hours
     (Free to Diamond and Platinum members)
Senior Discount: Various specials on
               Mon/Tue/Wed, if 50, orolder
Special Features: Land-based casino. Five themed gaming areas. Five-outlet food court. Daily live jazz music. $11.99 late-night buffet.

Harrah's Shreveport
315 Clyde Fant Parkway
Shreveport, Louisiana 71101
(318) 424-7777
Website: www.harrahs.com
Map Location: **#1**

Toll-Free Number: (800) HARRAHS
Rooms: 514 Price Range: $79-$200
Restaurants: 3 (1 open 24 hours)
Buffet: B/L-$9.99 D-$11.99/$15.99 (Thu-Fri)
Valet Parking: $2/$4 (Fri-Sun)
Casino Size: 30,000 Square Feet
Other Games: MB, CSP, LIR, TCP
Casino Marketing: (318) 424-7777
Special Features: 1,650-passenger paddle wheeler on the Red River.

Hollywood Casino Shreveport
451 Clyde Fant Parkway
Shreveport, Louisiana 71101
(318) 220-0711
Website: www.hollywoodcasino.com
Map Location: **#1**

Hotel Reservations: (877) 602-0711
Suites: 403 Price Range: $110-$230
Restaurants: 4
Buffet: B-$6.99 (Sun) L-$10.99
    D-$12.99/$18.99 (Fri)/$15.99 (Tue)
Casino Size: 29,607 Square Feet
Other Games: MB, CW, P, PGP, CSP, LIR, TCP
Special Features: 1,500-passenger paddle wheeler on the Red River. Large display of movie memorabilia. 100x odds on craps.

Horseshoe Casino Hotel - Bossier City
711 Horseshoe Boulevard
Bossier City, Louisiana 71111
(318) 742-0711
Website: www.horseshoe.com
Map Location: **#1** (across the Red River from Shreveport)

Toll-Free Number: (800) 895-0711
Suites: 606 Price Range: $110-$200
Restaurants: 5 (1 open 24 hours)
Buffets: B-$8.95 (Fri-Mon) L-$10.95
    D-$12.95/$13.95 (Mon-Tue)/$23.95 (Fri)
Other Games: MB, CSP, LIR, TCP
Casino Size: 29,500 Square Feet
Senior Discount: 10% buffet discount if 50+
Special Features: 2,930-passenger paddle wheeler on the Red River. 100x odds on craps.

Isle of Capri - Bossier City
711 Isle of Capri Boulevard
Bossier City, Louisiana 71111
(318) 678-7777
Website: www.isleofcapricasino.com
Map Location: **#1** (across the Red River from Shreveport)

Toll-Free Number: (800) 473-4753
Room Reservations: (800) 475-3847
Suites: 304 Price Range: $85-$125
Inn Rooms: 225 Price Range: $39-$69
Restaurants: 3 (1 open 24 Hours)
Buffets: B-$5.99 L-$7.99 D-$14.99
Casino Size: 30,000 Square Feet
Other Games: MB, PGP, CSP, LIR, TCP
Casino Marketing: (800) 475-3847
Senior Discount: Weekly specials, if 50, or older
Special Features: 1,650-passenger paddle wheeler on the Red River. Slot club members get $10 hotel discount.

Isle of Capri - Lake Charles
100 Westlake Avenue
Westlake, Louisiana 70669
(318) 430-0711
Website: www.isleofcapricasino.com
Map Location: **#2** (220 miles W. of New Orleans)

Toll-Free Number: (800) THE-ISLE
Rooms: 251 Price Range: $59-$139
Restaurants: 4 (1 snack bar on boat)
Buffets: B-$4.99 L-$6.99/$12.99 (Sat-Sun)
    D-$12.99
Casino Size: 48,900 Square Feet
Other Games: B, MB, P, CSP, LIR
Senior Discount: If 55, or older, go to Island
    Gold Club booth for special coupon book
Fun Book: Given when signing up for slot club
Special Features: Two 1,200-passenger paddle wheelers, *Crown* and *Grand Palais*, on Lake Charles.

Treasure Chest Casino
5050 Williams Boulevard
Kenner, Louisiana 70065
(504) 443-8000
Website: www.treasurechest.com
Map Location: **#4** (a suburb of New Orleans)

Toll-Free Number: (800) 298-0711
Restaurants: 2 (1 open 24 hours)
Buffets: B-$5.99/$15.99 (Sun) L-$9.99
        D-$12.99/$14.99 (Fri-Sat)
Casino Size: 25,767 Square Feet
Other Games: MB, CSP, LIR, TCP
Senior Discount: If 50, or older, join Treasured
        Friends for different monthly specials
Special Features: 1,900-passenger paddle
wheeler on Lake Pontchartrain. Buffet discounts for slot club members.

Indian Casinos

Cypress Bayou Casino
P.O. Box 519
Charenton, Louisiana 70523
(318) 923-7284
Website: www.cypressbayou.com
Map Location: **#5** (75 miles S. of Baton Rouge)

Toll-Free Number: (800) 284-4386
Restaurants: 3 Liquor: Yes
Casino Hours: 12pm-2am/4am (Fri-Sat)
Casino Size: 125,000 Square Feet
Other Games: B6, CSP, LIR, TCP
Special Features: Land-based casino. Gift
shop. Cigar bar. Oyster bar.

Grand Casino Coushatta
777 Coushatta Drive
Kinder Louisiana 70648
(318) 738-7300
Website: www.gccoushatta.com
Map Location: **#6** (35 miles N.E. of Lake
Charles)

Toll-Free Number: (800) 58-GRAND
Rooms: 373 Price Range: $69-$119
Suites: 90 Price Range: Casino Guests Only
Restaurants: 6 (1 open 24 hours) Liquor: Yes
Buffets: L-$8.50/$12.99 (Sun)
        D-$10.99/$14.99 (Fri-Sat)
Casino Size: 71,000 Square Feet
Other Games: MB, P, PGP, CSP, LIR, B6
Special Features: Land-based casino. 156-
space RV park. Kids Quest childcare center.
Video arcade. 18-hole golf course.

Paragon Casino Resort
711 Paragon Place
Marksville, Louisiana 71351
(318) 253-1946
Website: www.paragoncasinoresort.com
Map Location: **#7** (30 miles S.E. of Alexandria)

Toll-Free Number: (800) 946-1946
Rooms: 302 Price Range: $59-$119
Suites: 52 Price Range: $99-$149
Restaurants: 5 (1 open 24 hours) Liquor: Yes
Buffets: B-$6.99 L-$7.99
        D-$10.99/$14.99 (Fri)
Casino Size: 100,000 Square Feet
Other Games: B6, MB, P, PGP,
        CSP, LIR, TCP,
Special Features: Land-based casino. 166-
space RV Park. Kids Quest childcare center.
Video arcade. $10 room discount for AAA and
AARP members. 18-hole golf course.

Pari-Mutuels

Delta Downs Racetrack & Casino
2717 Highway 3063
Vinton, Louisiana 70668
(337) 589-7441
Website: www.deltadowns.com
Map Location: **#5** (75 miles S. of Baton Rouge)

Toll-Free Number: (800) 589-7441
Restaurants: 2 and 1 snack bar
Buffets: L-$7.99 D-$9.99/$12.99 (Fri-Sat)
Other Games: Only machines
Special Features: Live thoroughbred and quarter-horse racing (Thu-Sun) November through
June. Simulcasting offered all year.

MASSACHUSETTS

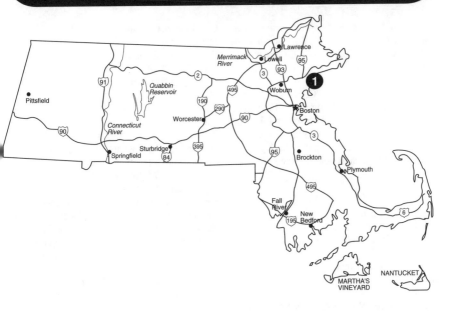

There is one gambling cruise ship in Massachusetts which sails three miles out into international waters where casino gambling is permitted.

The games offered include: blackjack, craps, roulette, baccarat, Caribbean stud poker, three-card poker, let it ride, slots, video poker and bingo.

For information on visiting Massachusetts call (800) 447-MASS.

Horizon's Edge Casino Cruises
76 Marine Boulevard
Lynn, MA 01905
Website: www.horizonsedge.com
Map Location: **#1** (8 miles N.E. of Boston)
(781) 581-7733

Toll-Free Reservations: (800) 582-5932
Gambling Age: 21
Ship's Registry: U.S.
Buffets: Included
Schedule:
    11:00am - 4:30pm
    7:00pm - 11:55pm/1:00am (Fri/Sat)
Prices: $25 (Mon-Fri Day/Sun-Thu Eve)
    $35 (Sat-Sun Day/Fri-Sat Eve)
Port Charges: Included
Parking: Free
Senior Discount: 2-for-1 admission Saturday
        morning if 55, or older
Special Features: 490-passenger *Horizon's Edge* sails from Marina off of Lynnway in Lynn. Sails seasonally from May through November, then travels to Riviera Beach, Florida. No one under 21 permitted to board.

MICHIGAN

One of Michigan's most popular casinos is actually in Canada. It's Casino Windsor in Ontario which is just across the river from downtown Detroit.

All winnings are paid in Canadian currency and the minimum gambling age is 19. The casino is open 24 hours and offers the following games: blackjack, craps, single-zero roulette, baccarat, mini-baccarat, big six wheel, pai-gow poker, Caribbean stud poker, three-card poker and let it ride.

Casino Windsor
377 Riverside Drive East
Windsor, Ontario N9A 7H7
(519) 258-7878
Website: www.casinowindsor.com
Map Location: **#12**

PRICES ARE IN CANADIAN DOLLARS
Toll-Free Number: (800) 991-7777
Room Reservations: (800) 991-8888
Rooms: 349 Price Range: $165-$300
Suites: 40 Price Range: $250-$1,000
Restaurants: 5 (1 open 24 hours)
Buffets: L-$15.65/$19.95 (Sat-Sun)
          D-$17.95/$22.95 (Fri-Sun)
Casino Size: 100,000 Square Feet
Special Features: Nautical theme with 60-foot waterfall, babbling brook, periodic water and light show. AARP 10% room discount (Sunday through Thursday only).

In November 1996 Detroit voters approved, by a 51% to 49% margin, a referendum to allow three casinos in the downtown area.

All three casinos are open 24 hours and offer the following games: blackjack, craps, roulette, baccarat, mini-baccarat, Caribbean stud poker, pai gow poker and let it ride. The minimum gambling age at all Detroit casinos is 21 and all three casinos offer free valet parking.

Greektown Casino
555 E. Lafayette Blvd.
Detroit, Michigan 48226
(313) 223-2999
Website:greektowncasino.com
Map Location: **#12**

Toll free Number: (888) 771-4386
Room Reservations: (800) 772-2323
Suites: 175 Price Range: $155-$950
Restaurants: 5 (1 open 24 hours)
Casino Size: 75,000 Square Feet
Other Games: Three-Card Poker
Special Features: Rooms are at Atheneum Hotel across the street from the casino. Restaurants, pastry shops and specialty boutiques are in off-property areas adjacent to the casino.

MGM Grand Detroit Casino
1300 John C. Lodge
Detroit Michigan 48226
(313) 393-7777
Website: http://detroit.mgmgrand.com
Map Location: **#12**

Toll-Free Number: (877) 888-2121
Restaurants: 4
Buffets: L- $14.95 D-$18.95
Casino Size: 75,000 Square Feet.
Other Games: Casino War, Spanish 21
Special Features: Packages offered by local hotels include: room, two buffets and free gift.

MotorCity Casino
2901 Grand River Avenue
Detroit, MI 48201
(313) 237-7711
Website: www.motorcitycasino.com
Map Location: **#12**

Toll-Free Number: (877) 777-0711
Restaurants: 4
Buffets: B-$10.95 L-$15.95 D-$19.95/$28.95 (Fri)
Casino Size: 75,000 Square Feet
Other Games: Casino War, Spanish 21

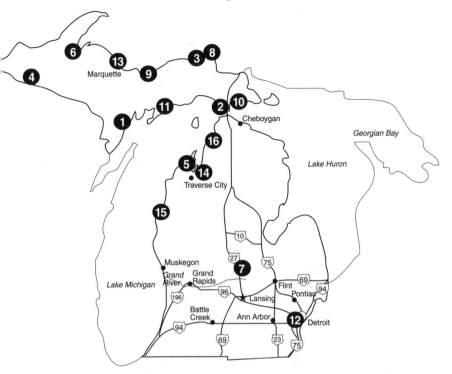

There are 16 Indian casinos in Michigan and the tribes are not required to release information on their slot machine payback percentages. However, according to officials at the Michigan Gaming Control Board, which is responsible for overseeing the tribal-state compacts, "the machines must meet the minimum standards for machines in Nevada or New Jersey." In Nevada the minimum return is 75% and in New Jersey it's 83%. Therefore, Michigan's Indian casinos must return at least 75% in order to comply with the law.

Unless otherwise noted, all Indian casinos in Michigan are open 24 hours and offer the following games: blackjack, slots and video poker. Other games offered include: craps (C), roulette (R), baccarat (B), mini-baccarat (MB), poker (P), Caribbean stud poker (CSP), let it ride (LIR), three-card poker (TCP), keno (K) and bingo (BG).

The minimum gambling age is 21 at all Indian casinos except for the following seven where it's 18: Leelanau Sands, Turtle Creek, Chip-In's, Ojibwa, Ojibwa II, Lac Vieux and Soaring Eagle.

For more information on visiting Michigan call the state's department of tourism at (800) 543-2937.

Bay Mills Resort & Casino
11386 Lakeshore Drive
Brimley, Michigan 49715
(906) 248-3715
Website: www.4baymills.com
Map Location: **#3** (12 miles S.W. of Sault Ste. Marie)

Toll-Free Number: (888) 4-BAY-MILLS
Rooms: 142 Price Range: $62-$109
Suites: 4 Price Range: $190-$230
Restaurants: 2 (1 open 24 hrs)   Liquor: Yes
Buffets: B-$5.95 L-$6.95
　　　　　D-$8.95/$10.95 (Fri/Sat)
Casino Size: 15,000 Square Feet
Other Games: C, R, CSP, LIR, K
Fun Book: Given with slot club membership
Senior Discount: 10% room discount (Sun-Thu). Wednesday is Senior's Day from 8am-2pm with buffet discounts and cash drawings, if 55, or older
Special Features: Free shuttle to King's Club and Kewadin casinos. 18-hole golf course.

Chip-In's Island Resort & Casino
P.O. Box 351
Harris, Michigan 49845
(906) 466-2941
Website: www.chipincasino.com
Map Location: **#1** (13 miles W. of Escanaba on Hwy. 41)

Toll-Free Number: (800) 682-6040
Rooms: 102 Price Range: $75-$144
Suites: 11 Price Range: $117-$144
Restaurants: 2 Liquor: Yes
Buffets: B-$7.95 L-$11.95 D-$12.95
Casino Size: 135,000 Square Feet
Other Games: C, R, P, CSP, TCP, LIR, K, BG
Special Features: 53-space RV park. Indoor heated pool. Fitness center.

Kewadin Casino - Christmas
N7761 Candy Cane Lane
Munising, Michigan 49862
(906) 387-5475
Website: www.kewadin.com
Map Location: **#9** (40 miles E. of Marquette)

Toll-Free Number: (800) KEWADIN
Restaurants: 1 Deli Liquor: Yes
Hours: 10am-2am/24 hours (May-November)
Casino Size: 3,060 Square Feet
Other Games: LIR, TCP
Senior Discount: Various specials Wednesdays from 9am to 7pm, if 50, or older
Special Features: Free local-area shuttle service. Coupon book distributed by local motels.

Kewadin Casino - Hessel
3 Mile Road, Box 789
Hessel, Michigan 49745
(906) 484-2903
Website: www.kewadin.com
Map Location: **#10** (20 miles N.E. of St. Ignace)

Toll-Free Number: (800) KEWADIN
Restaurants: 1 Deli Liquor: Yes
Hours: 9am-12am/1am (Fri/Sat)
Casino Size: 6,500 Square Feet
Senior Discount: Various specials Thursdays from 9am to 7pm, if 50, or older
Special Features: Free local-area shuttle service. BJ only open Thu-Sun from 2pm.

Kewadin Casino - Manistique
US 2 East, Rte 1, Box 1533D
Manistique, Michigan 49854
(906) 341-5510
Website: www.kewadin.com
Map Location: **#10** (95 miles S.E. of Marquette)

Toll-Free Number: (800) KEWADIN
Rooms: 40 Price Range: $45-$65
Restaurants: 1 Deli Liquor: Yes
Hours: 8am-3am/24 Hours (May-November)
Casino Size: 25,000 Square Feet
Other Games: C, R, LIR, TCP
Fun Book: On sale at Kewadin Inn
Senior Discount: Various specials Wednesdays from 8am to 7pm, if 50, or older
Special Features: Rooms are at Kewadin Inn about one mile from casino. Room discounts for AARP and AAA members. Sports bar. Gift shop. Free shuttle service from local motels. Coupon book distributed by local motels. Table games are only open 10am-2am daily.

Kewadin Casino Hotel - Sault Ste. Marie
2186 Shunk Road
Sault Ste. Marie, Michigan 49783
(906) 632-0530
Website: www.kewadin.com
Map Location: **#8**

Toll-Free Number: (800) KEWADIN
Rooms: 300 Price Range: $79-$89
Suites: 20 Price Range: $109-$119
Restaurants: 2 Liquor: Yes
Buffets: B-$5.95/$8.95 (Sun) L-$8.50
D-$11.95/$14.50 (Fri/Sat)
Casino Size: 85,123 Square Feet
Other Games: C, R, P, CSP, LIR, K, TCP
Casino Marketing: (906) 635-4968
Senior Discount: Various on Thu if 50 or older
Special Features: Free shuttle service to local motels and airport. 75-space RV park. Room discounts for AARP and AAA members.

Kewadin Casino - St. Ignace
3039 Mackinaw Trail
St. Ignace, Michigan 49781
(906) 643-7071
Website: www.kewadin.com
Map Location: **#2** (50 miles S. of Sault Ste. Marie)

Toll-Free Number: (800) KEWADIN
Restaurants: 1 Deli Liquor: Yes
Casino Size: 56,168 Square Feet
Other Games: C, R, P, PGP, CSP, LIR, K, TCP
Senior Discount: $5 in tokens on Thu if 50+
Special Features: Local motels/hotels offer packages with free shuttle service. Sports bar.

Kings Club Casino
12140 W. Lakeshore Drive
Brimley, Michigan 49715
(906) 248-3700
Website: www.4baymills.com
Map Location: **#3** (12 miles S.W. of Sault Ste. Marie)

Toll-Free Number: (888) 422-9645
Restaurants: 1 Deli Liquor: Yes
Casino Size: 7,400 Square Feet
Hours: 8am-2am/4am (Fri-Sat)
Seniors Discount: Various on Tue if 50 or older
Special Features: Four miles from and affiliated with Bay Mills Resort & Casino.

Lac Vieux Desert Casino
N 5384 US 45 North
Watersmeet, Michigan 49969
(906) 358-4226
Website: www.lacvieuxdesert.com
Map Location: **#4** (49 miles S.E. of Ironwood)

Toll-Free Number: (800) 583-3599
Room Reservations: (800) 634-3444
Rooms: 61 Price Range: $60-$75
Suites: 15 Price Range: $75-$140
Restaurants: 1 Liquor: Yes
Buffets: L-$7.95 D-$9.95/$15.95 (Fri-Sat)
Table Game Hours: 10am-4am Daily
Slot Hours: 24 Hours Daily
Other Games: C, R, LIR, BG
Casino Marketing: (906) 358-4423
Senior Discount: Specials on Tuesdays if 55 or older, 10% hotel and buffet discounts
Special Features: 9-hole golf course. 10% hotel discount for AAA and AARP members.

Leelanau Sands Casino
2521 N.W. Bayshore Drive
Sutton's Bay, Michigan 49682
(231) 271-4104
Website: www.casino2win.com
Map Location: **#5** (4 miles N. of Sutton's Bay)

Toll-Free Number: (800) 922-2946
Room Reservations: (800) 930-3008
Rooms: 51 Price Range: $89-$123
Restaurants: 1 Liquor: Yes
Buffets: B-$11.95 L-$7.95 D-$11.95
Casino Size: 72,000 Square Feet
Hours: 8am-3am/24 Hours (Fri/Sat)
Other Games: C, R, LIR, TCP
Senior Discount: Specials on Tuesdays if 55+
Special Features: Rooms are at nearby GTB Motel. Free breakfast buffet with rooms.

Little River Casino
2700 Orchard Drive
Manistee, Michigan 49660
(231) 723-1535
Website: www.littlerivercasinos.com
Map Location: **#15** (60 miles S.W of Traverse City)

Toll-Free Number: (888) 568-2244
Rooms: 88 Price Range: $79-$99
Suites: 12 Price Range: $109-$129
Restaurants: 1 Liquor: Yes
Buffets: B-$6.95 L-$8.95
          D-$12.95/$17.95 (Fri-Sat)
Casino Size: 75,000 Square Feet
Other Games: C, R, P, LIR, CSP, TCP
Senior Discount: Wednesday specials if 55+
Special Features: 46-space RV park open April-November.

Ojibwa Casino Resort
797 Michigan Avenue
Baraga, Michigan 49908
(906) 353-6333
Website: www.ojibwacasino.com
Map Location: **#6** (30 miles S. of Houghton)

Toll-Free Number: (800) 323-8045
Rooms: 38 Price Range: $54-$60
Suites: 2 Price Range: $75
Restaurants: 1 Liquor: Yes
Buffets: B-$7.95 (Sun) L-$5.95
          D-$8.95/$10.95 (Fri)
Casino Size: 17,000 Square Feet
Table Game Hours: 11am-2am/4am (Fri/Sat)
Slot Hours: 24 Hours Daily
Other Games: C, R, P, LIR, BG (Mon-Thu)
Casino Marketing: (800) 323-8045
Special Features: 8-lane bowling alley. Room discounts for AAA, AARP and club members.

Ojibwa Casino - Marquette
105 Acre Trail
Marquette, Michigan 49855
(906) 249-4200
Website: www.ojibwacasino.com
Map Location: **#13**

Toll-Free Number: (888) 560-9905
Restaurants: 1 Snack Bar Liquor: Yes
Table Hours: 12pm-4am/24 Hours (Fri/Sat)
Slot Hours: 24 Hours Daily
Other Games: C, R, P, LIR, TCP
Senior Discount: Monday specials if 55+

Soaring Eagle Casino & Resort
6800 E Soaring Eagle Boulevard
Mount Pleasant, Michigan 48858
(517) 775-5777
Website: www.soaringeaglecasino.com
Map Location: **#7** (65 miles N. of Lansing)

Toll-Free Number: (888) 7-EAGLE-7
Rooms: 491 Price Range: $129-$189
Suites: 21 Price Range: $269-$309
Restaurants: 3 (2 open 24 hrs) Liquor: Yes
Buffets: B:$8.75 L/D-$12.75
Casino Size: 210,000 Square Feet
Other Games: C, R, P, CSP, LIR, TCP, BG
Senior Discount: 50% off Wed b'fst if 55+
Special Features: Casino is in two separate buildings. Kid's Quest childcare center. Video arcade. Gift shop. Art gallery. 10% room discount for AAA and AARP members.

Turtle Creek Casino
7741 M-72 East
Williamsburg, Michigan 49690
(231) 267-9574
Website: www.casino2win.com
Map Location: **#14** (8 miles E. of Traverse City)

Toll-Free Number: (888) 777-8946
Restaurants: 1 Deli Liquor: Yes
Casino Size: 29,000 Square Feet
Other Games: C, R, P, CSP, LIR

Victories Casino
1966 U.S. 131
Petoskey, Michigan 49770
(231) 439-9100
Website: www.victories-casino.com
Map Location: **#16** (50 miles S.W of Cheboygan)

Toll-Free Number: 877-4-GAMING
Restaurants: 1 Liquor: Yes
Buffets: L-$9.00 (Sun)
Hours: 8am-4am Daily
Other Games: R, P, CSP, LIR
Senior Discount: Wednesday specials if 55+
Special Features: EconoLodge across the street. Free shuttle to/from local hotels.

MINNESOTA

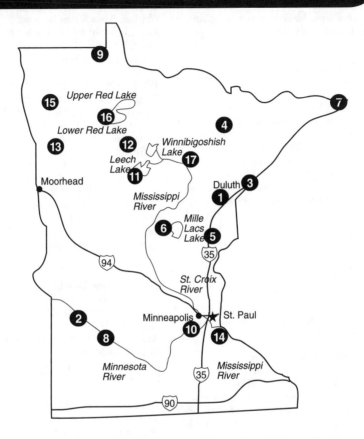

All Minnesota casinos are located on Indian reservations and under a compact reached with the state the only type of table game permitted is blackjack. Additionally, the only kind of slot machines allowed are the electronic video variety. Therefore, you will not find any mechanical slots that have traditional reels - only video screens.

The tribes are not required to release information on their slot machine percentage paybacks. According to the terms of the compact between the state and the tribes, however, the minimum and maximum payouts are regulated as follows: video poker and video blackjack - 83% to 98%, slot machines - 80% to 95%, keno - 75% to 95%. Each tribe is free to set its machines to pay back anywhere within those limits.

The hours of operation are listed for those casinos that are not open on a 24-hour basis. Unless otherwise noted, all casinos offer: video slots, video poker, video keno and blackjack. The minimum gambling age is 18 (21 if liquor is served).

For more information on visiting Minnesota call the state's office of tourism at (800) 657-3700.

Black Bear Casino & Hotel
1785 Highway 210
Carlton, Minnesota 55718
(218) 878-2327
Website: www.blackbearcasinohotel.com
Map Location: **#1** (130 miles N. of Twin Cities)

Toll-Free Number: (888) 771-0777
Reservation Number: (800) 553-0022
Rooms: 158 Price Range: $39-$109
Suites: 60 Price Range: $59-$169
Restaurants: 2 (open 24 hours) Liquor: Yes
Buffets: L-$6.95 D-$9.95/$19.95 (Fri)
Casino Size: 65,000 Square Feet
Other Games: Bingo, Video Craps
Senior Discount: Specials Mon/Tue if 55+
Special Features: Hotel has skywalk to casino. 10% AAA/AARP room discount.

Firefly Creek Casino
Route 2, Box 96
Granite Falls, Minnesota 56241
(320) 564-2121
Website: www.fireflycreek.com
Map Location: **#2** (110 miles W. of Twin Cities. Five minutes S.E. of Granite Falls on Highway 67 E.)

Restaurants: 1 Liquor: Yes
Casino Size: 26,000 Square Feet
Hours: 8am-2am/24 hours (Fri/Sat)
Senior Discount: Specials on Mondays if 55+
Special Features: New 89-room *Prairie's Edge Casino Resort* expected to open in early 2003 and it will replace the existing facility.

Fond-du-Luth Casino
129 E. Superior Street
Duluth, Minnesota 55802
(218) 722-0280
Website: www.fondduluthcasino.com
Map Location: **#3** (150 miles N.E. of Twin Cities)

Toll-Free Number: (800) 873-0280
Restaurants: 2 Snack Bars Liquor: Yes
Casino Size: 20,000 Square Feet
Casino Hours: 10am-2am/24 hours (Fri/Sat)
Other Games: Bingo
Senior Discount: Fun book Mon-Wed if 55+
Special Features: One hour free parking in lot adjacent to casino (must be validated in casino). Free shuttle to/from Black Bear Casino.

Fortune Bay Resort/Casino
1430 Bois Forte Road
Tower, Minnesota 55790
(218) 753-6400
Website: www.fortunebay.com
Map Location: **#4** (150 miles N.E. of Twin Cities. 24 miles N.E. of Virginia, MN on the S. shore of Lake Vermilion)

Toll-Free Number: (800) 992-7529
Hotel Reservations: (800) 555-1714
Rooms: 83 Price Range: $57-$101
Suites: 33 Price Range: $81-$151
Restaurants: 2 Liquor: Yes
Buffets: B-$4.95 L-$4.95/$8.95 (Mon/Thu)
    D-$11.95/$13.95 (Mon/Fri)/$14.95 (Sat)
Casino Size: 17,000 Square Feet
Other Games: Bingo (Wed-Sun), Keno
Senior Discount: Specials Mon & Thu if 55+
Special Features: Located on S.E. shore of Lake Vermilion. 34-space RV Park. Snowmobile and hiking trails. 18-hole golf course.

Grand Casino Hinckley
777 Lady Luck Drive
Hinckley, Minnesota 55037
(320) 384-7777
Website: www.grandcasinosmn.com
Map Location: **#5** (75 miles N. of Twin Cities. One mile E. of I-35's Hinckley exit on Hwy. 48)

Toll-Free Number: (800) 472-6321
RV/Chalet Reservations: (800) 995-4726
Hotel Reservations: (800) 468-3517
Rooms: 485 Price Range: $55-$105 (Hotel)
            Price Range: $40-$80 (Inn)
            Price Range: $55-$95 (Chalet)
Suites: 46 Price Range: $70-$300
Restaurants: 5 Liquor: Yes
Buffets: L-$6.99 D-$9.99/$10.99 (Fri-Sat)
            $16.99 (Tue)
Casino Size: 40,000 Square Feet
Other Games: Video Horse Racing, Video BJ
Video Craps, Video Roulette, Bingo(Thu-Tue)
Casino Marketing: (800) GRAND-76
Special Features: 222-space RV park. Kid's Quest childcare center. Video arcade. 18-hole golf course. Free pet kennel. AAA members receive 10% room discount.

Grand Casino Mille Lacs

777 Grand Avenue
Onamia, Minnesota 56359
(320) 532-7777
Website: www.grandcasinosmn.com
Map Location: **#6** (90 miles N. of Twin Cities. On Highway 169 on the W. shore of Lake Mille Lacs)

Toll-Free Number: (800) 626-LUCK
Room Reservations: (800) HOTEL-17
Rooms: 364 Price Range: $40-$139
Suites: 21 Price Range: $100-$300
Restaurants: 4 Liquor: No
Buffets: L-$6.99 D-$8.99(Mon/Tue/Thu)
$9.99 (Sat-Sun)/$12.99 (Wed)/$15.99 (Fri)
Casino Size: 42,000 Square Feet
Other Games: Bingo (Sun-Fri), Video Horse Racing, Video Blackjack, Video Craps, Video Roulette
Casino Marketing: (800) GRAND-76
Special Features: Resort has two hotels and one is off-property. Kid's Quest childcare center. Video arcade. Pet kennel. Free pet kennel. 222-space RV park. AAA members receive 10% room discount.

Grand Portage Lodge & Casino

P.O. Box 233
Grand Portage, Minnesota 55605
(218) 475-2401
Website: www.grandportagemn.com
Map Location: **#7** (N.E. tip of Minnesota. 300 miles N. of Twin Cities. On Highway 61, five miles from the Canadian border)

Reservation Number: (800) 543-1384
Rooms: 100 Price Range: $66-$85
Restaurants: 2 Liquor: Yes
Other Games: Bingo
Special Features: On shore of Lake Superior. Hiking, skiing and snowmobile trails. Gift shop. Marina. 10-space RV park and 10-tent campground. Free shuttle service to and from Thunder Bay, Ontario.

Jackpot Junction Casino Hotel

P.O. Box 420
Morton, Minnesota 56270
(507) 644-3000
Website: www.jackpotjunction.com
Map Location: **#8** (110 miles S.W. of Twin Cities)

Toll-Free Number: (800) WIN-CASH
Rooms: 253 Price Range: $55-$85
Suites: 23 Price Range: $100-$200
Restaurants: 3 (1 open 24 hours) Liquor: Yes
Buffets: B-$5.99 L-$6.99 D-$8.99
Other Games: Bingo (Thu-Tue)
Special Features: 40-space RV park. Kids Quest childcare center. 18-hole golf course. Gift shop.

Little Six Casino

2354 Sioux Trail N.W.
Prior Lake, Minnesota 55372
(952) 445-9000 (Mystic Lake)
Map Location: **#10** (25 miles S.W. of Twin Cities. On County Road 83, 3 miles S. of Canterbury Downs)

Toll-Free: (800) 262-7799 (Mystic Lake)
Restaurants: 1 Liquor: No
Hours: 10am-4am Daily/24 hours (Fri-Sat)
Special Features: 1/2-mile north of Mystic Lake Casino.

Mystic Lake Casino Hotel

2400 Mystic Lake Boulevard
Prior Lake, Minnesota 55372
(952) 445-9000
Website: www.mysticlake.com
Map Location: **#10** (25 miles S.W. of Twin Cities. On County Road 83, 3 miles S. of Canterbury Downs)

Toll-Free Number: (800) 262-7799
Reservation Number: (800) 813-7349
Rooms: 400 Price Range: $69-$109
Suites: 16 Price Range: $119-$359
Restaurants: 4 (3 open 24 hours) Liquor: No
Buffets: B-$12.95 (Sat-Sun) L-$8.95
D-$14.95/$19.95 (Wed)
Casino Size: 102,000 Square Feet
Other Games: Bingo, Video Roulette & Craps
Senior Discount: Free breakfast on Tues if 55+
Special Features: Has a second casino - Dakota Country with an 11-store retail arcade. 122-space RV park. Childcare facility.

Northern Lights Casino
6800 Y Frontage Rd NW
Walker, Minnesota 56484
(218) 547-2744
Website: www.northernlightscasino.com
Map Location: **#11** (175 miles N. of the Twin
Cities. Near the S. shore of Lake Leech four
miles S. of Walker, MN at the junction of Highways 371 & 200)

Toll-Free Number: (800) 252-7529
Toll-Free Number: (877) 544-4879
Restaurants: 2 Liquor: Yes
Buffets: B-$9.95 (Sat-Sun) L-$7.95
        D-$9.95/$14.95 (Fri-Sat)
Casino Size: 40,000 Square Feet
Other Games: Bingo
Casino Marketing: (800) 252-7529
Special Features: 90-foot dome simulates star
constellations. New hotel expected to open by
summer of 2003.

Palace Casino Hotel
6280 Upper Cass Frontage Rd NW
Cass Lake, Minnesota 56633
(218) 335-7000
Website: www.palacecasinohotel.com
Map Location: **#12** (220 miles N.W. of Twin
Cities)

Toll-Free Number: (800) 228-6676
Room Reservations: (800) 442-3910
Rooms: 54 Price Range: $35-$49
Suites: 16 Price Range $50-$70
Restaurants: 2 (1 open 24 hours) Liquor: No
Casino Size: 30,000 Square Feet
Other Games: Bingo
Special Features: Limited space RV park.

Seven Clans Casino Red Lake
Highway 1 East
Red Lake, MN 56671
(218) 679-2500
www.sevenclanscasino.com/redlake.htm
Map Location: **#16** (31 miles N. of Bemidji)

Toll-Free Number: (888) 679-2501
Restaurants: 1 Liquor: No
Casino Size: 19,800 Square Feet
Casino Hours: 10am-1am/9am-2am (Thu-Sat)
Other Games: Bingo (Wed-Sun)
Senior Discount: Specials on Mondays if 55+

Seven Clans Casino Thief River Falls
Rt 3, Box 168A
Thief River Falls, Minnesota 56701
(218) 681-4062
Website: www.sevenclanscasino.com
Map Location: **#15** (275 miles N.W. of Min-
neapolis)

Toll-Free Number: (800) 881-0712
Suites: 151 Price Range: $55-$109
Restaurants: 1 (open 24 hours) Liquor: No
Buffets: B-$5.99 L-$6.95 D-$9.95
Casino Size: 16,000 Square Feet
Other Games: Bingo (Mon)
Senior Discount: Specials on Tuesdays, if 55+
Special features: Indoor water park.

Seven Clans Casino Warroad
1012 E. Lake Street
Warroad, MN 56763
(218) 386-3381
www.sevenclanscasino.com/warroad.htm
Map Location: **#9** (400 miles N.W. of Twin
Cities)

Toll-Free Number: (888) 679-2501
Restaurants: 1 Liquor: No
Casino Hours: 10am-1am/9am-2am (Thu-Sat)
Casino Size: 19,875 Square Feet
Other Games Bingo (Wed-Sun), No Blackjack
Senior Discount: Specials on Thursdays if 55+

Shooting Star Casino Hotel
777 Casino Boulevard
Mahnomen, Minnesota 56557
(218) 935-2701
Website: www.starcasino.com
Map Location: **#13** (250 miles N.W. of Twin
Cities)

Room Reservations: (800) 453-STAR
Rooms: 360 Price Range: $47-$100
Suites: 30 Price Range: $65-$160
Restaurants: 3 Liquor: Yes
Buffets: B-$ 4.99 L-$6.99
        D-$8.99/$11.99 (Fri-Sat)
Other Games: Bingo, Poker
Senior Discount: $5 off room, if 50, or older
Special Features: 47-space RV park. Childcare
facility.

Treasure Island Resort Casino
5734 Sturgeon Lake Road
Red Wing, Minnesota 55066
(651) 388-6300
Website: www.treasureislandcasino.com
Map Location: **#14** (40 miles S.E. of Twin Cities. Halfway between Hastings and Red Wing, off Highway 61 on County Road 18)

Toll-Free Number: (800) 222-7077
Room Reservations: (888) 867-7829
Restaurants: 3 Liquor: Yes
Rooms: 250 Price Range: $30-$92
Suites: 28 Price Range: $115-$215
Buffets: B-$10.75 (Sat/Sun) L-$8.25
        D-$11.25-$14.95
Casino Size: 110,000 Square Feet
Other Games: Bingo, Video Craps and Roulette
Casino Marketing: (800) 222-7077
Senior Discount: First Wednesday of each
    month 10am-2pm get coupon book if 55+
Special Features: 95-space RV Park. Marina. Dinner and sightseeing cruises on yacht.

White Oak Casino
45830 US Hwy 2
Deer River, MN 56636
(218) 246-9600
Website: www.whiteoakcasino.com
Map Location: **#17** (5 miles N.W. of Grand Rapids)

Toll-Free Number: (800) 653-2412
Restaurants: 1 Snack Bar Liquor: Yes
Casino Size: 11,000 Square Feet
Senior Discount: Buy $5, get $5 Tue, if 50+

Pari-Mutuel

Canterbury Park
1100 Canterbury Road
Shakopee, Minnesota 55379
(952) 445-7223
Website: www.canterburypark.com
Map Location: **#10** (22 miles S.W. of Twin Cities.)

Toll-Free Number: (800) 340-6361
Admission: $4
Self-Parking: Free   Valet Parking: $6
Restaurants: 2 Buffets: D-$12.95 (Thu-Sun)
Other Games: Blackjack, Poker, Pai Gow Poker, Let It Ride, Caribbean Stud Poker
Casino Marketing: (800) 815-8293
Special Features: Only offers card games and players must pay a commission on each hand. Live horse racing May-September. Daily simulcasting.

MISSISSIPPI

Mississippi was the third state to legalize riverboat gambling when it was approved by that state's legislature in 1990. The law restricts casinos to coast waters (including the Bay of St. Louis and the Back Bay of Biloxi) along the Mississippi River and in navigable waters of counties that border the river.

Mississippi law also requires that riverboats be permanently moored at the dock and they are not permitted to cruise. This allows the riverboats to offer 24-hour dockside gambling. The Isle of Capri in Biloxi was the first casino to open on August 1, 1992 followed one month later by The President.

Since the law does not require that the floating vessel actually resemble a boat, almost all of the casinos are built on barges. This gives them the appearance of a land-based building, rather than a riverboat.

The Mississippi Gaming Commission does not break down its slot statistics by individual properties. Rather, they are classified by region. The **Coastal** region includes Biloxi, Gulfport and Bay Saint Louis. The **North** region includes Tunica, Greenville and Lula. The **South** region includes Vicksburg and Natchez.

With that in mind here's information, as supplied by the Mississippi Gaming Commission, showing the machine payback percentages for each area's casinos for the one-year period from June 1, 2001 through May 30, 2002:

	Coastal	North	South
5¢ Slots	91.70%	90.42%	**91.76%**
5¢ Prog.	89.51%	**89.92%**	89.92%
25¢ Slots	**92.80%**	92.45%	92.78%
25¢ Prog.	**88.56%**	88.32%	87.84%
$1 Slots	95.20%	95.08%	**95.27%**
$1 Prog.	88.58%	88.33%	**91.88%**
$5 Slots	95.65%	**96.84%**	95.28%

These numbers reflect the percentage of money returned on each denomination of machine and encompass all electronic machines including video poker and video keno. The best returns for each category are highlighted in bold print and you can see that all of the gaming areas offer rather similar returns on their machines.

Mississippi is one of the few states that breaks down its progressive machine statistics separately and you can see that the return is always less on machines with progressive jackpots.

Unless otherwise noted, all casinos are open 24 hours and offer: slots, video poker, blackjack, craps, roulette and Caribbean stud poker.

Other game listings include: baccarat (B), mini-baccarat (MB), poker (P), pai gow poker (PGP), let it ride (LIR), three card poker (TCP), big six wheel (B6) and keno (K). The minimum gambling age is 21.

For more information on visiting Mississippi call the state's tourism department at (800) 927-6378. For Biloxi tourism information call (800) 237-9493 and for tourism information on Robinsonville call (888) 4-TUNICA.

Bay St. Louis

Map Location: **#2** (on St. Louis Bay, 40 miles E. of New Orleans)

Casino Magic - Bay St. Louis
711 Casino Magic Drive
Bay St. Louis, Mississippi 39520
(228) 467-9257
Website: www.casinomagic.com

Toll-Free Number: (800) 5-MAGIC-5
Rooms: 498 Price Range: $59-$159
Suites: 78 Price Range: $175-$295
Restaurants: 5 (1 open 24 hours)
Buffets: B-$6.95 L-$8.95 D-$12.95
Casino Size: 39,500 Square Feet
Other Games: MB, PGP, LIR, TCP
Casino Marketing: (800) 5-MAGIC-5
Special Features: 100 hook-up RV Park. 25-slip marina. 18-hole golf course.

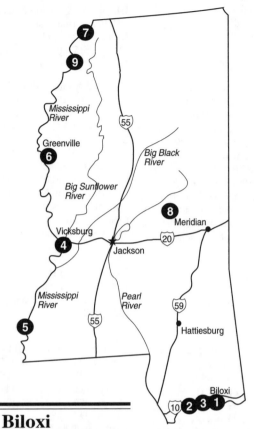

Biloxi

Map Location: **#1** (On the Gulf of Mexico, 80 miles E. of New Orleans)

Beau Rivage
875 Beach Boulevard
Biloxi, Mississippi 39530
(228) 386-7111
Website: www.beaurivageresort.com

Toll-Free Number: (888) 750-7111
Room Reservations: (888) 56-ROOMS
Rooms: 1,780 Price Range: $59-$249
Suites: 66   Price Range: $275-$350
Restaurants: 12 (1 open 24 hours)
Buffets: B-$8.99/$14.99 (Sat/Sun)
        L-$10.99 D-$14.99
Casino Size: 71,669 Square Feet
Other Games: B, MB, PGP, LIR, TCP
Casino Marketing: (800) 239-2771
Special Features: Microbrewery. Health spa and salon. 31-slip marina. Retail shopping promenade.

Boomtown Casino - Biloxi
676 Bayview Avenue
Biloxi, Mississippi 39530
(228) 435-7000
Website: www.boomtownbiloxi.com

Toll-Free Number: (800) 627-0777
Restaurants: 2 (1 open 24 hours)
Buffets: B-$5.99 L-$7.99 D-$12.99
Casino Size: 33,632 Square Feet
Other Games: PGP, TCP, No CSP
Casino Marketing: (800) 627-0777 ext. 5011
Senior Discount: If 50, or older, join Wild
    Bunch Seniors Club for various discounts
Fun Book: Look for rack card in local hotels
            or at Welcome Center on Hwy 90
Special Features: Family video arcade. Western gift and clothing shop. 24-hour bakery.

Casino Magic - Biloxi
195 E. Beach Boulevard
Biloxi, Mississippi 39530
(228) 386-4600
Website: www.casinomagic.com

Toll-Free Number: (800) 5-MAGIC-5
Rooms: 292 Price Range: $65-$149
Suites: 86 Price Range: $99-$199
Restaurants: 4 (1 open 24 hours)
Buffets: B-$6.45 L-$8.99 D-$14.99
Casino Size: 48,860 Square Feet
Other Games: MB, PGP, LIR, TCP
Casino Marketing: (800) 5-MAGIC-5
Fun Book: Available through local hotels/motels
Senior Discount: 1/2 off Wed b'fst buffet if 50+
Special Features: Free comedy club show on
Monday nights. All suites features jacuzzis.

Grand Casino Biloxi
265 Beach Boulevard
Biloxi, Mississippi 39530
(228) 436-2946
Website: www.grandbiloxi.com

Toll-Free Number: (800) WIN-2-WIN
Rooms: 1,000 Price Range: $49-$179
Suites: 64 Price Range: $159-$209
Restaurants: 6 (1 open 24 hours)
Buffets: B-$7.99 L-$8.99 D-$12.99
Casino Size: 106,300 Square Feet
Other Games: MB, PGP, LIR, TCP, P, B6
Special Features: Kid's Quest childcare center. Video arcade. Spa. Specialty retail shops.
Golf packages.

Imperial Palace Hotel & Casino
850 Bayview Avenue
Biloxi, Mississippi 39530
(228) 436-3000
Website: www.ipbiloxi.com

Toll-Free Number: (800) 436-3000
Toll-Free Number: (888) WIN-AT-IP
Room Reservations: (800) 634-6441
Rooms: 1,000 Price Range: $49-$129
Suites: 14 Price Range: $79-$189
Restaurants: 10 (1 open 24 hours)
Buffets: B-$4.95/$8.95 (Sun) L-$6.95
          D-$12.95/$12.95 (Fri)
Casino Size: 70,000 Square Feet
Other Games: MB, PGP, LIR, TCP, B6
Special Features: Six-screen movie theater.
Comedy Club. Health spa. Video arcade.

Isle of Capri Casino & Hotel - Biloxi
151 Beach Boulevard
Biloxi, Mississippi 39530
(228) 435-5400
Website: www.isleofcapricasino.com

Toll-Free Number: (800) 843-4753
Rooms: 367 Price Range: $79-$139
Suites: 4 Price Range: $219
Restaurants: 3 (1 open 24 hours)
Buffets: B-$6.75/$11.95 (Sun)
          L-$8.50 D-$12.95
Casino Size: 32,500 Square Feet
Other Games: PGP, LIR, TCP
Senior Discount: Various if 50+
Special Features: Slot club members receive
room discounts. 10% room discount for AAA
and AARP members. Health club.

Palace Casino Resort
158 Howard Avenue
Biloxi, Mississippi 39530
(228) 432-8888
Website: www.palacecasinoresort.com

Toll-Free Number: (800) PALACE-9
Rooms: 234 Price Range: $59-$149
Suites: 2 Price Range: $500
Restaurants: 3 (1 open 24 hours)
Buffets: B-$7.49 L-$8.99/$12.99 (Sun)
          D-$13.99
Casino Size: 43,500 Square Feet
Other Games: PGP, TCP
Special Features: Health spa. 20-slip marina.

President Casino Broadwater Resort
2110 Beach Boulevard
Biloxi, Mississippi 39531
(228) 385-3500
Website: www.broadwater.com

Toll-Free Number: (800) THE-PRES
Rooms: 500 Price Range: $59-$125
Suites: 12 Price Range: $120-$330
Restaurants: 3 (1 open 24 hours)
Buffets: B-$4.95 L-$7.95/$11.95 (Fri-Sat)
          D-$11.95
Casino Size: 38,000 Square Feet
Other Games: P, PGP, LIR, TCP
Fun Book: Need coupon from local card racks
Senior Discount: $2.95 breakfast and $5.75
          lunch Mon-Thu, if 50, or older
Special Features: Covered marina. Golf packages.

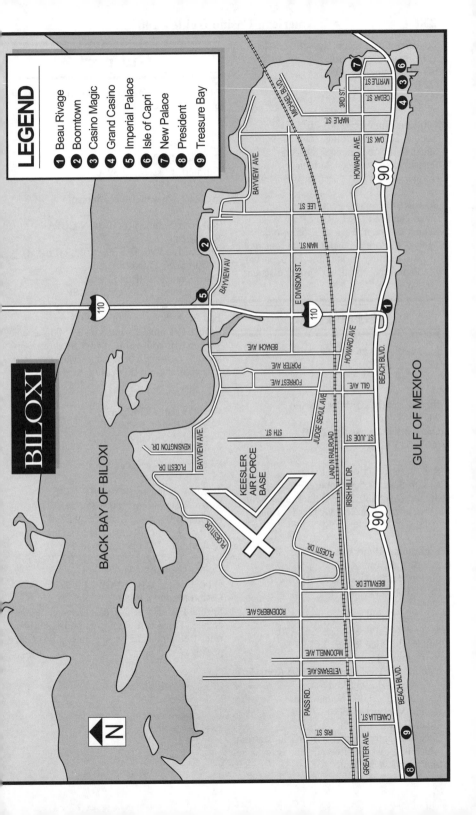

Treasure Bay Casino Resort
1980 Beach Boulevard
Biloxi, Mississippi 39531
(228) 385-6000
Website: www.treasurebay.com

Toll-Free Number: (800) PIRATE-9
Rooms: 262 Price Range: $59-$119
Suites: 8 Price Range: $189-$338
Restaurants: 3 (1 open 24 hours)
Buffets: B-$5.95/$12.95 (Sun) L-$7.95
      D-$12.95
Size: 40,000 Square Feet
Other Games: PGP, LIR, TCP
Senior Discount: Various if 55 or older
Special Features: Casino is 400-foot replica
of 18th century pirate ship built on barge.
Microbrewery. AARP 10% room discount.

Greenville

Map Location: **#6** (On the Mississippi River,
121 miles N.W. of Jackson)

Bayou Caddy's Jubilee Casino
242 S. Walnut Street
Greenville, Mississippi 38701
(662) 335-1111

Restaurants: 3 (1 open 24 hours)
Casino Size: 28,500 Square Feet
Senior Discount: Join Wild Bunch Seniors
Club for free Hot Seat Wednesdays entry.

Lighthouse Point Casino
199 N. Lakefront Road
Greenville, Mississippi 38701
(662) 334-7711

Toll-Free Number: (800) 878-1777
Rooms: 148 Price Range: $51-$79
Suites: 19 Price Range: $67-$79
Restaurants: 1
Buffets: B-$11.95 (Sun) L-$6.95 (Mon-Fri)
      D-$12.95 (Wed-Sat)
Casino Size: 22,000 Square Feet
Casino Marketing: (800) 878-1777
Other Games: No CSP
Special Features: Hotel is Fairfield Marriottt
which is across the street. Casino is on an ac-
tual paddlewheel boat.

Gulfport

Map Location: **#3** (On the Gulf of Mexico, 70
miles E. of New Orleans)

Copa Casino
P.O. Box 1600
Gulfport, Mississippi 39502
(228) 863-3330
Website: www.thecopacasino.com

Toll-Free Number: (800) WIN-COPA
Restaurants: 1
Buffets: L-$5.99 D-$7.99/$10.99 (Fri-Sat)
Casino Size: 27,000 Square Feet
Other Games: TCP, No Poker
Other Games: LIR, TCP, No CSP
Senior Discount: Various, if 40 or older
Fun Book: Show out-of-state ID to receive
Special Features: Casino is on a 1,500-passen-
ger modern cruise ship. $1.99 Steak & Eggs
special (7am-mid). New barge casino expected
to replace current ship casino by early 2003.

Grand Casino Gulfport
3215 W. Beach Boulevard
Gulfport, Mississippi 39501
(228) 870-7777
Website: www.grandgulfport.com

Toll-Free Number: (800) WIN-7777
Room Reservations: (800) 354-2450
Rooms: 1000 Price Range: $59-$199
Suites: 74   Price Range: $149 and up
Restaurants: 7 (1 open 24 hours)
Buffets: L-$8.99 D-$11.99/$14.99 (Wed/Fri)
Casino Size: 105,000 Square Feet
Other Games: MB, P, PGP, LIR, TCP
Casino Marketing: (800) WIN-7777
Special Features: Kids Quest childcare. Video
arcade. Three-acre pool area and lazy river
ride. Bellisimo unisex spa and salon. Golf
packages.

The Best Places To Play On The Gulf Coast

Roulette - There are no casinos on the Gulf Coast that offer single-zero roulette.

Craps -The Imperial Palace offers 20x odds, which is the highest in the area. Almost all other casinos on the Gulf Coast (including Casino Magic in Bay St. Louis) offer 10x odds. The two exceptions are Boomtown and Beau Rivage which both limit players to 5x odds.

Blackjack - Gulf Coast casinos offer some of the best blackjack outside of Nevada and, unlike downtown Las Vegas, there are no casinos that hit soft 17. This rule is advantageous for the player by .20%. All of the recommendations in this section apply to players using perfect basic strategy for each particular game.

Only four casinos offer single-deck games. The Copa in Gulfport's rules are: double down on any two card total of 10 or more, splitting allowed, late surrender and no doubling after splitting. The casino edge in this game is .23%. A slightly better single-deck game can be found at Casino Magic in Bay St. Louis which doesn't allow surrender but does allow resplitting of aces. The casino advantage here is .22%. The two Grand Casinos offer a single-deck game that pays even-money on blackjack but you should definitely avoid this game because the casino edge is more than 2%.

Several casinos are tied for best double-deck and they all have the following rules: double down on any first two cards, re-split any pair (including aces) and doubling allowed after splitting. This works out to a casino edge of just .14% and it's offered at: Casino Magic in Bay St. Louis, both Grand Casinos, Imperial Palace, New Palace and Treasure Bay. The Copa in Gulfport offers a similar game except late surrender is allowed in place of resplitting aces. The casino edge here is also .14%.

Next best are four casinos that offer the same rules as the Copa's, with the exception of late surrender: Beau Rivage, Boomtown, President and Isle of Capri. The casino edge in these games is .19%.

For six-deck shoe games the best place to play is Beau Rivage which allows doubling down on any first two cards, doubling after splitting, late surrender and resplitting of aces. The casino advantage in this game is .26%. That same game, without resplitting of aces, is offered at the Copa and the edge there works out to .33%. Next best are both Casino Magic properties, both Grand Casinos, Imperial Palace, New Palace and Treasure Bay which all offer the same rules as Beau Rivage with the exception of late surrender. The edge in these games is .34%.

Boomtown, Isle of Capri and the President all offer standard six-deck shoe games that allow doubling down on any first two cards and doubling after splitting. The edge on these games is .41%.

Casino Magic in Bay St. Louis and the Grand Casino in Gulfport offer eight-deck shoe games with doubling on any two cards, double after split and resplitting aces allowed which works out to a .36% casino advantage. Isle of Capri offers the same eight-deck shoe game with no resplitting of aces and this works out to a .43% casino advantage.

Video Poker - Good video poker players know that three of the best varieties of machines to look for are: 9/6 Jacks or Better, 10/7 Double Bonus and full-pay Deuces Wild. By only playing these three kinds of machines, playing the maximum coin and using perfect strategy you can achieve the following payback percentages: 99.5% on 9/6 Jacks or Better, 100.1% on 10/7 Double Bonus and 100.7% on full-pay Deuces Wild. Unfortunately, the Gulf Coast's choice of machines is not nearly as good as in Nevada which still offers the country's best paying machines. As a matter of fact, only the Copa has Deuces Wild machines available with a full-pay schedule and it's the only casino outside of Nevada to offer that game. The Copa also has full-pay Kings or Better Joker's Wild which has a payback percentage of 100.64%.

10/7 Double Bonus can be found at Casino Magic in Bay St. Louis which has 25¢ machines. It's also available at the Copa which has 25¢ games, plus some $1 machines with a progressive jackpot.

Full-pay All American (100.72% payback), which is a rather rare machine to find outside of Missouri, is available at the Isle of Capri which has a few of them at the 25¢ level.

Quarter 9/6 Jacks or Better machines with a progressive jackpot for the royal flush can be found at Casino Magic (Biloxi), Treasure Bay, the President and the Isle of Capri. Casino Magic (Bay St. Louis), Copa and Imperial Palace also have quarter 9/6 machines but without the progressive jackpot. Casino Magic (Bay St. Louis), New Palace, Imperial Palace and Beau Rivage have $1 9/6 machines while Treasure Bay, President and the Copa all offer dollar 9/6 machines with a progressive jackpot.

Both Grand Casinos advertise "over 99% payback video poker" but this only applies to certain machines in the casino that are clearly marked. Some of these are standard 9/7 Double Bonus games but they also offer Jacks or Better machines with the following pay table (per coin with maximum coins played): Royal Flush -800; Straight Flush -50; 4-of-a-Kind (A) -80; 4-of-a-Kind (J-Q-K) -40; 4-of-a-Kind (2-10) -25; Full House -8; Flush -5; Straight -4; 3-of-a-Kind -3; 2 Pair -2; Jacks or Better -1. These same kind of machines are known in the Las Vegas market as 8/5 Bonus Poker Aces and Faces. With perfect strategy (and maximum coins played) they return 99.3%.

Slots - For slot players both Grand casinos also offer 98% paybacks on some of their $1 slots. The machines with these paybacks are grouped in different areas and clearly marked with signage, so be aware that not all machines are guaranteed to return that high an amount. Statistics from the Mississippi Gaming Commission show that the average $1 slot returns around 95% so it's probably worthwhile to search around for the "certified" machines if you're a $1 player.

Lula

Map Location: **#9** (On the Mississippi River, 70 miles S. of Memphis, TN)

Isle of Capri Casino & Hotel - Lula
777 Isle of Capri Parkway
Lula, Mississippi 38644
(662) 363-4600
Website: www.isleofcapricasino.com

Toll-Free Number: (800) 789-LUCK
Toll-Free Number: (800) THE-ISLE
Rooms: 173 Price Range: $40-$99
Suites: 4   Price Range: $55-$120
Restaurants: 4 (1 open 24 hours)
Buffets: B-$5.95 L-$8.95 D-$12.95
Casino Size: 55,000 Square Feet
Other Games: LIR, TCP
Special Features: Two movie theaters. 10% hotel discount for AAA and AARP members.

Natchez

Map Location: **#5** (on the Mississippi River, 102 miles S.W. of Jackson)

Isle of Capri Casino & Hotel - Natchez
53 Silver Street
Natchez, Mississippi 39120
(601) 445-0605
Website: www.isleofcapricasino.com

Toll-Free Number: (800) 722-LUCK
Toll-Free Number: (800) THE-ISLE
Rooms: 147 Price Range: $49-$99
Suites: 5 Price Range: $135-$165
Restaurants: 2
Buffets: L-$8.95 D-$12.95
Size: 14,300 Square Feet
Other Games: TCP
Special Features: Casino is built on barge that resembles 1860's paddle wheel steamboat.

Tunica

Map Location: **#7** (on the Mississippi River, 28 miles S. of Memphis, TN)

Bally's Casino Tunica
1450 Bally's Boulevard
Robinsonville, Mississippi 38664
(662) 357-1500
Website: www.ballysms.com

Toll-Free Number: (800) 382-2559
Rooms: 235 Price Range: $29-$109
Suites: 8 Price Range: $250-$425
Restaurants: 2 (1 open 24 hours)
Buffets: B-$6.95 L-$7.95 D-$11.95
Casino Size: 40,000 Square Feet
Other Games: TCP, B6
Senior Discount: If 55, or older, receive 50% off daily buffets, if players club member
Special Features: Free breakfast with every room stay. Mini Jacuzzi's and refrigerators in every room. Free buffet on Thursdays for ladies who are slot club members.

Fitzgeralds Casino/Hotel
711 Lucky Lane
Robinsonville, Mississippi 38664
(662) 363-5825
Website: www.fitzgeraldstunica.com

Toll-Free Number: (800) 766-LUCK
Room Reservations: (888) 766-LUCK
Rooms: 507 Price Range: $29-$99
Suites: 70 Price Range: $69-$199
Buffets: B-$6.95/$9.50 (Sun)
          L-$7.95 D-$10.50
Restaurants: 3 (1 open 24 hours)
Casino Size: 33,000 Square Feet
Casino Marketing: (800) 766-LUCK
Other Games: LIR, TCP
Senior Discount: 10% AARP room discount
Special Features: Indoor pool and spa. Sports pub with 8 tv's.

Gold Strike Casino
100 Casino Center Drive
Robinsonville, Mississippi 38664
(662) 357-1111
Website: www.goldstrikemississippi.com

Toll-Free Number: (888) 24K-PLAY
Room Reservations: (888) 245-7829
Rooms: 1,130 Price Range: $49-$99
Suites: 70 Price Range: $169-$239
Restaurants: 3
Buffets: B-$6.95 L-$7.95
         D-$13.95/$16.95 (Fri)
Casino Size: 50,486 Square Feet
Other Games: LIR, P, TCP
Casino Marketing: (800) 871-CLUB
Special Features: McDonald's. Krispy Kreme.

Grand Casino Tunica
13615 Old Highway 61 N.
Robinsonville, Mississippi 38664
(662) 363-2788
Website: www.grandtunica.com

Toll-Free Number: (800) 946-4946
Rooms: 1,356 Price Range: $39-$139
Suites: 117 Price Range: $149-$220
Restaurants: 8 (1 open 24 hours)
Buffets: B-$7.99 L-$9.89
         D-$12.99/$16.49 (Fri-Sat)
Casino Size: 140,000 Square Feet
Other Games: MB, P, PGP, LIR, TCP, B6
Special Features: World's largest dockside casino. 18-hole golf course. Kid's Quest childcare center. 200-space RV park. Spa.

Harrah's Tunica
1100 Casino Strip Boulevard
Robinsonville, Mississippi 38664
(662) 363-7777
Website: www.harrahs.com

Reservation Number: (800) HARRAHS
Rooms: 180 Price Range: $59-$129
Suites: 20 Price Range: $149 and up
Restaurants: 3 (open 24 hours)
Buffets: L-$8.75 D-$12.99
Casino Size: 50,000 Square Feet
Other Games: LIR, TCP
Casino Marketing: (888) 789-7900
Senior Discount: 10% room discount for
             AARP members (Sun-Thu)
Special Features: River Bend Links golf course.

Hollywood Casino Tunica
1150 Casino Strip Resorts Boulevard
Robinsonville, Mississippi 38664
(662) 357-7700
Website: www.hollywoodtunica.com

Toll-Free Number: (800) 871-0711
Rooms: 451 Price Range: $59-$149
Suites: 55 Price Range: $129-$350
Restaurants: 3 (1 open 24 hours)
Buffets: B-$6.99/$10.99 (Sun) L-$7.99
         D-$10.99/$16.99 (Fri)
Size: 54,000 Square Feet
Other Games: MB, LIR, P, TCP
Special Features: Casino features a collection of Hollywood memorabilia. 123-space RV park. Slot club members get 10-15% discount in hotel, restaurants and gift shop. Indoor pool and jacuzzi. 18-hole golf course.

Horseshoe Casino & Hotel
1021 Casino Center Drive
Robinsonville, Mississippi 38664
(662) 357-5500
Website: www.horseshoe.com

Toll-Free Number: (800) 303-7463
Rooms: 200 Price Range: $59-$89
Suites: 311 Price Range: $99-$129
Restaurants: 2 (1 open 24 hours)
Buffets: B-$7.75 L-$8.75
         D-$14.75/$17.75 (Fri)
Casino Size: 63,000 Square Feet
Other Games: MB, LIR, P, PGP, TCP
Special Features: Blues & Legends Hall of Fame Museum. Bluesville Nightclub.

Sam's Town Hotel & Gambling Hall
1477 Casino Strip Boulevard
Robinsonville, Mississippi 38664
(662) 363-0711
Website: www.samstowntunica.com

Toll-Free Number: (800) 456-0711
Rooms: 850 Price Range: $39-$109
Suites: 44 Price Range: $115-$199
Restaurants: 4 (1 open 24 hours)
Buffets: B-$7.95 L-$9.95
         D-$12.95/$17.95 (Fri-Sat)
Size: 96,000 Square Feet
Other Games: MB, K, P, PGP, LIR, TCP
Senior Discount: Various discounts if 50+
Special Features: 18-hole golf course. Slot club members get buffet discount.

The Best Places To Play In Tunica

Roulette -The only single-zero roulette wheel can be found at the Grand Casino. The house edge in this game is cut from 5.26% down to a more reasonable 2.70%. Be aware, however, that the Grand only has one table in the casino that offers this single-zero game while there are five other tables with the more common double-zero wheel.

Craps - All Tunica casinos offer 20x odds. Some casinos also pay triple (rather than double) on 12 in the field which cuts the house edge on this bet in half from 5.6% to 2.8%. The four casinos offering this slightly better field bet are: Hollywood, Horseshoe, Gold Strike and Sam's Town.

Blackjack - The blackjack games in Tunica are most similar to those offered in downtown Las Vegas. Every casino offers both single and double-deck games, as well as six-deck shoe games. That's good. The bad part, however, is that dealers hit soft 17 at all blackjack games, except for the six-deck game at the Grand Casino. This results in an extra advantage for the house of .20%. All of the following recommendations apply to players using perfect basic strategy for each particular game.

For single-deck players, Tunica has some of the best games in the country because all allow doubling down on any first two cards (but no doubling after splitting). The best one-deck games can be found at the Horseshoe, Gold Strike, Grand and Sheraton which all allow resplitting of pairs, including aces. The casino edge in this game is .15%.

At Sam's Town they offer a game identical to the above game except won't allow you to resplit aces and this results in a slightly higher house edge of .18%. Bally's has those same single-deck rules in place, except they won't allow you to resplit *any* pair and the casino edge in their game works out to .22%.

The Grand, Bally's, Gold Strike, Hollywood, Sheraton and Horseshoe are the best places to play double-deck because their games have the following rules: double down on any first two cards, resplit any pair (including aces), and double down after split. This works out to a casino edge of .35%.

Tunica's remaining three casinos: Sam's Town, Harrah's and Fitzgeralds, all offer the next best game. The only rule change from the previous casinos is that you aren't allowed to resplit aces and the casino edge in this game is .40%.

The best six-deck blackjack game in Tunica can be found at the Grand which has rules identical to those offered in the best two-deck games, plus they allow you to double after splitting and it's the only game in town where the dealer stands on soft 17. The casino advantage in this game is .34%.

Bally's, Gold Strike, Hollywood, Horseshoe and Sheraton have games identical to the Grand game except they hit soft 17 and that results in a slightly higer casino advantage of .56%.

The remaining six-deck games are those offered at Fitzgeralds, Harrah's and Sam's Town. All three offer a game with a slightly higher casino edge of .63% because they hit soft 17 and won't allow you to resplit aces.

Video Poker -Good video poker players know that three of the best machines to look for are: 9/6 Jacks or Better, 10/7 Double Bonus and full-pay Deuces Wild. By only playing these three kinds of machines, playing the maximum coin and using perfect strategy you can achieve the following payback percentages: 99.5% on 9/6 Jacks or Better, 100.17% on 10/7 Double Bonus and 100.76% on full-pay Deuces Wild. Unfortunately, Tunica's choice of machines is not nearly as good as in Nevada which still offers the country's best paying machines. As a matter of fact, there are no full-pay Deuces Wild machines in Tunica, nor are there any 10/7 Double Bonus machines. 9/6 machines are available but they're difficult to find, especially for higher level players.

The most 25¢ 9/6 Jacks or Better games can be found at the Hollywood Casino. Other casinos offering quarter games are Gold Strike, Harrah's and Fitzgeralds.

For 50¢ players, 9/6 Jacks or Better games can be found at Harrah's, Sheraton and Hollywood. These casinos also offer 9/6 games at the $1 level. Additionally, Harrah's has $1and $5 Triple-Play 9/6 games.

Quarter 9/7 Double Bonus machines (99.11% payback) can be found at the Grand Casino, Sam's Town and Gold Strike (Fitzgeralds has them in nickels). $1 9/7 games can be found at Horseshoe and Harrah's. Most of the other Tunica casinos have 9/6 Double Bonus games in both quarter and dollar machines, but with an expected return of just 97.81% you would be better off seeking out the higher paying 9/7 machines.

The Grand Casino has some standard 9/7 Double Bonus games but they also offer Jacks or Better machines with the following pay table (per coin with maximum coins played): Royal Flush -800; Straight Flush -50; 4-of-a-Kind (A) -80; 4-of-a-Kind (J-Q-K) -40; 4-of-a-Kind (2-10) -25; Full House -8; Flush -5; Straight -4; 3-of-a-Kind -3; 2 Pair -2; Jacks or Better -1. These same kind of machines are known in the Las Vegas market as 8/5 Bonus Poker Aces and Faces. With perfect strategy (and maximum coins played) they return 99.3%.

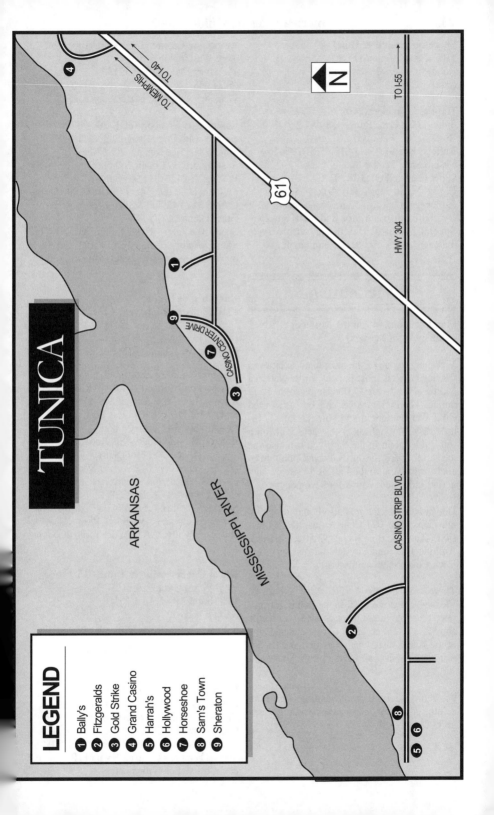

Sheraton Casino & Hotel
1107 Casino Center Drive
Robinsonville, Mississippi 38664
(662) 363-4900

Toll-Free Number: (800) 391-3777
Suites: 140 Price Range: $89-$129
Restaurants: 4 (1 open 24 hours)
Buffets: B/L-$7.95 D-$12.95/$16.95 (Fri)
Casino Size: 32,800 Square Feet
Other Games: PGP, LIR, TCP
Casino Marketing: (800) 391-3777
Senior Discount: If 55, or older, receive $2
    buffet discount Mon and Fri 10am-2pm
Special Features: Health spa with private
massages, Jacuzzis, saunas and tanning.

Vicksburg

Map Location: **#4** (on the Mississippi River,
44 miles W. of Jackson)

Vicksburg is one of the most historic cities in
the South and is most famous for its National
Military Park where 17,000 Union soldiers are
buried. The Park is America's best-preserved
Civil War battlefield and you can take a 16-
mile drive through the 1,858-acre Park on a
self-guided tour. In the Park you can also see
the U.S.S. Cairo, the only salvaged Union Iron-
clad. Admission to the Park is $4 per car and
allows unlimited returns for seven days.

Downtown Vicksburg is also home to several
museums: The Old Court House ($3 admis-
sion), Gray and Blue Naval ($2.50 admission),
Antique Doll and Toy ($2 admission); and
Coca-Cola ($2.95 admission).

There are also about 12 historic homes in
Vicksburg that are open to the public for nar-
rated tours. Admission prices are $5 for adults
and $2 to $3 for children 12 and under. Some
of the homes also function as Bed and Breakfasts and rooms can be rented for overnight
stays.

For more information on visiting Vicksburg
call the city's Convention and Visitors Bureau
at (800) 221-3536.

Ameristar Casino Hotel - Vicksburg
4146 Washington Street
Vicksburg, Mississippi 39180
(601) 638-1000
Website: www.ameristarcasinos.com

Reservation Number: (800) 700-7770
Rooms: 146 Price Range: $39-$119
Suites: 4   Price Range: $99-$189
Restaurants: 3 (1 open 24 hours)
Buffets: L-$4.99/$11.99 (Sun)
       D-$9.99/$14.99 (Fri)/$13.99 (Sat)
Casino Size: 42,500 Square Feet
Other Games: LIR, TCP
Special Features: $2 off buffets and 20% off
rooms for slot club members. AARP and AAA
members receive 10% hotel discount.

Harrah's Vicksburg
1310 Mulberry Street
Vicksburg, Mississippi 39180
(601) 636-DICE
Website: www.harrahs.com

Toll-Free Number: (800) 843-2343
Reservation Number: (800) HARRAHS
Rooms: 101 Price Range: $69-$129
Suites: 16 Price Range: Casino Use Only
Restaurants: 3 (1 open 24 hours)
Buffets: B-$4.99/$6.99 (Sat-Sun)
       L-$6.99/$11.99 (Sun)
       D-$10.99/$12.99 (Fri-Sun)
Casino Size: 20,909 Square Feet
Other Games: TCP, No CSP
Special Features: Casino is on 1,200-passen-
ger paddlewheel riverboat. Planet 4 Kids
childcare facility. AAA/AARP room discount.

Isle of Capri Casino & Hotel - Vicksburg
3990 Washington Street
Vicksburg, Mississippi 39180
(601) 636-5700
Website: www.isleofcapricasino.com

Toll-Free Number: (800) THE-ISLE
Rooms: 61 Price Range: $40-$99
Suites: 61 Price Range: $79-$149
Restaurants: 2 (1 open 24 hours)
Buffets: B-$5.95 L-$6.95 D-$13.99
Casino Size: 24,000 Square Feet
Other Games: TCP
Senior Discount: Various discounts if 50+
Special Features: 67-space RV park. Room dis-
count for slot club members.

Rainbow Casino
1380 Warrenton Road
Vicksburg, Mississippi 39182
(601) 636-7575
Website: www.rainbowcasino.com

Toll-Free Number: (800) 503-3777
Rooms: 85 Price Range: $45-$75
Restaurants: 1
Buffets: B-$3.99 L-$5.75/$6.25 (Fri/Sat)
        D-$6.95/$11.99 (Fri/Sat)
Casino Size: 25,000 Square Feet
Other Games: TCP
Senior Discount: Various discounts if 50+
Special Features: Hotel is Amerihost Inn which offers complimentary continental breakfast and morning newspaper.

Indian Casino

Pearl River Resort & Casino
Highway 16 West
Philadelphia, Mississippi 39350
(601) 650-1234
Website: www.pearlriverresort.com
Map Location: **#8** (81 miles N.E. of Jackson)

Toll-Free Number: (800) 557-0711
Silver Star Rooms: 450 Prices: $79-$124
Silver Star Suites: 50 Prices: Private Use
Golden Moon Rooms: 572 Prices: $99-$144
Golden Moon Suites: 144 Prices: Private Use
Restaurants: 12 (1 open 24 hours)
Buffets: L-$7.50/$11.25 (Sun)
        D-$9.95/$15.75 (Fri)
Silver Star Casino Size: 90,000 Square Feet
Golden Moon Casino Size: 90,000 Square Feet
Other Games: B, MB, LIR, P, TCP, B6
Special Features: Resort consists of two separate hotel/casinos across the street from each other. 18-hole golf course. 15-acre water theme park. Health spa. Beauty salon. Gift shop. Specialty retail shops. 10% room discount for AAA and AARP members (Sun-Thu).

MISSOURI

In November, 1992 Missouri voters approved a state-wide referendum to allow riverboat gambling. That made Missouri the fifth state to approve riverboat casinos. There is no limit to the number of licenses that may be issued by the state's gaming commission and all boats remain dockside.

Missouri's riverboat casinos initially conducted two-hour gaming sessions with a $500 loss-limit on each session. In early 2000 the law was changed to allow offer continuous boardings. However, the state's loss limit provision is still in force and you are not allowed to lose more than $500 within a two-hour period. All casinos base that two-hour period beginning on even hour times: 12-2, 2-4, 4-6, 6-8, 8-10, 10-12.

When you first enter a casino you must present an ID to receive a slot club card which will be used to track your chip and/or slot token purchases. Once you have purchased $500 worth of chips or tokens you will not be able to buy anymore until the beginning of the next even hour. There is no limit on winnings.

Admission is free to all Missouri casinos except for the President and Aztar. However, if you're a rated player from another casino you may get free admission to those casinos. Call ahead to ask them about their requirements.

Unlike dockside gaming in Mississippi, most Missouri casinos are not open 24 hours and the hours of operation are listed for each casino.

Here's information from the Missouri Gaming Commission regarding the payback percentages for each casino's electronic machines for the six-month period from December 1, 2001 through May 31, 2002:

CASINO	PAYBACK %
Argosy	94.37
Isle of Capri K.C.	93.65
President	93.50
Ameristar-St. Charles	93.25
Harrah's K.C.	93.21
Harrah's M.H.	93.15
Ameristar-K. C.	93.13
St. Jo Frontier	92.77
Mark Twain	92.65
Isle of Capri-Boonville	92.53
Aztar	89.79

These figures reflect the total percentages returned by each casino for all of their electronic machines including slot machines, video poker, video keno, etc. As you can see, Argosy Casino returned the most to its slot machine players, while Casino Aztar returned the least. Although these numbers are only for a six-month period they pretty much remain constant with the same casinos at the top and bottom of the list.

Unless otherwise noted, all casinos offer: slots, video poker, craps, blackjack, roulette and Caribbean stud poker. Optional games include: baccarat (B), mini-baccarat (MB), poker (P), pai gow poker (PGP), let it ride (LIR), Spanish 21 (S21) and 3-Card Poker (TCP). The minimum gambling age is 21.

For more information on visiting Missouri call the state's Travel Center at (800) 877-1234.

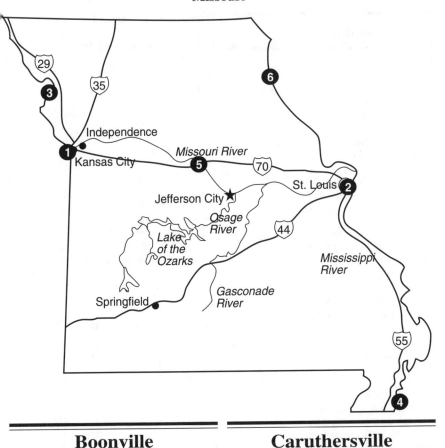

Boonville

Map Location: **#5** (100 miles E. of Kansas City)

Isle of Capri Casino - Boonville
100 Isle of Capri Boulevard
Boonville, Missouri 65233
(660) 882-1200
Website: www.isleofcapricasino.com

Toll-Free Number: THE-ISLE
Restaurants: 3
Buffets: B-$6.99 (Sat-Sun) L-$8.99 D-$14.99
Hours: 8am-5am/24 hours (Fri-Sat)
Valet Parking: Free
Casino Size: 28,000 Square Feet
Other Games: LIR, TCP
Senior Discount: Free buffet on Tue/Thu with qualified slot play and if 50 or older
Special Features: 600-passenger barge that remains dockside on the Missouri River.

Caruthersville

Map Location: **#4** (200 miles S. of St. Louis)

Casino Aztar
777 East Third Street
Caruthersville, Missouri 63830
(573) 333-6000

Toll-Free Number (800) 679-4945
Restaurants: 1
Buffets: D-$11.99 (Fri-Sat)
Hours: 10am-2am/4am (Fri-Sat)
Admission: $3
Valet Parking: $2
Senior Discount: Free Wed and Sun cruises, free valet parking on Sun
Casino Size: 12,000 Square Feet
Other Games: LIR, TCP
Special Features: 875-passenger sternwheeler that remains dockside on the Mississippi River. Restaurant and sports bar. Gift shop. Live music Thu-Sat.

Kansas City

Map Location: **#1**

Ameristar Casino Hotel Kansas City
3200 North Station Drive
Kansas City, Missouri 64161
(816) 414-7000
Website: www.ameristarcasinos.com
Map Location: **#1**

Toll-Free Number: (800) 499-4961
Rooms: 176 Price Range: $79-$169
Suites: 12 Price Range: $349
Restaurants: 14
Buffets: B-$7.49 L-$8.99/$12.99 (Sun)
          D-$14.99/$12.99 (Sun)
Hours: 8am-5am/24hrs (Fri/Sat)
Valet Parking: $5
Other Games: S21, MB, P, PGP, LIR, TCP
Special Features: 4,000-passenger barge that remains dockside on the Missouri River. Nine fast food outlets. Bavarian brew pub. 18 theater movie complex. Buffet discounts for AAA and slot club members.

Argosy Casino
777 N.W. Argosy Parkway
Riverside, Missouri 64150
(816) 746-3100
Website: www.argosycasinos.com
Map Location: **#1** (3 miles W. of Kansas City)

Toll-Free Number: (800) 900-3423
Restaurants: 4 (Deli on boat)
Buffets: B-$5.95 L-$6.95
          D-$11.95/$17.95 (Fri-Sat)
Hours: 8am-5am/24 hours (Fri/Sat)
Valet Parking: $4
Casino Size: 30,000 Square Feet
Other Games: S21, PGP, LIR, TCP
Senior Discount: SVP club members receive discounts on select days, if 55, or older
Special Features: 1,800-passenger old-fashioned paddle wheeler that remains dockside on the Missouri River. Slot club and AAA members receive dining discounts.

Harrah's North Kansas City
One Riverboat Drive
Kansas City, Missouri 64116
(816) 472-7777
Website: www.harrahs.com
Map Location: **#1**

Toll-Free Number: (800) HARRAHS
Rooms: 200 Price Range: $89-$150
Suites: 15 Price Range: $139-$190
Restaurants: 4 (Deli on both boats)
Buffets: B-$6.99/$10.99 (Sat/Sun) L-$7.99
          D-$11.99/$16.99 (Mon/Wed/Fri/Sat)
Hours: 8am-5am/24 Hrs (Fri/Sat)
Casino Size: 60,000 Square Feet
Valet Parking: $5
Other Games: MB, LIR, PGP, TCP
Special Features: 1,700-passenger paddle-wheeler that remains dockside on the Missouri River. Sports bar. Video arcade. Room discount and $1 buffet discount with Harrah's card.

Isle of Capri Casino - Kansas City
1800 E. Front Street
Kansas City, Missouri 64120
(816) 855-7777
Website: www.isleofcapricasino.com
Map Location: **#1**

Toll-Free Number: (800) 946-8711
Restaurants: 3
Buffets: B-$3.95/$10.95 (Sun) L-$8.95
          D-$16.95
Hours: 8am-5am/24 hours (Fri/Sat)
Valet Parking: Free
Casino Size: 30,000 Square Feet
Other Games: LIR, PGP
Senior Discount: Food discounts on
          Thursdays if slot club member and 50+
Special Features: 2,000-passenger Caribbean-themed barge that remains dockside in a man-made lake fed by the Missouri River.

The Ameristar Casino in Kansas City is the largest casino complex in Missouri. It features a 184-room hotel, two 3,000-passenger barges, 12 food outlets, a Bavarian brew pub, a Kid's Quest supervised children's entertainment center and a movie complex with 18 theaters.

La Grange

Map Location: **#6** (150 miles N.W. of St. Louis)

Mark Twain Casino
104 Pierce Street
La Grange, Missouri 63348
(573) 655-4770
Website: www.casinomarktwain.com

Toll-Free Number: (866) 454-5825
Restaurants: 2
Buffets: B:$2.99 (Mon-Tue) L-$6.95 (Sun)
Hours: 8am-2am/4am (Fri/Sat)
Casino Size: 8,000 Square Feet
Other Games: S21, TCP
Senior Discount: 10% off food Mon-Wedif 55+
Special Features: 600-passenger barge that remains dockside on the Mississippi River. 8-space RV park.

St. Joseph

Map Location: **#3** (55 miles N. of Kansas City)

St. Jo Frontier Casino
77 Francis Street
St. Joseph, Missouri 64501
(816) 279-5514
Website: www.stjocasino.com

Toll-Free Number: (800) 888-2946
Restaurants: 4
Buffets: B-$4.49 L-$5.99 D-$8.49
Hours: 8am-2am/4am (Fri/Sat)
Valet Parking: Not Offered
Casino Size: 9,260 Square Feet
Other Games: S21, LIR, TCP
Casino Marketing: (800) WIN-STJO
Senior Discount: 2-for-1 breakfast buffet on Wed, if 55, or older
Special Features: 600-passenger paddlewheel boat that remains docked on the Missouri River. Entertainment barge next to the casino has a bar and gift shop. Conference center.

St. Louis

Map Location: **#2**

In addition to the three St. Louis-area casinos shown below, the Casino Queen in E. St. Louis, Illinois is also a nearby casino. It is located on the other side of the Mississippi river from downtown St. Louis. Additionally, the Alton Belle in Alton, Illinois is about 25 miles north of St. Louis. Both Illinois casinos are not restricted by the $500 loss limit (per two-hours) that is in effect in Missouri casinos.

Ameristar Casino St. Charles
P.O. Box 720
St. Charles, Missouri 63302
(314) 949-4300
Website: www.ameristarcasinos.com
Map Location: **#2** (5 miles W. of St. Louis)

Toll-Free Number: (800) 325-7777
Restaurants: 3
Buffets: B-$4.99 L-$6.99/$8.99 (Sun)
        D-$9.99 (Mon/Wed/Sat)/$12.99
Hours: 8am-5am/24hrs (Fri-Sat)
Valet Parking: $5
Casino Size: 115,000 Square Feet
Other Games: LIR, P, PGP, TCP
Senior Discount: Mon-Thu from 8am-6pm
    receive double points, gift shop discounts,
    $1 lunch and free valet parking, by joining *Golden Opportunities*, if 55, or older
Special Features: 2,000-passenger barge that remains dockside on the Missouri River.

Harrah's St. Louis
777 Casino Center Drive
Maryland Heights, Missouri 63043
(314) 770-8100
Website: www.harrahs.com
Map Location: **#2** (6 miles W. of St. Louis)

Toll-Free Number: (800) HARRAHS
Rooms: 277 Price Range: $79-$199
Suites: 14 Price Range: $169-$299
Restaurants: 6
Buffets: B-$6.95 L-$8.95
        D-$12.95/$16.95 (Mon/Wed/Fri/Sat)
Hours:
Island: 11am-5am/24 hours (Fri-Sat)
Mardi Gras: 8am-5am/24 hours (Fri-Sat)
Valet Parking: $5
Senior Discount: $1.50 off breakfast and
                 lunch buffets
Casino Size: 120,000 Square Feet Total
Other Games: S21, MB, LIR, TCP
Senior Discount: $1.50 off lunch buffet, 10%
    gift shop discount, cash drawings Tue/Fri,
    if 50, or older with Player's Club Card
Special Features: Two 3,200-passenger barges that remain dockside on the Missouri River.

President Casino - St. Louis
800 North First Street
St. Louis, Missouri 63102
(314) 622-3000
Website: www.presidentcasino.com
Map Location: **#2**

Toll-Free Number: (800) 772-3647
Restaurants: 2
Buffets: L-$7.95 D-$12.95
Hours: 8am-4am/24hrs (Fri/Sat)
Admission: $2
Parking: Free with casino validation
Valet Parking: $5
Other Games: LIR, P, PGP, TCP
Senior Discount: 2-for-1lunch buffet and other
                 discounts on Thursdays, if 55, or older
Special Features: 2,500-passenger, art deco riverboat that remains dockside on the Mississippi River near the Gateway Arch. Free shuttle service to and from all downtown hotels. One block from Laclede's Landing Metro Link Light Rail Station.

MONTANA

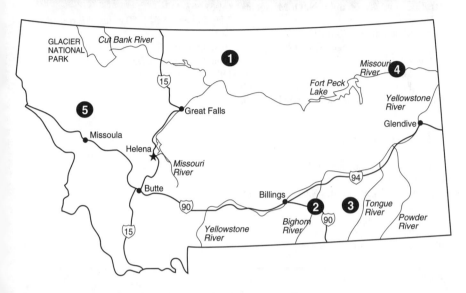

Montana law permits bars and taverns to have up to 20 video gaming devices that play video poker, video keno, or video bingo. These machines are operated in partnership with the state and are not permitted to pay out in cash; instead, they print out a receipt which must be taken to a cashier. The maximum bet on these machines is $2 and the maximum payout is limited to $800. Montana gaming regulations require these machines to return a minimum of 80%.

There are five Indian Tribes offering video gaming machines that also print out a receipt. The maximum bet on these machines is $2 and the maximum payout is capped at $1,000. According to Wilbur Raymond of Montana's Gambling Control Division, there are no minimum payback amounts required for gaming machines on Indian reservations. The minimum gambling age in Montana is 18.

For Montana tourism information call (800) VISIT-MT.

Charging Horse Casino
P.O. Box 128
Lame Deer, Montana 59043
(406) 477-6677
Map Location: **#3** (90 miles S.E. of Billings on Hwy. 212)

Restaurants: 1 Snack Bar Liquor: No
Hours: 7am-2am Daily

4 C's Cafe & Casino
Rocky Boy Route, Box 544
Box Elder, Montana 59521
(406) 395-4863
Map Location: **#1** (75 miles N.E. of Great Falls)

Restaurants: 1 Liquor: No
Hours: 9am-2:30am Daily

KwaTaqNuk Casino Resort
303 Highway 93
E. Polson, Montana 59860
(406) 883-3636
Map Location: **#5** (65 miles N. Of Missoula)

Room Reservations: (800) 882-6363
Rooms: 112 Price Range: $79-$129
Restaurants: 1 Liquor: Yes
Hours: 24 Hours Daily
Special Features: Hotel is Best Western. 10%
AAA room discount. Indoor pool and hot tub.

SilverWolf Casino
Highway 25 East
P.O. Box 726
Wolf Point, Montana 59201
(406) 653-3476
Map Location: **#4** (180 miles N.E of Billings)

Restaurants: 1 Snack Bar Liquor: No
Hours: 11am-Mid Daily
Other Games: Bingo

Little Big Horn Casino
P.O. Box 580
Crow Agency, Montana 59022
(406) 638-4000
Map Location: **#2** (65 miles S.E. of Billings)

Restaurants: 1 Liquor: No
Hours: 9am-2am/4am (Fri/Sat)
Other Games: Bingo (Thu-Sat)

NEVADA

All Nevada casinos are open 24 hours and, unless otherwise noted, offer: slots, video poker, craps, blackjack, and roulette. The minimum gambling age is 21.

Other games in the casino listings include: sports book (SB), race book (RB), baccarat (B), mini-baccarat (MB), pai gow (PG), poker (P), pai gow poker (PGP), Caribbean stud poker (CSP), let it ride (LIR), Spanish 21 (S21), sic bo (SIC), three-card poker (TCP), keno (K), big 6 wheel (B6) and bingo (BG).

Amargosa Valley

Map Location: **#8** (91 miles N.W. of Las Vegas on Hwy. 95)

Longstreet Inn and Casino
Route 373, HCR 70
Amargosa Valley, Nevada 89020
(775) 372-1777
Website: www.longstreetinn.com

Toll-Free Number: (800) 508-9493
Rooms: 46 Price Range: $59-$69
Suites: 14 Price Range: $89
Restaurants: 2
Other Games: No Craps or Roulette
Senior Discount: 20% off meals, if 65 or older
Special Features: 50-space RV Park. 9-hole par-3 golf course. 24-hour convenience store.

Stateline Saloon
Route 15, Box 566R
Amargosa Valley, Nevada 89020
(775) 372-5238

Restaurants: 1
Other Games: No Craps or Roulette

Battle Mountain

Map Location: **#9** (215 mile N.E. of Reno on I-80)

Nevada Hotel & Casino
8 E. Front Street
Battle Mountain, Nevada 89820
(775) 635-2453

Rooms: 13 Price Range: $17-$60
Restaurants: 1
Casino Size: 840 Square Feet
Other Games: No Craps or Roulette

Beatty

Map Location: **#10** (120 miles N.W. of Las Vegas on Hwy. 95)

Burro Inn Motel & Casino
Highway 95 South
Beatty, Nevada 89003
(775) 553-2225

Reservation Number: (800) 843-2078
Rooms: 61   Price Range: $35-$45
Suites: 1   Price Range: $65
Restaurants: 1
Other Games: No Craps or Roulette
Fun Book: Given to hotel guests.
Special Features: 43-space RV park. Four miles from Rhyolite ghost town.

Exchange Club Casino & Motel
119 N. Main Street
Beatty, Nevada 89003
(775) 553-2368

Rooms: 44 Price Range: $38-$45
Suites: 1 Price Range: $68
Restaurants: 1 (open 24 hours)
Casino Size: 7,620 Square Feet
Other Games: P, No Craps or Roulette
Fun Book: Ask at motel office

Stagecoach Hotel & Casino
P.O. Box 836
Beatty, Nevada 89003
(775) 553-2419
Website: www.stagecoachhotel.com

Reservation Number: (800) 4-BIG-WIN
Rooms: 50 Price Range: $35-$40
Restaurants: 2
Casino Size: 8,800 Square Feet
Other Games: P, B6, No Roulette
Fun Book: Ask at front desk or cashier cage
Special Features: Swimming pool and Jacuzzi. Seven miles from Rhyolite ghost town. 90-space RV Park next door (775) 553-2238.

Boulder City

Map Location: **#11** (22 miles S.E. of Las Vegas on Hwy. 93)

Hacienda Hotel & Casino
U.S. Highway 93
Boulder City, Nevada 89005
(702) 293-5000
Website: www.haciendaonline.com

Reservation Number: (800) 245-6380
Rooms: 378 Price Range: $29-$79
Restaurants: 3
Buffets: L-$4.99 D-$6.99
Casino Size: 17,942 Square Feet
Other Games: SB, RB, P

Carson City

Map Location: **#7** (32 miles S. of Reno on Hwy. 395)

Carson Nugget
507 N. Carson Street
Carson City, Nevada 89701
(775) 882-1626
Website: www.ccnugget.com

Toll-Free Number: (800) 426-5239
Reservation Number: (800) 338-7760
Rooms: 82 Price Range: $38-$61
Restaurants: 5
Buffets: L-$5.95/$7.95 (Sat-Sun)
       D-$7.95/$13.95 (Fri)
Casino Size: 24,320 Square Feet
Other Games: SB, RB, LIR, TCP, K, BG
Fun Book: Available at local motels
Senior Discount: 10% off room/food, if 50+
Special Features: Rare gold display.

Carson Station Hotel/Casino
900 S. Carson Street
Carson City, Nevada 89702
(775) 883-0900

Reservation Number: (800) 528-1234
Rooms: 92 Price Range: $55-$85
Suites: 3 Price Range: $80-$105
Restaurants: 2
Casino Size: 6,750 Square Feet
Other Games: SB, RB, K
Special Features: Hotel is Best Western.

Piñon Plaza Casino Resort
2171 Highway 50 East
Carson City, Nevada 89701
(775) 885-9000
Website: www.pinonplaza.com

Toll-Free Number: (877) 519-5567
Rooms: 148 Price Range: $50-$90
Suites: 22 Price Range: $90-$125
Restaurants: 2
Casino Size: 16,926 Square Feet
Other Games: SB, RB
Fun Book: Given to resort/RV guests
Senior Discount: 10% off food, if 55 or older
Special Features: Hotel is Best Western. 30-space RV park. 32-lane bowling center. 10% off room for AAA and AARP members.

Elko

Map Location: **#3** (289 miles N.E. of Reno on I-80)

Commercial Casino
345 4th Street
Elko, Nevada 89801
(775) 738-3181
Website: www.fh-inc.com

Toll-Free Number: (800) 648-2345
Restaurants: 2
Casino Size: 6,440 Square Feet
Other Games: TCP, No Craps or Roulette
Fun Book: Show out-of-Elko ID at cashier cage
Special Features: Oldest continually operating casino in Nevada. 10-foot-tall stuffed polar bear in casino. Large gunfighter art collection.

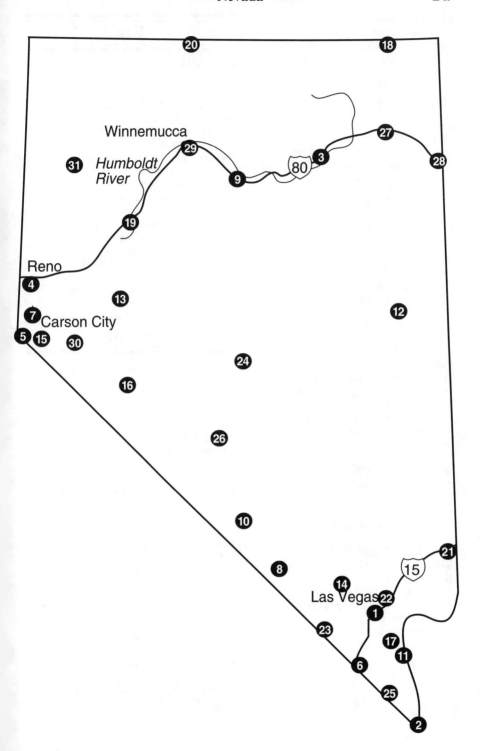

Gold Country Motor Inn
2050 Idaho Street
Elko, Nevada 89801
(775) 738-8421

Room Reservations: (800) 621-1332
Rooms: 140   Price Range: $69-$109
Rooms: 11   Price Range: $99-$119
Restaurants: 1
Casino Size: 2,359 Square Feet
Other Games: No Craps or Roulette
Special Features: Motor Inn is Best Western.

Red Lion Inn & Casino
2065 Idaho Street
Elko, Nevada 89801
(775) 738-2111
Website: www.redlioncasino.com

Reservation Number: (800) 545-0044
Rooms: 223 Price Range: $76-$119
Suites: 2 Price Range: $259
Restaurants: 2 (1 open 24 hours)
Buffets: B-$7.25 L-$7.50
            D-$9.50/$12.50 (Sat)/$15.95 (Fri)
Casino Size: 20,350 Square Feet
Other Games: SB, RB, P, LIR, K, BG
Fun Book: Ask at Player's Club Booth
Special Features: Air junkets offered from 90
U.S. cities-call (800) 258-8800. Sports bar.
AAA and AARP room discount.

Stockmen's Hotel & Casino
340 Commercial Street
Elko, Nevada 89801
(775) 738-5141
Website: www.fh-inc.com

Reservation Number: (800) 648-2345
Rooms: 141 Price Range: $31-$60
Restaurants: 2
Buffets: D-$7.95/$11.95 (Fri)
Casino Size: 7,030 Square Feet
Other Games: SB, TCP
Fun Book: Show out-of-Elko ID at cashier cage
Special Features: 24-hour shuttle service.

Ely

Map Location: **#12** (317 miles E. of Reno on
Hwy. 50)

Hotel Nevada & Gambling Hall
501 Aultman Street
Ely, Nevada 89301
(775) 289-6665
Website: www.hotelnevada.com

Reservation Number: (888) 406-3055
Rooms: 45   Price Range: $19-$48
Restaurants: 1
Casino Size: 2,980 Square Feet
Other Games: P, No Craps or Roulette
Fun Book: Ask at front desk
Special Features: Built in 1929. Historical dis-
play of mining, ranching and railroad artifacts.
10% room discount to AARP members

Fallon

Map Location: **#13** (61 miles E. of Reno on
Hwy. 50)

Bird Farm
128 E. Williams Avenue
Fallon, Nevada 89406
(775) 423-7877

Other Games: P, No Blackjack or Roulette
Special Features: Craps played after 7pm.

Bonanza Inn & Casino
855 W. Williams Avenue
Fallon, Nevada 89406
(775) 423-6031

Reservation Number: (702) 423-6031
Rooms: 74 Price Range: $39-$50
Suites: 2 Price Range: $50-$68
Restaurants: 1
Casino Size: 5,830 Square Feet
Other Games: K, No Craps or Roulette
Fun Book: Only given to hotel guests
Senior Discount: $5 off room, if 55 or older

Depot Casino & Restaurant
875 W. Williams Avenue
Fallon, Nevada 89406
(775) 423-2411

Restaurants: 1
Casino Size: 4,655 Square Feet
Other Games: BG, No Craps or Roulette
Special Features: BJ open Wed-Sat after 6pm.

Stockman's Casino
1560 W. Williams Avenue
Fallon, Nevada 89406
(775) 423-2117

Toll-Free Number: (800) HOLIDAY
Rooms: 60 Price Range: $39-$54
Suites: 8 Price Range: $89-$129
Restaurants: 2
Casino Size: 7,587 Square Feet
Other Games: K, No Roulette or Craps
Senior Discount: Various, if 60 or older
Special Features: Hotel is Holiday Inn Express.
10% AAA room discount.

Gardnerville

Map Location: **#15** (45 miles S. of Reno on
Hwy. 395)

Sharkey's Nugget
P.O. Box 625
Gardnerville, Nevada 89410
(775) 782-3133

Restaurants: 1
Casino Size: 694 Square Feet
Other Games: No Craps or Roulette. BJ opens
at 3pm/12pm (Fri-Sat)

Topaz Lodge & Casino
1979 Highway 395 South
Gardnerville, Nevada 89410
(775) 266-3338
Website: www.enterit.com/topaz3338

Reservation Number: (800) 962-0732
Rooms: 59 Price Range: $40-$58
Restaurants: 1
Buffets: B-$6.95 (Sun)
         D-$13.95(Fri)/$7.95(Sat)
Casino Size: 12,800 Square Feet
Other Games: BG, No Roulette

Gerlach

Map Location: **#31** (107 miles N.E. of Reno)

Bruno's Country Club
445 Main Street
Gerlach, Nevada
(775) 557-2220

Rooms: 40 Price Range: $45-$55
Restaurants: 1
Other Games: No Craps or Roulette

Hawthorne

Map Location: **#16** (138 miles S.E. of Reno
on Hwy. 95)

El Capitan Resort Casino
540 F Street
Hawthorne, Nevada 89415
(775) 945-3321

Rooms: 103 Price Range: $35-$72
Restaurants: 1
Casino Size: 10,000 Square Feet
Other Games: No Craps or Roulette
Fun Book: Ask at front desk

Henderson

Map Location: **#17** (15 miles S.E. of Las Vegas on Hwy. 93)

Barley's Casino & Brewing Co.
4500 E. Sunset Road #30
Henderson, Nevada 89014
(702) 458-2739

Restaurants: 1
Casino Size: 10,000 Square Feet
Other Games: SB
Special Features: Located in a strip mall. Four
varieties of beer micro-brewed on the pre-
mises.

Eldorado Casino
140 Water Street
Henderson, Nevada 89015
(702) 564-1811
Website: www.boydgaming.com

Restaurants: 2
Casino Size: 17,756 Square Feet
Other Games: SB, PGP, K, BG

Fiesta Henderson Casino Hotel
777 West Lake Mead Drive
Henderson, Nevada 89015
(702) 558-7000

Toll-Free Number: (866) 469-7666
Rooms: 200 Price Range: $19-$99
Restaurants: 4 (1 open 24 hours)
Buffets: B-$9.99 (Sat/Sun) L-$6.99
  D-$9.99/$14.99 (Fri)/$10.99 (Wed/Sat/Sun)
Casino Size: 65,560 Square Feet
Other Games: SB, PGP, LIR, TCP, K, BG
Senior Discount: Join Fun Club, if 50 or older
Special Features: Nils Lofgren guitar bar. Beer
garden. Video arcade.

Green Valley Ranch Resort
2300 Paseo Verde Drive
Henderson, Nevada 89012
(702) 617-7777
Website: www.greenvalleyranchresort.com

Reservation Number: (866) 782-9487
Rooms: 200 Price Range: $129-$239
Suites: 45 Price Range: $204-$354
Restaurants: (1 open 24 hours)
Buffets: B-$5.99 L-$7.99
       D-$12.99/$14.99 (Fri-Sun)
Casino Size: 50,000 Square Feet
Other Games: SB, RB, B, MB, PGP,LIR, TCP

Hyatt Regency Lake Las Vegas Resort
101 Montelago Boulevard
Las Vegas, Nevada 89011
(702) 567-1234
Web site: www.lakelasvegas.hyatt.com

Reservation Number: (800) 55-HYATT
Rooms: 449 Price Range: $115-$525
Suite: 47 Price Range: $750-$900
Restaurants: 4
Casino Size: 6,500 Square Feet
Other Games: MB
Special Features: Located by large private lake.
18-hole Jack Nicklaus designed golf course.

Jokers Wild
920 N. Boulder Highway
Henderson, Nevada 89015
(702) 564-8100
Website: www.boydgaming.com

Restaurants: 1
Buffets: L-$4.49 D-$5.99/$8.99 (Fri)
Casino Size: 23,698 Square Feet
Other Games: SB, K
Senior Discount: $1 off dinner, if 55 or older

Klondike Sunset Casino
444 West Sunset
Henderson, Nevada 89015
(702) 568-7575

Restaurants: 1
Casino Size: 7,700 Square Feet
Other Games: No Craps

Railroad Pass Hotel & Casino
2800 S. Boulder Highway
Henderson, Nevada 89015
(702) 294-5000
Website: www.railroadpass.com

Toll-Free Number: (800) 654-0877
Rooms: 100 Price Range: $29-$59
Suites: 20 Price Range: $36-$79
Restaurants: 3 (1 open 24 hours)
Buffets: B-$5.99 (Sat-Sun) L-$4.99
       D-$6.99/$7.99 (Fri-Sat)
Casino Size: 23,584 Square Feet
Other Games: SB, RB
Fun Book: Show out-of-state ID at front desk
Senior Discount: Food discount Mon, if 55+
Special Features: Video arcade. Gift shop.

Skyline Restaurant & Casino
1741 N. Boulder Highway
Henderson, Nevada 89015
(702) 565-9116

Restaurants: 1
Buffets: L-$4.45
Casino Size: 8,500 Square Feet
Other Games: SB, RB, No Craps or Roulette
Fun Book: Available at local hotels/motels

Sunset Station Hotel and Casino
1301 W. Sunset Road
Henderson, Nevada 89014
(702) 547-7777
Website: www.sunsetstation.com

Reservation Number: (888) 786-7389
Rooms: 448 Price Range: $45-$105
Suites: 18 Price Range: $99-$139
Restaurants: 12 (1 open 24 hours)
Buffets: B-$4.99/$8.99 (Sat-Sun) L-$6.99
D-$9.99/$11.99 (Thu)/$15.99 (Fri)
Casino Size: 133,409 Square Feet
Other Games: SB, RB, S21, MB, P, PGP,
LIR, TCP, K, BG
Special Features: 13 movie theaters. Kid's
Quest childcare center. Video arcade.

Indian Springs

Map Location: **#14** (35 miles N.W. of Las Vegas on Hwy. 95)

Indian Springs Casino
372 Tonopah Highway
Indian Springs, Nevada 89018
(702) 879-3456
Website: www.wherethehellisindiansprings.com

Reservation Number: (877) 977-7746
Restaurants: 1
Rooms: 45 Price Range: $35-$49
Other Games: No Craps or Roulette
Funbook: Ask at cashier cage
Special Features: RV park. Convenience store.

Jackpot

Map Location: **#18** (Just S. of the Idaho border on Hwy. 93)

Barton's Club 93
Highway 93
Jackpot, Nevada 89825
(775) 755-2341

Toll-Free Number: (800) 258-2937
Rooms: 98 Price Range: $43-$70
Suites: 4 Price Range: $90-$135
Restaurants: 2
Buffets: B-$5.93 (Sat-Sun) D-$4.93 (Wed)/
$5.93 (Thu/Sun)/$9.93 (Fri-Sat)
Casino Size: 9,550 Square Feet
Other Games: K, LIR
Fun Book: Ask at registration desk

Cactus Pete's Resort Casino
1385 Highway 93
Jackpot, Nevada 89825
(775) 755-2321
Website: www.ameristarcasinos.com

Reservation Number: (800) 821-1103
Rooms: 272 Price Range: $37-$89
Suites: 28 Price Range: $125-$185
Restaurants: 5
Buffets: B-$5.99 (Sat)/$8.99 (Sun)
L-$5.99 D-$7.99/$10.99 (Fri-Sat)
Casino Size: 25,351 Square Feet
Other Games: SB, P, PGP, K
Senior Discount: 15% off room/restaurant,
20% off gift shop, if 60 or older
Special Features: Every Wed 5pm-11pm all
restaurants are half-price. 18-hole golf course.
Free dinner on birthday and anniversary.

Horseshu Hotel & Casino
Highway 93
Jackpot, Nevada 89825
(702) 755-7777
Website: www.ameristars.com

Reservation Number: (800) 432-0051
Rooms: 110 Price Range: $27-$85
Suites: 10 Price Range: $125-$185
Restaurants: 1
Casino Size: 3,520 Square Feet
Other Games: K, No Roulette

Jean

Map Location: **#6** (22 miles S.W. of Las Vegas on I-15; 12 miles from the California border)

Gold Strike Hotel & Gambling Hall
1 Main Street/P.O. Box 19278
Jean, Nevada 89019
(702) 477-5000
Website: www.goldstrike-jean.com

Reservation Number: (800) 634-1359
Rooms: 800 Price Range: $19-$49
Suites: 13 Price Range: $24-$110
Restaurants: 5
Buffets: B-$7.50 (Sat/Sun) L-$6.96
D-$8.03/$9.64 (Fri)/$9.11 (Sat)
Casino Size: 37,006 Square Feet
Other Games: CSP
Fun Book: Ask at hotel registration desk
Special Features: Free shuttle to Nevada Landing. $1.99 breakfast special. Burger King.

Nevada Landing Hotel & Casino
2 Goodsprings Road/P.O. Box 19278
Jean, Nevada 89019
(702) 387-5000
Website: www.nevadalanding.com

Reservation Number: (800) 628-6682
Rooms: 287 Price Range: $19-$54
Suites: 16 Price Range: $70-$125
Restaurants: 4
Buffets: B-$7.50 (Sat/Sun) L-$6.96
        D-$8.03/$9.64 (Fri)/$9.11 (Sat)
Casino Size: 35,700 Square Feet
Other Games: SB, PGP, CSP
Fun Book: Ask at hotel registration desk
Special Features: Free shuttle to Gold Strike.
$1.99 breakfast special.

Lake Tahoe

Map Location: **#5** (directly on the Nevada/
California border; 98 miles northeast of Sacramento and 58 miles southwest of Reno).

The area is best known for its many recreational activities with skiing in the winter and water sports in the summer. Lake Tahoe Airport is located at the south end of the basin. The next closest airport is in Reno with regularly scheduled shuttle service by bus. Incline Village and Crystal Bay are on the north shore of Lake Tahoe, while Stateline is located on the south shore. For South Lake Tahoe information call the Lake Tahoe Visitors Authority at (800) AT-TAHOE and for North Lake Tahoe information call the Incline Village/Crystal Bay Convention & Visitors Authority at (800) GO-TAHOE.

Here's information, as supplied by Nevada's State Gaming Control Board, showing the slot machine payback percentages for all of the south shore casinos for the fiscal year beginning July 1, 2001 and ending June 30, 2002:

Denomination	Payback %
5¢ Slots	90.98
25¢ Slots	93.43
$1 Slots	95.22
$1 Megabucks	84.90
$5 Slots	95.67
All Slots	94.39

And here's that same information for the north shore casinos:

Denomination	Payback %
5¢ Slots	93.21
25¢ Slots	94.26
$1 Slots	95.57
$1 Megabucks	89.30
$5 Slots	95.28
All Slots	94.51

These numbers reflect the percentage of money returned to the players on each denomination of machine. All electronic machines including slots, video poker and video keno are included in these numbers.

Optional games in the casino listings include: sports book (SB), race book (RB), baccarat (B), mini-baccarat (MB), poker (P), pai gow poker (PGP), Caribbean stud poker (CSP), let it ride (LIR), keno (K) and bingo (BG).

Bill's Casino
U.S. Highway 50/P.O. Box 8
Stateline, Nevada 89449
(775) 588-2455
Website: www.harrahs.com

Restaurants: 1 (open 24 hours)
Casino Size: 18,000 Square Feet
Special Features: Separate casino that is owned by Harrah's Lake Tahoe.

Caesars Tahoe
55 Highway 50
Stateline, Nevada 89449
(775) 588-3515
Website: www.caesars.com

Reservation Number: (800) 648-3353
Rooms: 403 Price Range: $69-$160
Suites: 37 Price Range: $379-$750
Restaurants: 5 (1 open 24 hours)
Buffets: B/L-$9.99/$10.99 (Sat)/$14.99 (Sun)
        D-$12.99/$19.99 (Fri-Sat)/$13.99 (Sun)
Casino Size: 40,500 Square Feet
Other Games: SB, RB, B, MB, PG, PGP
        CSP, LIR, TCP, B6, K
Special Features: On south shore of Lake Tahoe. Health spa. Planet Hollywood restaurant.

Cal-Neva Lodge Resort
Hotel, Spa & Casino
P.O. Box 368
Crystal Bay, Nevada 89402
(775) 832-4000
Website: www.calnevaresort.com

Reservation Number: (800) CAL-NEVA
Rooms: 180 Price Range: $79-$139
Suites: 27 Price Range: $169-$209
Restaurants: 1
Casino Size: 10,020 Square Feet
Other games: P
Special Features: Straddles California/Nevada
state line on north shore of Lake Tahoe. Lake
view rooms. European Spa. Three wedding
chapels. Florist. Photo studio. Bridal boutique.
Gift shop. Airport shuttle. Internet cafe.

Harrah's Lake Tahoe
Highway 50/P.O. Box 8
Stateline, Nevada 89449
(775) 588-6611
Website: www.harrahs.com

Reservation Number: (800) HARRAHS
Rooms: 451 Price Range: $129-$259
Suites: 62 Price Range: $199-$800
Restaurants: 7 (1 open 24 hours)
Buffets: B-$9.99/$16.99 (Sun) L-$10.99
        D-$16.99/$24.99 (Fri)/$22.99 (Sat)
Casino Size: 83,388 Square Feet
Casino Marketing: (800) 346-6569
Other Games: SB, RB, B, MB, PG, PGP
        CSP, LIR, TCP, K
Special Features: On south shore of Lake
Tahoe. Health club. Pet kennel.

Harveys Resort Hotel/Casino - Lake Tahoe
P.O. Box 128 - Highway 50
Stateline, Nevada 89449
(775) 588-2411
Website: http://www.harrahs.com/
our_casinos/hlt/

Toll-Free Number: (800) 553-1022
Reservation Number: (800) HARVEYS
Rooms: 740 Price Range: $99-$279
Suites: 36 Price Range: $300-$679
Restaurants: 8 (1 open 24 hours)
Buffets: B-$8.50/$11.95 (Sat)/$14.95 (Sun)
        L-$9.95 D-$14.50/$22.95 (Fri-Sat)

Casino Size: 81,731 Square Feet
Other Games: SB, RB, S21, B, MB, P,
        PGP, CSP, LIR, TCP, B6, K
Special Features: On south shore of Lake
Tahoe. AAA room discount. Health Club.

Hyatt Regency Lake Tahoe
Resort & Casino
P.O. Box 3239
Incline Village, Nevada 89450
(775) 832-1234
Website: www.laketahoehyatt.com

Toll-Free Number: (800) 553-3288
Reservation Number: (800) 233-1234
Rooms: 412 Price Range: $99-$230
Suites: 48 Price Range: $425-$900
Restaurants: 2 (1 open 24 hours)
Buffets: B-$12.95
        D-$22.00 (Fri)/$20.00 (Sat)
Casino Size: 18,900 Square Feet
Other Games: SB, CSP, LIR, TCP
Senior Discount: Up to 50% off room, if 62+
Special Features: On north shore of Lake
Tahoe. Two Robert Trent Jones golf courses.

Lake Tahoe Horizon
50 Highway 50/P.O. Box C
Lake Tahoe, Nevada 89449
(775) 588-6211
Website: www.horizoncasino.com

Toll-Free Number: (800) 322-7723
Reservation Number: (800) 648-3322
Rooms: 519 Price Range: $39-$169
Suites: 20 Price Range: $300-$500
Restaurants: 5 (1 open 24 hours)
Buffets: D-$9.95/$11.95 (Fri-Sat)
Casino Size: 30,999 Square Feet
Other Games: SB, RB, S21, P, PGP, TCP, K
Senior Discount: 10% to 25% off room,if 50+
Special Features: On south shore of Lake
Tahoe. Outdoor heated pool with 3 hot tubs.
Wedding chapel. Video arcade. Baskin-
Robbins store.

Lakeside Inn & Casino
Highway 50 & Kingsbury Grade
Stateline, Nevada 89449
(775) 588-7777
Website: www.lakesideinn.com

Toll-Free Number: (800) 523-1291
Room Reservations: (800) 624-7980
Rooms: 123 Price Range: $79-$119
Suites: 2 Price Range: $110-$280
Restaurants: 2 (open 24 hours)
Casino Size: 18,175 Square Feet
Other Games: SB, RB, K
Special Features: On south shore of Lake Tahoe. Gift shop. Video arcade.

Tahoe Biltmore Lodge & Casino
#5 Highway 28/P.O. Box 115
Crystal Bay, Nevada 89402
(775) 831-0660
Website: www.tahoebiltmore.com

Reservation Number: (800) BILTMOR
Rooms: 92 Price Range: $49-$119
Suites: 7 Price Range: $119-$159
Restaurants: 2 (1 open 24 hours)
Casino Size: 10,480 Square Feet
Other Games: SB, RB, K
Funbook: Show out-of-state ID at casino cage
Special Features: On north shore of Lake Tahoe. All rooms include free breakfast. Video arcade.

Las Vegas

Map Location: **#1**

Las Vegas is truly the casino capital of the world! While many years ago the city may have had a reputation as an "adult playground" run by "shady characters," today's Las Vegas features many family-oriented facilities run by some of America's most familiar corporate names.

Las Vegas has more hotel rooms - 130,000 - than any other city in the U.S. and it attracts more than 31 million visitors each year. The abundance of casinos in Las Vegas forces them to compete for customers in a variety of ways and thus, there are always great bargains to be had, but only if you know where to look.

Las Vegas Advisor newsletter publisher, Anthony Curtis is the city's resident expert on where to find the best deals. His monthly 12-page publication is always chock full of powerful, money-saving, profit-making and vacation enhancing tips for the Las Vegas visitor and here are some of his thoughts on the Best of Las Vegas:

Best Las Vegas Bargain
Shrimp Cocktail, 99¢, Golden Gate

The Golden Gate's 99¢ shrimp cocktail is not only the current best bargain in town, it's been one of the best for more than 40 years. The six-ounce sundae glass full of shrimp was introduced back in 1957 for 50¢ and remained at that price until it was raised to 99¢ in 1991. All shrimp. No filler. Served 24 hours a day.

Best Room Rate
Free, Las Vegas Hotel-Casinos

The only other vacation scenario that includes this possibility involves a tent, sleeping bag, and a lot of wilderness. Why would casinos give rooms away? Competition. Hotels with 3,000, 4,000, and 5,000 rooms open, and the owners of hotels with only 1,000 or 2,000 rooms get nervous. Lulls, city-wide occupancy levels sometimes plummet below 90%, especially in December. Gasp! But mostly, it's the gambling. Gambling winnings subsidize the room department (and the food department, and the alcohol department, and the entertainment department, and ...). The best way to get in on the free-room bonanza is to join slot clubs.

Best Loss Leader
5¢ Coffee, Westward Ho

Coffee is cheap, but it's not this cheap. For a super nostalgia blast from the past, grab a cuppa Joe at the Ho for just a nickel at Nickel Nick's snack bar. Another five thin dimes get you a fresh donut. Throw in an eight-bit newspaper and you've got the All-American breakfast for less than one smacker.

Best Breakfast

Old Guard—Steak & Eggs, $2.49,
Arizona Charlie's East
New Guard—Any breakfast buffet, about $5

The Arizona Charlie's deal has been around for several years now; however, it's now limited to the East location on Boulder Hwy. (the tab at West has been raised to $2.99). This is a four- to six-ounce sirloin steak and eggs served 24 hours in the coffee shop. The compact steak is thick enough to cook perfectly to order, and because they serve so many, the preparation is expert.

While prices climb for lunch and dinner buffets, breakfast buffets continue to be a low-priced constant. Get eggs cooked to order, breakfast meats, fresh fruit, pastries and rolls, plus all the beverages you desire, in many buffets for less than $6.

Best Buffet

Ports O' Call, $4.45-$8.95, Gold Coast

The incredible Ports O' Call now takes top honors over Las Vegas' 50 or so buffet offerings. It's another multi-station superbuffet, offering Italian, Mexican, Chinese, seafood, barbecue, even a Mongolian grill. While several Las Vegas buffets boast similar quality, none can compare for price, at $4.45 for breakfast, $6.45 for lunch, and $8.95 for dinner or an outstanding Sunday brunch.

Best Sunday Brunch

$55, Bally's

A vacation-topping Sunday brunch is the perfect Las Vegas splurge, and the epic Sterling Brunch at Bally's is as good as it gets. Despite being the highest-priced spread in town, the Sterling Brunch still qualifies as a bargain, offering sushi, oysters and clams, lobster tail, prime meats, and fantastic desserts, including goblets of fresh berries. The brand of champagne changes, but it's always a step or two above that served at the other brunches in town.

Best Meal

Steak Dinner, $4.95, Ellis Island

Carrying on the tradition of the legendary Las Vegas steak dinners is the Ellis Island "filet-cut" sirloin. This complete dinner comes with choice of soup or salad, baked potato, and garlic toast for just $4.95. The 10-ounce steak is thick, so it can be cooked perfectly to specifications. Though available 24 hours a day seven days a week in the cafe, this great dinner is listed nowhere on the menu; you have to ask for it.

Best Snack Bar

Binion's Horseshoe

Prices have nudged up just a touch, but the two 24-hour snack bars at Binion's Horseshoe are still tops in town. The soup of the day is $2, the greasy-but-tasty chili is $3, and the turkey sandwiches—still made from real turkey—are $3.50. The best deal remains the daily chef's special of ham and beans (a different bean every day), served with cornbread, for $3.

Best Prime Rib

Cortez Room, $8.95, Gold Coast

Prices at former prime rib king Jerry's Nugget have risen precipitously, but that's not a problem. You can still get great prime rib dinners for under $10 all over town. The best is the special in the Cortez Room at the Gold Coast. Somehow they manage to hold the line on this great deal, served in the atmosphere of an old-time Las Vegas gourmet room. As is the custom at Gaughan gourmet rooms (they're also at El Cortez and Plaza), meals come with crudités and hot bread, as well as a big baked potato and vegetable of the day. You can get this dinner for just $5.50 when you combine it with the good Honky Tonk Angels show ($16.50).

Best Freebie
Pirate Show, Treasure Island

This swashbuckling, cannon-firing, powder-keg-exploding free show is a definite must-see, and more than once. It plays six times a night, weather cooperating, every 90 minutes starting at 4:30 p.m. The best viewing area, at the north end of the veranda at the Battle Bar, should be staked out as early as 45 minutes prior to show times. Another good viewing locale is the plank bridge between the ships, as close to the frigate-side rope railing as possible. It is necessary to arrive at least 30 minutes prior to show time to secure a good spot. It's a good show for young children, unless they are bothered by crowds, in which case you should watch from the sidewalk across the street.

Best Funbook
Hard Rock, Free

The Hard Rock distributes the "Six Pack" funsheet, which includes good gambling and dining coupons, and best of all, a free logo shot glass. This is such a good assemblage of offers, the Hard Rock has tightened up on distribution and the voucher you need to get the Six Pack is getting harder to find. One tried-and-true source is the freebie magazine Showbiz. Requirements change, so ask a slot club booth worker how to obtain a voucher.

5¢ Slot Machines
The Strip - 90.95%
Downtown - 91.97%
Boulder Strip - 93.28%
N. Las Vegas - 92.90%

25¢ Slot Machines
The Strip - 92.71%
Downtown - 94.90%
Boulder Strip - 96.38%
N. Las Vegas - 96.75%

$1 Slot Machines
The Strip - 94.74%
Downtown - 95.43%
Boulder Strip - 96.45%
N. Las Vegas - 97.25%

$1 Megabucks Machines
The Strip - 88.03%
Downtown - 87.97%
Boulder Strip - 87.90%
N. Las Vegas - 88.20%

$5 Slot Machines
The Strip - 95.75%
Downtown - 95.87%
Boulder Strip - 96.89%
N. Las Vegas - N/A

All Slot Machines
The Strip - 93.85%
Downtown - 94.47%
Boulder Strip - 95.48%
N. Las Vegas - 95.61%

Unlike New Jersey, the Nevada Gaming Control Board does not break down its slot statistics by individual properties. Rather, they are classified by area. The annual gaming revenue report breaks the Las Vegas market down into two different areas: the Strip and downtown. There is also a very big locals market in Las Vegas and those casinos are shown in the gaming revenue report for the North Las Vegas area. When choosing where to do your slot gambling, you may to keep in mind the following slot payback percentages for Nevada's fiscal year beginning July 1, 2001 and ending June 30, 2002:

These numbers reflect the percentage of money returned to the players on each denomination of machine. All electronic machines including slots, video poker and video keno are included in these numbers.

As you can see, the machines in downtown Las Vegas pay out 1% to 2% more than those located on the Las Vegas Strip for the lower denomination 5¢ and 25¢ machines. When you get to the $1 and $5 machines the difference is less noticeable but you can clearly see that the downtown casinos almost always return more than the Strip area casinos. This information is pretty well known by the locals and that's why many of them do their slot gambling away from the Strip unless they are drawn by a special slot club benefit or promotion.

Returns even better than the downtown casinos can be found at some of the other locals casinos along Boulder Highway such as Boulder Station and Sam's Town. The best returns of all, however, can be found at the locals casinos in the North Las Vegas area which would include the Fiesta, Santa Fe Station and Texas Station casinos. Not only are those numbers the best returns in the Las Vegas area, they are also the best payback percentage returns for anywhere in the United States.

As mentioned before, one of the best sources for finding out about the best "deals" on a current basis in the Las Vegas area is the *Las Vegas Advisor*. It is a 12-page monthly newsletter published by gaming expert Anthony Curtis. *Las Vegas Advisor* accepts no advertising and each issue objectively analyzes the best values in lodging, dining, entertainment and gambling to help you get the most for your money when visiting Las Vegas. The newsletter is especially well known for its "Top Ten Values" column which is often quoted by major travel publications. Each subscription also comes with a benefit package valued at more than $600. Ordering information for *Las Vegas Advisor* can be found later in this section.

There are many free tourist magazines that run coupon offers for casino fun books or special deals. Some sample titles are: *Tour Guide, Showbiz, What's On In Las Vegas, Best Read Guide* and *Today in Las Vegas*. All of these magazines are usually available in the hotel/motel lobbies or in the rooms themselves. If a fun book listing in this section says to look for an ad in a magazine, then it can probably be found in one of these publications. For Nevada tourism information call (800) NE-VADA-8. For Las Vegas information call the city's Convention & Visitors Authority at (702) 892-0711, or visit their Website at: www.lasvegas24hours.com.

Other games in the casino listings include: sports book (SB), race book (RB), baccarat (B), mini-baccarat (MB), pai gow (PG), poker (P), pai gow poker (PGP), Caribbean stud poker (CSP), three-card poker (TCP), let it ride (LIR), red dog (RD), big 6 wheel (B6), sic bo (SIC), keno (K) and bingo (BG).

Aladdin Hotel & Casino
3667 Las Vegas Boulevard S.
Las Vegas, Nevada 89109
(702) 785-5555
Website: www.aladdincasino.com

Reservation Number: (877) 333-9474
Rooms: 1,878 Price Range: $99-$299
Parlor Rooms: 466 Price Range: $279-$349
Suites: 223 Price Range: $299-$1,199
Restaurants: 21
Buffets: B-$10.99 L-$12.99 D-$18.99
Casino Size: 102,916 Square Feet
Other Games: SB, RB, B, MB, PG, PGP, CSP, LIR, TCP, B6, K
Special Features: 130-store retail mall. 7,000-seat Theater of the Performing Arts. Health spa and salon.

Arizona Charlie's - East
4575 Boulder Highway
Las Vegas, Nevada 89121
(702) 951-9000
Website: www.azcharlies.com

Reservation Number: (888) 236-9066
Rooms: 300 Price Range: $35-$65
Restaurants: 3 (1 open 24 hours)
Buffets: B-$4.29 L-$5.75 D-$7.75
Casino Size: 23,826 Square Feet
Other Games: SB, RB, PGP, BG
Senior Discount: 10% off buffet, if 55 or older
Special Features: 239-space RV park. $2.49 steak & eggs special.

Arizona Charlie's - West
740 S. Decatur Boulevard
Las Vegas, Nevada 89107
(702) 258-5200
Website: www.azcharlies.com

Reservation Number: (800) 342-2695
Rooms: 245 Price Range: $34-$89
Suites: 10 Price Range: $75-$195
Restaurants: 5 (1 open 24 hours)
Buffets: B-$4.29 L-$5.75 D-$7.75
Casino Size: 63,933 Square Feet
Other Games: SB, RB, P, PGP, K, BG
Senior Discount: 10% off buffet, if 55 or older
Special Features: 24-hour 50-lane bowling center. Video arcade. $2.49 steak & eggs special.

Bally's Las Vegas
3645 Las Vegas Blvd. South
Las Vegas, Nevada 89109
(702) 739-4111
Website: www.ballyslv.com

Toll-Free Number: (800) 7-BALLYS
Reservation Number: (888) 215-1078
Rooms: 2,814 Price Range: $59-$220
Suites: 265 Price Range: $160-$499
Restaurants: 6 (1 open 24 hours)
Buffets: B-$10.95 L-$12.95 D-$17.95
Casino Size: 68,278 Square Feet
Other Games: SB, RB, S21, B, MB, PG,
        PGP, CSP, LIR, TCP, B6, K
Senior Discount: 15% off rooms, if 50 or older
Fun Book: Given to hotel guests at check-in
Special Features: 20 retail stores. Free monorail service to MGM Grand. "Jubilee" stage show.

Barbary Coast Hotel & Casino
3595 Las Vegas Blvd. South
Las Vegas, Nevada 89109
(702) 737-7111
Website: www.barbarycoastcasino.com

Reservation Number: (888) 227-2279
Rooms: 200 Price Range: $49-$199
Suites: 12 Price Range: Casino Use Only
Restaurants: 3 (1 open 24 hours)
Casino Size: 32,000 Square Feet
Other Games: SB, RB, MB, LIR, TCP, PGP
Fun Book: Given to hotel guests at check-in

Barcelona Hotel & Casino
5011 E. Craig Road
Las Vegas, Nevada 89115
(702) 644-6300
Website: www.barcelonalasvegas.com

Toll-Free Number: (800) 223-6330
Rooms: 178 Price Range: $42-$60
Restaurants: 1 (open 24 hours)
Casino Size: 2,220 Square Feet
Other Games: SB, RB, No Craps
Senior Discount: $5 off room, if 62, or older,
Special Features: Special weekly and monthly room rates. $5 AAAroom discount.

Bellagio
3600 Las Vegas Blvd. South
Las Vegas, Nevada 89109
(702) 693-7111
Website: www.bellagioresort.com

Reservation Number: (888) 987-6667
Rooms: 2,688 Price Range: $159-$469
Suites: 308 Price Range: $325-$5,500
Restaurants: 12 (2 open 24 hours)
Buffets: B-$12.95/$22.95 (Sat-Sun)
      L-$16.95 D-$25.95
Casino Size: 156,257 Square Feet
Other Games: SB, RB, B, MB, P, PG, SIC
        PGP, CSP, LIR, TCP, B6, K
Special Features: Lake with nightly light and water show. Shopping mall. Two wedding chapels. Beauty salon and spa. Cirque du Soleil's "O" stage show.

Binion's Horseshoe Casino and Hotel
128 E. Fremont Street
Las Vegas, Nevada 89101
(702) 382-1600
Website: www.binions.com

Toll-Free Number: (800) 937-6537
Reservation Number: (800) 622-6468
Rooms: 300 Price Range: $29-$189
Suites: 34 Price Range: $55-$500
Restaurants: 3 (1 open 24 hours)
Casino Size: 56,929 Square Feet
Other Games: SB, RB, MB, P, LIR,
        TCP, B6, K, BG
Special Features: Home of World Series of Poker. Steak House on 23rd floor offers panoramic views of Las Vegas.

Boardwalk Hotel and Casino
3750 Las Vegas Blvd. South
Las Vegas, Nevada 89109
(702) 735-2400
Website: www.hiboardwalk.com

Reservation Number: (800) 635-4581
Rooms: 645 Price Range: $59-$129
Suites: 11 Price Range: $125-$750
Restaurants: 5 (2 open 24 hours)
Buffets: B-$6.99 L-$7.99 D-$9.49
Casino Size: 23,000 Square Feet
Other Games: SB, RB, LIR, TCP
Special Features: 24-hour buffet.

The Best Places To Play In Las Vegas

Roulette - The best roulette game in Las Vegas can be found in the London Club at the Aladdin which has single-zero wheel with a surrender rule in effect. Single-zero roulette has only a 2.70% edge as compared to the usual 5.26% edge on a double-zero roulette wheel. Additionally, the surrender rule means that if you make an even-money bet (odd-even, red-black, or high-low) and zero comes in, then you only lose half of your bet. This lowers the house edge to just 1.35% on those particular bets. The minimum bet is $10.

Single-zero wheels, without a surrender rule, can be found at Monte Carlo, Stratosphere, MGM Grand, Caesars Palace, Bellagio, Mandalay Bay, Paris and Venetian. The house edge in this game is 2.70%. Be aware, however, that only the Reserve has single-zero roulette exclusively. All of the other casinos offer it at just some of their roulette games and not all of them. Only the Stratosphere offers $5 minimum bets, the minimum is $25 at all others (sometimes $10 during the day), except for Bellagio ($100 minimum).

Craps - Only one casino allows up to 100x odds on their crap tables: Casino Royale (minimum bet is $1).

Mini-Baccarat - The normal 5% commission charged on winning bank bets in this game is reduced to only 4% at Binion's Horseshoe. This lowered commission reduces the house edge on bank bets from the standard 1.17% to just .067%.

Blackjack - All recommendations in this section apply to basic strategy players. For single-deck players the best game is at Slots A Fun (located next to Circus Circus) which offers one table that is a dead-even game and has no advantage for the casino! The rules are: dealer stands on soft 17, double down on any first two cards totaling 8,9,10 or 11, re-split any pair (except aces) and double after split. (They also have one other table with identical rules except that they hit soft 17. The casino advantage in this game is .19%)

Next best are the Fiesta (Rancho) and Silverton which both have the same rules as Slots A Fun except: the dealer hits soft 17 and you're allowed to double down on any two cards. The casino edge in this game is .06%. A similar game is offered at the Horseshoe except that you can't double after splitting but you are allowed to re-split aces. Tha casino advantage in this game is .15%

Next best are seven casinos that offer single-deck with the same rules as the last two, except they don't allow doubling after splitting: El Cortez, Four Queens, Golden Gate, Gold Spike, Lady Luck, Las Vegas Club and the Western. The casino edge here is .18%.

The best double-deck game in Las Vegas is offered at Caesars Palace with the following rules: dealer stands on soft 17, double down on any first two cards, re-split any pair (except aces), double down after split and late surrender. This works out to a casino edge of just .14% but there is a minimum bet requirement of $100.

Next best are eight casinos that offer those same rules, except for late surrender: Venetian, Bellagio, Mirage, Monte Carlo, Riviera, San Remo, Stardust and Treasure Island. The casino edge in these games is .19%. Keep in mind that these games aren't offered at every table, just some of them, so you'll have to look around each casino to find these better game. Also, these casinos will require higher minimum bets (usually $25 and up).

For six-deck shoe games the best casinos have these rules: dealer stands on soft 17, double after split allowed, late surrender offered and resplitting of aces allowed. The casino edge in this game works out to .26% and you can find it at many of the major casino properties: Bellagio, Caesars Palace, Golden Nugget, Luxor, Palms, Aladdin, Mandalay Bay, MGM Grand, Mirage, New York New York, Hard Rock, Treasure Island and the Venetian. The minimum bet at some of these casino casinos can be as high as $50 but a few are as low as $10 (Stardust). Many of these casinos also offer this same game with identical rules except that they will hit soft 17. The limits in the game are lower ($5 to $10) but the casino's mathematical edge in this game is raised to .46% Casinos offering this version of the game are: Treasure Island, Palms, Texas Station, Golden Nugget, New York New York and MGM Grand.

Video Poker - Las Vegas is the best place in the world for video poker. The three best varieties to look for are: 9/6 Jacks or Better, 10/7 Double Bonus and full-pay Deuces Wild. By only playing these three kinds of machines, playing the maximum coin and using perfect strategy you can achieve, theoretically, the following payback percentages: 99.54% on 9/6 Jacks or Better, 100.17% on 10/7 Double Bonus and 100.76% on full-pay Deuces Wild. All three kinds can be found in 25-cent denominations in the following casinos: Arizona Charlie's (East and West), California, Barbary Coast, El Cortez, both Fiestas, Gold Coast, Hard Rock, Plaza, Orleans, Sam's Town, San Remo, Santa Fe, Suncoast, Texas Station, Palace Station, Castaways and Silverton. By restricting your play to just these machines and taking advantage of the slot club benefits offered at these casinos you should be able to play at a 100%+ level.

Sometimes 10/7 Double Bonus games can be found with a payoff of 80-for-1 on straight flushes. That higher payoff on straight flushes raises the overall return to 100.51%. These better-paying quarter games can be found at the Four Queens, Gold Coast, Riviera, Arizona Charlie's West and Boulder Station. Additionally, the Plaza in downtown has some full pay Deuces Wild machines that pay 4,700 coins for the royal flush which raises the return to 101.07% on these games. The Stratosphere also offers some unique 25-cent Jacks or Better games: 9/7 (100.8%) and 10/6 (100.7%).

$1 full-pay Deuces Wild machines are extremely rare (if not extinct). 9/6 games can be found at the $1 level in many casinos ($1 10/7 games are rarer). There are rarer machines that return over 100% including joker's wild kings or better and All-American which can occassionally be found.

On the Strip generally the best machines you will find are 9/6 Jacks or Better. The only Strip locations to offer 10/7 Double Bonus are Circus Circus, Barbary Coast, Riviera, San Remo and Stratosphere. Only the Barbary Coast, Boardwalk, San Remo and Stratosphere offer full pay Deuces Wild on the Strip.

Slots - For slot players it pays to play where the machines are set to return the most. According to the Nevada Gaming Control Board, for the fiscal year ending June 30, 2002 the average Las Vegas Strip slot machine returned 93.85% while the average downtown casino's slots returned 94.47%. Among Boulder Highway casinos such as Sam's Town and Boulder Station the average return was 95.48%. The highest returns of all, however, were found in north Las Vegas which is home to the "locals" casinos: Fiesta, Jerry's Nugget, Texas Station and Santa Fe Station. The average return on these machines was 95.61%.

TOP 10 Reasons to Subscribe to

A Anthony Curtis' LAS VEGAS ADVISOR

---

10. Reliability. Since 1983 the *Las Vegas Advisor* has helped readers get more out of Las Vegas than Las Vegas gets out of them.

9. Special Offers. Receive extras on top of the Pocketbook of Values (see #2). Free rooms, free food, free shows and more.

8. Absolutely no casino advertising.

7 . Expert Advice. Gaming's best writers give tips and strategies in every issue.

6. First-class delivery every month.

5. Discounts on all new books published by Huntington Press.

4. Free Great Stuff for Gamblers Catalog loaded with the top gambling and Las Vegas products available anywhere.

3. Free LVA Reference Guide — a handy listing of show and dining specials, plus a detailed map of the city.

2. LVA Pocketbook of Values — exclusive offers from over 30 properties worth more than $700, Rooms, meals, shows, gambling, car rentals and more.

1. 12 issues of the *Las Vegas Advisor* newsletter. The best values in dining, entertainment, gambling, comps and everything you'll need to know about Las Vegas.

Bravo! I have never seen such a collection of coupons in the 27 years I have been visiting Las Vegas. The *Las Vegas Advisor* not only gives you the most reliable, up-to-date news about Las Vegas month after month, but now they give you a phenomenal package of coupons worth much, much more than the cost of a subscription. This is a no-brainer. My advice - RUSH your subscription order today for the LVA.

— Henry Tamburin, bestselling gambling author

Subscribe Today

One Year Subscription - $50

100% Money-Back Guarantee

Call (800) 741-1596

or mail check or money order to:

Casino Vacations
P.O. Box 703
Dania, FL 33004

Boulder Station Hotel & Casino
4111 Boulder Highway
Las Vegas, Nevada 89121
(702) 432-7777
Website: www.stationcasinos.com

Toll-Free Number: (800) 981-5577
Reservation Number: (800) 683-7777
Rooms: 300 Price Range: $42-$109
Restaurants: 13 (1 open 24 hours)
Buffets: B-$4.99/$8.99 (Sun) L-$6.99
      D-$9.99/$10.99(Sun)/$16.99 (Fri)
Casino Size: 89,433 Square Feet
Other Games: SB, RB, MB, P, PGP,
      LIR, TCP, K, BG
Special Features: $1.49 Sauza margaritas. 11-screen movie complex. Kid Quest childcare center.

Caesars Palace
3570 Las Vegas Blvd. South
Las Vegas, Nevada 89109
(702) 731-7110
Website: www.caesars.com

Toll-Free Number: (800) 634-6001
Reservation Number: (800) 634-6661
Rooms: 2,469 Price Range: $99-$500
Suites: 250 Price Range: $450-$5,000
Restaurants: 9 (1 open 24 hours)
Buffets: B-$9.99/$16.99 (Sat-Sun) L-$11.99
      D-$16.99/$24.99 (Fri-Sat)
Casino Size: 125,000 Square Feet
Other Games: SB, RB, S21, B, MB, PG,
      PGP, CSP, LIR, TCP, B6, K
Special Features: Health spa. Beauty salon. Shopping mall with 125 stores and interactive attractions.

California Hotel & Casino
12 Ogden Avenue
Las Vegas, Nevada 89101
(702) 385-1222
Website: www.thecal.com

Reservation Number: (800) 634-6505
Rooms: 781 Price Range: $45-$110
Suites: 74 Price Range: Casino Use Only
Restaurants: 4 (1 open 24 hours)
Casino Size: 35,848 Square Feet
Other Games: SB, PGP, CSP, LIR, TCP,K
Special Features: 93-space RV park. Offers many charter packages from Hawaii.

Casino Royale & Hotel
3411 Las Vegas Blvd. South
Las Vegas, Nevada 89109
(702) 737-3500
Website: www.casinoroyalehotel.com

Toll-Free Number: (800) 854-7666
Rooms: 151 Price Range: $39-$99
Suites: 3 Price Range: $150-$299
Restaurants: 3 (1 open 24 hours)
Casino Size: 15,000 Square Feet
Other Games: S21, CSP
Fun Book: Given with slot initial club sign-up
Special Features: TCBY, Denny's and Subway. Refrigerator in every room. Low-limit games.

Castaways Hotel Casino & Bowling Center
2800 Fremont Street
Las Vegas, Nevada 89104
(702) 385-9123
Website: www.castaways-lv.com

Reservation Number: (800) 826-2800
Rooms: 416 Price Range: $29-$89
Suites: 4 Price Range: $99-$199
Restaurants: 3 (1 open 24 hours)
Buffets: B-$8.95 (Sat-Sun) L-$6.49
D-$8.95/$13.95 (Wed)/$12.95 (Sat)/$14.95 (Fri)
Casino Size: 74,300 Square Feet
Other Games: SB, RB, PGP, LIR,
      TCP, B6, K, BG
Special Features: 106-lane bowling center. $2.50 late-night buffet (10:30pm-7am) Sun-Thu.

Circus Circus Hotel & Casino
2880 Las Vegas Blvd. South
Las Vegas, Nevada 89109
(702) 734-0410
Website: www.circuscircus.com

Reservation Number: (800) 634-3450
Rooms: 3,770 Price Range: $34-$139
Suites: 122 Price Range: $99-$278
Restaurants: 9 (2 open 24 hours)
Buffets: B-$6.99 L-$6.99 D-$8.99
Casino Size: 107,195 Square Feet
Other Games: SB, RB, MB, P, PGP,
      CSP, LIR, B6, K
Special Features: Free circus acts 11 a.m. to midnight. 370-space RV park. Wedding chapel. Midway and arcade games. Indoor theme park.

Free Things To See In Las Vegas!

Masquerade Village

The Masquerade Show in the Sky is a $25-million extravaganza in the sky and on the stage at the Rio Hotel & Casino. Five floats travel on an overhead track above the casino, while numerous dancers, musicians, aerialists and stiltwalkers perform on stage, or from attractions that drop from the ceiling or from two circular lifts that rise from the floor.

There are four differently themed shows on a rotating schedule daily at 3:30, 4:30, 5:30, 7, 8, 9 and 10 p.m.

El Cortez Hotel & Casino
600 E. Fremont Street
Las Vegas, Nevada 89101
(702) 385-5200
Website: www.elcortezhotelcasino.com

Reservation Number: (800) 634-6703
Rooms: 299 Price Range: $25-$45
Suites: 10 Price Range: $40-$47
Restaurants: 2 (1 open 24 hours)
Casino Size: 45,300 Square Feet
Other Games: SB, RB, MB, P, K
Special Features: Video arcade. Gift shop and ice cream parlor. Barber shop. Beauty salon.

Ellis Island Casino
4178 Koval Lane
Las Vegas, Nevada 89109
(702) 734-8638
Website: www.ellisislandcasino.com

Restaurants: 2
Casino Size: 12,466 Square Feet
Other Games: SB
Special Features: Super 8 Motel next door. Microbrewery. $4.95 steak dinner. Single-deck blackjack.

Excalibur Hotel/Casino
3850 Las Vegas Blvd. South
Las Vegas, Nevada 89109
(702) 597-7777
Website: www.excaliburcasino.com

Reservation Number: (800) 937-7777
Rooms: 4,008 Price Range: $49-$209
Suites: 46 Price Range: $275-$375
Restaurants: 5 (1 open 24 hours)
Buffets: B-$8.99 L-$9.99 D-$11.49
Casino Size: 121,544 Square Feet
Other Games: SB, RB, S21, MB, P, PGP,
           CSP, LIR, B6, K, Casino War
Fun Book: Given to hotel guests at check-in
Special Features: Wedding chapel. Strolling entertainers. Video arcade and midway games. Nightly "Tournament of Kings" dinner show.

Fitzgeralds Las Vegas
301 Fremont Street
Las Vegas, Nevada 89101
(702) 388-2400
Website: www.fitzgeralds.com

Reservation Number: (800) 274-5825
Rooms: 634 Price Range: $28-$80
Suites: 14 Price Range: $100-$250
Restaurants: 4 (1 open 24 hours)
Buffets: B-$6.49 L-$6.99 D-$9.99
Casino Size: 42,301 Square Feet
Other Games: SB, LIR, TCP, K
Fun Book: Coupons given at promotions kiosk
Senior Discount: 10% off room, if 55 or older

Flamingo Las Vegas
3555 Las Vegas Blvd. South
Las Vegas, Nevada 89109
(702) 733-3111
Website: www.flamingolasvegas.com

Reservation Number: (800) 732-2111
Rooms: 3,565 Price Range: $60-$250
Suites: 215 Price Range: $350-$750
Restaurants: 8 (1 open 24 hours)
Buffets: B-$8.75 L-$9.95 D-$14.95
Casino Size: 76,763 Square Feet
Casino Marekting: (800) 225-4882
Other Games: SB, RB, S21, B, MB, P, PGP,
          CSP, LIR, TCP, SIC, B6, K
Special Features: Health Spa. Shopping arcade.
Afternoon "Bottoms Up" stage show.

Four Queens Hotel/Casino
202 Fremont Street
Las Vegas, Nevada 89101
(702) 385-4011
Website: www.fourqueens.com

Reservation Number: (800) 634-6045
Rooms: 690 Price Range: $35-$89
Suites: 48 Price Range: $74-$240
Restaurants: 4 (1 open 24 hours)
Casino Size: 27,389 Square Feet
Other Games: SB, RB, PGP, CSP, LIR, TCP, K
Special Features: 99¢ shrimp cocktail.

Fremont Hotel & Casino
200 E. Fremont Street
Las Vegas, Nevada 89101
(702) 385-3232
Website: www.fremontcasino.com

Reservation Number: (800) 634-6460
Rooms: 428 Price Range: $35-$99
Suites: 24 Price Range: Casino Use Only
Restaurants: 4 (1 open 24 hours)
Buffets: B-$5.99/$8.99 (Sat/Sun) L-$6.49
        D-$9.99/$14.99 (Sun/Tue/Fri)
Casino Size: 30,244 Square Feet
Other Games: SB, RB, PGP, CSP, LIR, TCP, K
Special Features: 99¢ shrimp cocktail.

Gold Coast Hotel & Casino
4000 W. Flamingo Road
Las Vegas, Nevada 89103
(702) 367-7111
Website: www.goldcoastcasino.com

Toll-Free Number: (800) 331-5334
Room Reservations: (888) 402-6278
Rooms: 750 Price Range: $29-$109
Suites: 26 Price Range: $175-$225
Restaurants: 5 (1 open 24 hours)
Buffets: B-$4.45/$8.95 (Sun) L-$6.45
        D-$8.95/$9.95 (Sun)
Casino Size: 71,000 Square Feet
Other Games: SB, RB, MB, PGP, LIR, K, BG
Special Features: 72-lane bowling center. 2
movie theaters. Dance hall. Free childcare.

Gold Spike Hotel & Casino
400 E. Ogden Avenue
Las Vegas, Nevada 89101
(702) 384-8444
Website: www.goldspikehotelcasino.com

Reservation Number: (800) 634-6703
Rooms: 100 Price Range: $25-$30
Suites: 7 Price Range: $35-$40
Restaurants: 1 (open 24 hours)
Casino Size: 5,820 Square Feet
Other Games: K, No Craps or Roulette

Golden Gate Hotel & Casino
One Fremont Street
Las Vegas, Nevada 89101
(702) 385-1906
Website: www.goldengatecasino.net/
index.cfm

Reservation Number: (800) 426-1906
Rooms: 106 Price Range: $32-$55
Restaurants: 2 (2 open 24 hours)
Casino Size: 9,090 Square Feet
Other Games: SB, RB, CSP, LIR
Special Features: 99¢ shrimp cocktail (24
hours). Oldest hotel in Vegas (opened 1906).

The Best Vegas Values

By H. Scot Krause

Welcome to "Vegas Values!" For those of you who may be unfamiliar with the title, it's an exclusive weekly column found only at: www.americancasinoguide.com, the companion website to this book. The column is updated weekly with what we consider to be some of the best, current entertainment, gambling and dining values, and promotions located throughout Las Vegas. Tune in and click on every week beginning Sunday for the latest news and information for the upcoming week, along with a steady, growing list of ongoing promotions. Listed below are examples and excerpts from the "Vegas Values" column. We hope at least some of the listings are enlightening for you, and will help you enjoy your Las Vegas vacation a little more by taking advantage of these promotions and specials.

Binion's Horseshoe: The old downstairs coffee shop reopened this past year. The famous late-night steak dinner isn't as cheap as it once was, but is still a great deal at $4.99. The 10-oz NY strip steak special is served as a complete dinner with salad and potato from 11:00 p.m. to 7:00 a.m. nightly.

Barbary Coast: Offering a 24-hour Prime Rib or 16 oz. T-Bone Special in The Victorian Room for $10.95. Dinners include soup or salad and choice of potato. (Note: This is a small Coffee Shop-type restaurant and is often crowded and on a waiting list. Try off-peak times for faster service or arrive early to put your name on the waiting list while you play first.)

Boulder Station (and Sunset Station): Purchase an entree at Guadalajara (Mexican Restaurant) on your Birthday and receive a FREE Dessert along with a FREE T-Shirt.

California: A sort of "nice touch" when you hit a royal flush or top slot jackpot, the California Hotel will take a Polaroid photo of you with your " lucky" machine as a souvenir gift and present it to you in a little display card. They will also include the photo in their monthly newsletter. They almost always give some little "extra" gift when you hit the jackpot, too, like a t-shirt, stuffed animal, or beanie baby.

Flamingo: Two FREE Show Tickets to "The Best of Bottoms Up," are available with a coupon found in the current edition of the American Casino Guide. Look in the promotional magazines found around town for additional coupons if needed. Advertised as, "The only topless afternoon show in Las Vegas," there are two show times at 2 and 4 pm, Monday through Saturday. Each person must purchase a beverage for $5.95 with the FREE coupon and gratuity is not included. Regular show ticket price is $12.95.

Gold Coast: They have long offered one of the best steak specials in all of Las Vegas. It's a huge Texas T-Bone that includes potato, onion rings, Texas toast, baked beans and a 16 oz. draft beer, all for $7.95. Its available 24 hours a day, seven days a week.

Gold Coast: Play Freeno, a FREE Keno game anytime you visit the property. Register six keno numbers and watch for your numbers on the boards located throughout the casino. You win $500 if all six of your numbers are drawn between 7am-8am or 7pm-8pm and $100 all other times. If you win, you must collect your prize prior to the start of the next game. Register only once. They will become your permanent numbers to watch anytime you return to the casino.

Main Street Station: An often overlooked promotion called "Score with Four," continues at MSS. Hit any 4-of-a-kind, straight flush, royal flush or 300-coin slot win and receive a scratch card for additional cash. Most of the scratch cards are of the $1.00 to $5.00 variety, but they claim to offer cards valued at $20, $50 and $100, as well as rare $5,000 cards.

Orleans: Play the Big Easy Sunday Night Free Entry Keno Contest. No minimum buy-in. Just register at the Keno Department for the contest before you play, with a chance to win the first prize of $500. Second place is $200 and prizes are awarded through fifth place, for cash and dinners. Contest starts at 5:30 p.m. every Sunday night.

Orleans and Suncoast: Late-night Breakfast Specials served in the coffee shop including Steak and Eggs with potatoes and toast for $1.95 and three additional breakfast specials for 99 cents each. Served from 12 midnight to 9:00 a.m. to guests over 21 years of age.

Palms: Earn 600 points in any one day and receive a $3.00 off coupon for the buffet. Ongoing promotion. After earning the 600 points, visit the Slot Club Booth for your voucher.

Tropicana: New members who sign-up for the Tropicana Winner's Slot Club receive double cash back on their first 24 hours of play. Bonus cash must be redeemed on current trip and a minimum of 30 minutes play is required. New sign-ups also receive a FREE Tropicana T-shirt.

Venetian: New members who sign-up for The Venetians Slot Club Player's Card and earn 25 points get a FREE spin on the Prize Wheel for a chance to win up to $500. Earn an additional 25 points (50 total,) and receive a complimentary meal. Earn another 50 points (100 total,) and get $10 cash back. First two rewards must be earned within your first trip. See Player's Club for details.

Westward Ho: Play Bingo for FREE on Tuesdays and Fridays at 4:00 pm. Ongoing promotion. No cost to play. Locals and tourists are welcome. Eight games are played at each session with a $50 Bingo prize jackpot up for grabs for each game.

That's it for this edition.....
Luck, Royals, Good Food and Jackpots to all......
(Author not responsible for omissions, changes and/or errors. Always call ahead to verify all offers.)

The author, H. Scot Krause, originally from Cleveland, Ohio, is a seven year resident of Las Vegas who reports, researches, and writes about casino games, events and promotions for The American Casino Guide as well as other publications and marketing/consulting firms. Questions or comments for Scot may be addressed to the discussion board at: www.americancasinoguide.com

Free Things To See In Las Vegas!

Buccaneer Bay

Cannons fire, pyrotechnics explode and stuntmen are thrown into the waters of Buccaneer Bay as the British Royal Navy challenges the pirates in a battle to the finish at the front entrance of Treasure Island.

Live action shows daily at 5:30, 7, 8:30, 10 and 11:30p.m (Fri-Sat only). Lines start forming in front about 45 minutes before showtime. To avoid the huge crowds get there early and then go into the resort and head to the Battle Bar. Grab a table near the railing, order a soda for $2.25, or a domestic draft beer for $2.75 and you'll have a front row seat for the show!

The Golden Nugget
129 E. Fremont Street
Las Vegas, Nevada 89101
(702) 385-7111
Website: www.goldennugget.com

Toll-Free Number: (800) 634-3403
Reservation Number: (800) 634-3454
Rooms: 1,805 Price Range: $54-$139
Suites: 102   Price Range: $175-$3,750
Restaurants: 5 (1 open 24 hours)
Buffets: B-$5.50/$10.50 (Sun)
　　　　　　L-$7.25 D-$9.95
Casino Size: 34,680 Square Feet
Other Games: SB, RB, MB, PGP, CSP, LIR, TCP, B6, K
Special Features: World's largest gold nugget (61 pounds) on display.

Hard Rock Hotel & Casino
4455 Paradise Road
Las Vegas, Nevada 89109
(702) 693-5000
Website: www.hardrockhotel.com

Toll-Free Number: (800) HRD-ROCK
Rooms: 340   Price Range: $59-$299
Suites: 28   Price Range: $350-$500
Restaurants: 2 (1 open 24 hours)
Casino Size: 30,000 Square Feet
Other Games: SB, RB, B, MB, PGP, CSP, LIR, TCP, B6
Special Features: Rock and Roll memorabilia display. Beach Club with whirlpools, spas, cabanas and sandy beaches. Athletic club.

Harrah's Las Vegas
3475 Las Vegas Blvd. South
Las Vegas, Nevada 89109
(702) 369-5000
Website: www.harrahs.com

Toll-Free Number: (800) 392-9002
Reservation Number: (800) HARRAHS
Rooms: 2,672 Price Range: $49-$195
Suites: 94 Price Range: $250-$350
Restaurants: 8 (1 open 24 hours)
Buffets: B-$9.99/$14.99 (Sat-Sun)
　　　　　　L-$10.99 D-$14.99
Casino Size: 87,700 Square Feet
Other Games: SB, RB, B, MB, P, PGP, CSP, LIR, TCP, B6, K
Special Features: Mardi Gras-themed casino. "Clint Holmes" and "Skintight" stage shows. Afternoon "Mac King" stage show. Improv Comedy Club.

Hotel San Remo Casino & Resort
115 East Tropicana Avenue
Las Vegas, Nevada 89109
(702) 739-9000
Website: www.sanremolasvegas.com

Reservation Number: (800) 522-7366
Rooms: 694 Price Range: $29-$149
Suites: 17 Price Range: $109-$209
Restaurants: 4 (1 open 24 hours)
Other Games: SB, PGP, CSP, LIR, K
Casino Size: 27,000 Square Feet
Special Features: "Showgirls of Magic" show.

Imperial Palace Hotel & Casino
3535 Las Vegas Blvd. South
Las Vegas, Nevada 89109
(702) 731-3311
Website: www.imperialpalace.com

Reservation Number: (800) 634-6441
Rooms: 2,700 Price Range: $52-$102
Suites: 225 Price Range: $92-$282
Restaurants: 9 (1 open 24 hours)
Buffets: B-$6.25 L-$7.50 D-$8.50
Casino Size: 47,780 Square Feet
Other Games: SB, RB, MB, PGP,
                    CSP, LIR, TCP, B6, K
Casino Marketing: (800) 351-7400
Special Features: Auto museum (admission charge). Video arcade. Wedding chapel. Independent medical facility.
Show: "Legends In Concert" $34.50/$19.50 children under 12, 7:30/10:30 nightly, dark Sun. Price includes two drinks, tax and tip.

Jerry's Nugget
See North Las Vegas section

Key Largo Casino & Quality Inn
377 East Flamingo Road
Las Vegas, Nevada 89109
(702) 733-7777

Reservation Number: (800) 634-6617
Rooms: 314 Price Range: $40-$129
Restaurants: 1
Casino Size: 9,172 Square Feet
Other Games: SB, RB No Craps or Roulette
Fun Book: Given to hotel guests at check-in
Senior Discount: 10% off room, if 50 or older
Special Features: All rooms are mini-suites with wet bars/refrigerators. Coin laundry. Gift shop. Free airport/Strip shuttle 8am-11:30pm daily.

Klondike Hotel & Casino
5191 Las Vegas Boulevard S.
Las Vegas, Nevada 89119
(702) 739-9351

Rooms: 150 Price Range: $29-$99
Restaurants: 1
Casino Size: 7,700 Square Feet
Other Games: No Craps

Lady Luck Casino Hotel
206 N. Third Street
Las Vegas, Nevada 89101
(702) 477-3000
Website: www.ladyluck.com

Toll-Free Number: (800) 634-6580
Room Reservations: (800) LADY-LUCK
Rooms: 792 Price Range: $29-$109
Suites: 134 Price Range: $44-$124
Restaurants: 4 (1 open 24 hours)
Buffets: B-$6.95 D-$10.95/$14.95 (Sat)
Casino Size: 17,150 Square Feet
Other Games: SB, RB, PG, PGP, LIR, TCP
Fun Book: Ask at Mad Money booth

Las Vegas Auto/Truck Plaza
8050 S. Industrial Road
Las Vegas, Nevada 89118
(702) 361-1176

Restaurants: 1 (Open 24 hours)
Casino Size: 1,700 Square Feet
Other Games: LIR, No Craps or Roulette
Special Features: Players Club gives table players comps/discounts in stores and restaurants.

Las Vegas Club Hotel & Casino
18 E. Fremont Street
Las Vegas, Nevada 89101
(702) 385-1664
Website: www.playatlvc.com

Reservation Number: (800) 634-6532
Rooms: 410 Price Range: $29-$89
Suites: 7 Price Range: $129-$179
Restaurants: 4 (1 open 24 hours)
Casino Size: 48,500 Square Feet
Other Games: SB, RB, MB, LIR, PGP, K
Special Features: Sports themed-casino with large collection of sports memorabilia.

Free Things To See In Las Vegas!

Fremont Street Experience

This $70 million computer-generated sound and light show takes place 90 feet in the sky over a pedestrian mall stretching four city blocks in downtown Las Vegas. It has more than 2.1 million lights, 208 speakers and needs 121 computers to make it all run like clockwork.

There are more than eight different shows with themes that include Country Western, Las Vegas Legends, a special Christmas Show, and more. Showtimes are 7:30 p.m. and then on the hour from 8 p.m. through midnight. (During winter months the 7:30 p.m. show is moved to 7 p.m.)

Las Vegas Hilton
3000 Paradise Road
Las Vegas, Nevada 89109
(702) 732-5111
Website: www.lvhilton.com

Reservation Number: (800) 732-7117
Rooms: 2,900 Price Range: $39-$159
Suites: 305 Price Range: $359-$995
Restaurants: 13 (1 open 24 hours)
Buffets: B-$8.99/$12.99 (Sat/Sun)
L-$9.99 D-$13.99
Casino Size: 78,882 Square Feet
Other Games: SB, RB, S21, B, MB, PG, PGP,
CSP, LIR, TCP, B6, K
Casino Marketing: (800) 457-3307
Special Features: *Star Trek: The Experience* -
an interactive adventure. World's largest race and sports book. Health club. Jogging track.

Longhorn Casino
5288 Boulder Highway
Las Vegas, Nevada 89122
(702) 435-9170

Restaurants: 1 (open 24 hours)
Casino Size: 1,675 Square Feet
Other Games: No Craps or Roulette
Special Features: $1 blackjack games.

Luxor Las Vegas
3900 Las Vegas Blvd. South
Las Vegas, Nevada 89119
(702) 262-4000
Website: www.luxor.com

Reservation Number (800) 288-1000
Rooms: 3,962 Price Range: $69-$209
Suites 464 Price Range: $169-$500
Restaurants: 9 (1 open 24 hours)
Buffets: B-$9.49 L-$9.99 D-$15.99
Casino Size: 100,000 Square Feet
Other Games: SB, RB, B, MB, PG, PGP,
P, CSP, LIR, TCP, B6, K
Casino Marketing: (800) 956-0289
Special Features: 30-story pyramid-shaped hotel with Egyptian theme. "Blue Man Group" and "Midnight Fantasy" stage shows.

Main Street Station Hotel & Casino
200 N. Main Street
Las Vegas, Nevada 89101
(702) 387-1896
Website: www.mainstreetcasino.com

Toll-Free Number: (800) 713-8933
Reservation Number: (800) 465-0711
Rooms: 406 Price Range: $35-$125
Suites: 14 Price Range: Casino Use Only
Restaurants: 4 (1 open 24 hours)
Buffets: B-$5.29/$8.99 (Sat-Sun) L-$7.49
D-$10.29/$14.99 (Fri)/$11.99 (Tue/Thu)
Casino Size: 27,798 Square Feet
Other Games: PGP, LIR, TCP

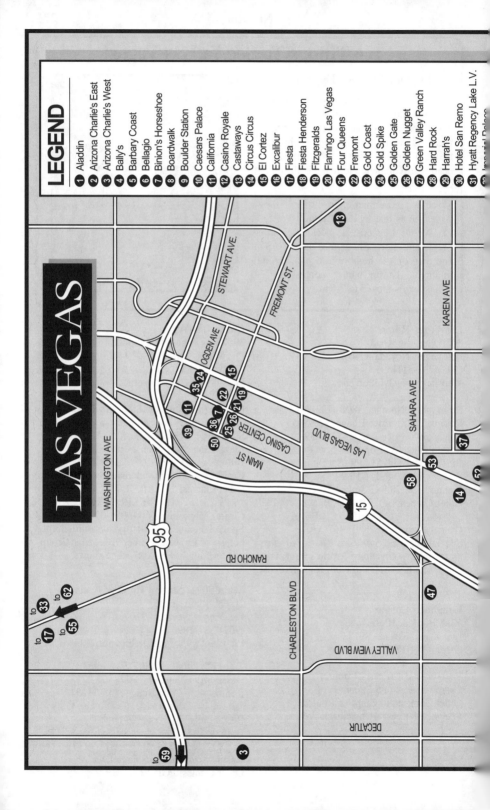

LAS VEGAS

LEGEND

1. Aladdin
2. Arizona Charlie's East
3. Arizona Charlie's West
4. Bally's
5. Barbary Coast
6. Bellagio
7. Binion's Horseshoe
8. Boardwalk
9. Boulder Station
10. Caesars Palace
11. California
12. Casino Royale
13. Castaways
14. Circus Circus
15. El Cortez
16. Excalibur
17. Fiesta
18. Fiesta Henderson
19. Fitzgeralds
20. Flamingo Las Vegas
21. Four Queens
22. Fremont
23. Gold Coast
24. Gold Spike
25. Golden Gate
26. Golden Nugget
27. Green Valley Ranch
28. Hard Rock
29. Harrah's
30. Hotel San Remo
31. Hyatt Regency Lake L.V.

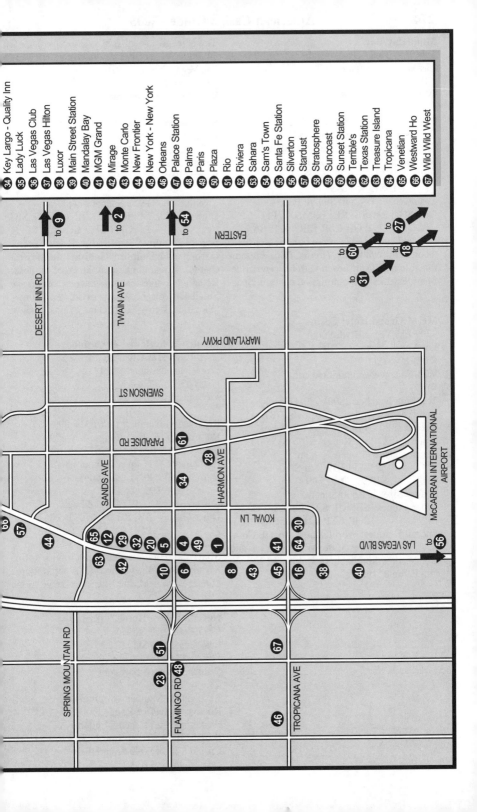

34 Key Largo - Quality Inn
35 Lady Luck
36 Las Vegas Club
37 Las Vegas Hilton
38 Luxor
39 Main Street Station
40 Mandalay Bay
41 MGM Grand
42 Mirage
43 Monte Carlo
44 New Frontier
45 New York - New York
46 Orleans
47 Palace Station
48 Palms
49 Paris
50 Plaza
51 Rio
52 Riviera
53 Sahara
54 Sam's Town
55 Santa Fe Station
56 Silverton
57 Stardust
58 Stratosphere
59 Suncoast
60 Sunset Station
61 Terrible's
62 Texas Station
63 Treasure Island
64 Tropicana
65 Venetian
66 Westward Ho
67 Wild Wild West

Mandalay Bay
3950 Las Vegas Blvd. South
Las Vegas, Nevada 89109
(702) 632-7777
Web Sit: www.mandalaybay.com

Reservation Number: (877) 632-7000
Rooms: 3,220 Price Range: $119-$449
Suites: 436 Price Range: $149-$899
Restaurants: 16 (1 open 24 hours)
Buffets: B-$11.75/$20.75 (Sun)
L-$13.75 D-$20.75
Casino Size: 137,540 Square Feet
Other Games: SB, RB, B, MB, P, PG,
PGP, CSP, LIR, TCP, B6
Special Features: 424-room Four Seasons Hotel on 35th-39th floors. *House of Blues* restaurant. Sand and surf beach with lazy river ride. Shark Reef exhibit (admission charge). Spa.

MGM Grand Hotel Casino
3799 Las Vegas Blvd. South
Las Vegas, Nevada 89109
(702) 891-1111
Web-Site: www.mgmgrand.com

Toll-Free Number: (800) 929-1111
Reservation Number: (800) 646-7787
Rooms: 5,005 Price Range: $99-$349
Suites: 752 Price Range: $199-$15,000
Restaurants: 8 (1 open 24 hours)
Buffets: B-$9.99/$12.99 (Sat-Sun)
L-$10.99 D-$15.99
Casino Size: 171,500 Square Feet
Other Games: SB, RB, S21, B, MB, PG,
PGP, CSP, LIR, TCP, B6, K
Special Features: World's largest hotel. Comedy Club. Rainforest Cafe. Midway games and arcade. Free lion habitat exhibit. "EFX" and "La Femme" stage shows.

The Mirage
3400 Las Vegas Blvd. South
Las Vegas, Nevada 89109
(702) 791-7111
Website: www.themirage.com

Reservation Number: (800) 627-6667
Rooms: 3,044 Price Range: $99-$399
Suites: 281 Price Range: $275-$2,500
Restaurants: 11 (1 open 24 hours)
Buffets: B-$8.95/$14.95 (Sun) L-$9.95
D-$14.95
Casino Size: 92,952 Square Feet
Other Games: SB, RB, S21, B, MB, PG, SIC
P, PGP, CSP, LIR, TCP, B6, K
Special Features: Siegfried & Roy's Secret Garden and Dolphin Habitat (admission charge). Aquarium display at check-in desk. Royal white tiger habitat viewing area (free). Simulated volcano with periodic "eruptions." "Siegfried & Roy" and "Danny Gans" shows.

Monte Carlo Resort & Casino
3770 Las Vegas Blvd. South
Las Vegas, Nevada 89109
(702) 730-7777
Website: www.montecarlo.com

Reservation Number: (800) 311-8999
Rooms: 3,002 Price Range: $69-$299
Suites: 259 Price Range: $139-$169
Restaurants: 7 (1 open 24 hours)
Buffets: B-$9.49/$14.95 (Sun)
L-$9.99 D-$13.75
Casino Size: 102,197 Square Feet
Other Games: SB, RB, B, MB, PG, P,
PGP, CSP, LIR, TCP, B6, K
Special Features: McDonald's, Nathan's, Sbarro's, Haagen Daz and bagel shop. Microbrewery. Lazy river ride. 12 retail shops. "Lance Burton, Master Magician" stage show.

Nevada Palace Hotel & Casino
5255 Boulder Highway
Las Vegas, Nevada 89122
(702) 458-8810
Website: www.nvpalace.com

Reservation Number: (800) 634-6283
Rooms: 210 Price Range: $40-$75
Restaurants: 2 (1 open 24 hours)
Buffets: B-$4.99 (Sat-Sun) D-$5.99/$9.99 (Fri)
Casino Size: 15,000 Square Feet
Other Games: SB, K

Free Things To See In Las Vegas!

MGM Grand Lion Habitat

MGM Grand's $9 million Lion Habitat is located inside the property near the entertainment dome and it showcases up to five lions daily.

The Habitat is open from 11 a.m. to 10 p.m. daily and features four separate waterfalls, overhangs, a pond and Acacia trees. There are numerous viewing areas that will allow you to get an upclose view of the lions, including overhead and beneath you as you follow the walkway.

The Habitat has a retail souvenir shop and, for a $20 fee, you can have your photo taken with a lion club. For more information on the Lion Habitat you can call the MGM Grand at (800) 929-1111, or visit their web site at www.mgmgrand.com

---

New Frontier Hotel & Casino
3120 Las Vegas Blvd. South
Las Vegas, Nevada 89109
(702) 794-8200
Website: www.frontierhotelcasino.com

Toll-Free Number: (800) 421-7806
Reservation Number: (800) 634-6966
Rooms: 550   Price Range: $39-$129
Suites: 434 Price Range: $59-$199
Restaurants: 4 (1 open 24 hours)
Buffets: B-$7.50 L-$7.95 D-$11.95
Casino Size: 42,609 Square Feet
Other Games: SB, RB, S21, MB, P, PGP
          CSP, LIR, TCP, B6, K, BG
Fun Book: Ask at slot club booth

New York-New York Hotel & Casino
3790 Las Vegas Blvd. South
Las Vegas, Nevada 89109
(702) 740-6969
Website: www.nynyhotelcasino.com

Reservation Number: (800) 693-6763
Rooms: 2,024 Price Range: $75-$189
Suites: 12 Price Range: Casino Use Only
Restaurants: 7 (1 open 24 hours)
Casino Size: 88,254 Square Feet
Other Games: SB, RB, MB, PG, PGP, SIC
          CSP, LIR, TCP, B6, K
Special Features: Replica Statue of Liberty and Empire State Building. *Manhattan Express* roller coaster. *ESPN Zone* restaurant.

Orleans Hotel & Casino
4500 W. Tropicana Avenue
Las Vegas, Nevada 89103
(702) 365-7111
Website: www.orleanscasino.com

Reservation Number: (800) ORLEANS
Rooms: 825 Price Range: $30-$139
Suites: 15 Price Range: $175-$325
Restaurants: 10 (1 open 24 hours)
Buffets: B-$5.49/$9.95 (Sun) L-$6.95
          D-$9.95/$14.95 (Mon)/$10.95 (Wed)
Casino Size: 94,380 Square Feet
Other Games: SB, RB, MB, P, PGP, LIR, K
Special Features: Wedding chapel. 70-lane bowling center. 12 movie theaters. Starbucks. Free shuttle service to Strip and other Coast properties.

O'Shea's Casino
3555 Las Vegas Blvd. South
Las Vegas, Nevada 89109
(702) 697-2767

Toll-Free: (800) 329-3232 ask for O'Shea's
Other Games: S21, LIR
Fun Book: Ask at cashier cage
Special Features: Property is part of the Flamingo. Burger King.

Palace Station Hotel & Casino
2411 West Sahara Avenue
Las Vegas, Nevada 89102
(702) 367-2411
Website: www.palacestation.com

Reservation Number: (800) 634-3101
Rooms: 949 Price Range: $29-$99
Suites: 82 Price Range: $89-$139
Restaurants: 5 (1 open 24 hours)
Buffets: B-$4.99/$8.99 (Sat/Sun) L-$6.99
      D-$9.99/$9.99 (Thu/Fri/Sat)
Casino Size: 84,000 Square Feet
Other Games: SB, RB, MB, P, PG, PGP,
      CSP, LIR, TCP, K, BG
Special Features: Nonsmoking slot area.

The Palms
4321 Flamingo Road
Las Vegas, Nevada 89103
(702) 942-7001
Website: www.thepalmslasvegas.com

Toll Free Number: (866) 942-7777
Reservation Number: (866) 942-7770
Rooms: 447 Price Range: $59-$149
Suites: 60 Price Range: $109-$600
Restaurants: 7 (1 open 24 hours)
Buffets: B-$5.99/$8.99 (Sat-Sun) L-$6.99
      D-$9.99/$15.99 (Wed)
Casino Size: 57,120 Square Feet
Other Games: SB, RB, B, MB, P,
      PGP, LIR, TCP, K, BG
Special Features: 14 theater cineplex.

Paris Casino Resort
3645 Las Vegas Blvd. South
Las Vegas, Nevada 89109
(702) 946-7000
Website: www.paris-lv.com

Reservation Number: (888) BON-JOUR
Rooms: 2,914 Price Range: $65-$260
Suites: 300 Price Range: $350-$1,250
Restaurants: 8 (1 open 24 hours)
Buffets: B-$11.95 L-$16.95 D-$21.95
Casino Size: 66,451 Square Feet
Other Games: SB, RB, S21, MB,
      PGP, CSP, LIR
Special Features: Replicas of Arc de Triomphe, Opera House, Parc Monceau and 50-story Eiffel Tower with restaurant/observation deck.

Plaza Hotel & Casino
1 Main Street
Las Vegas, Nevada 89101
(702) 386-2110
Website: www.plazahotelcasino.com

Reservation Number: (800) 634-6575
Rooms: 1,037 Price Range: $35-$80
Suites: 60 Price Range: $70-$300
Restaurants: 3 (1 open 24 hours)
Casino Size: 60,060 Square Feet
Other Games: SB, RB, MB, P, LIR, K, BG
Special Features: Domed restaurant offers full view of Fremont Street Experience.

Rio Suite Hotel & Casino
3700 W. Flamingo Road
Las Vegas, Nevada 89103
(702) 252-7777
Website: www.playrio.com

Reservation Number: (800) PLAY RIO
Suites: 2,563 Price Range: $89-$425
Restaurants: 16 (1 open 24 hours)
Buffets: B-$7.99 L-$10.99 D-$14.99
Seafood Buffets: D-$26.99 (opens 4pm)
Casino Size: 118,320 Square Feet
Other Games: SB, RB, B, MB, PG, PGP,
      CSP, LIR, TCP, B6, K
Special Features: Free "Masquerade Show in the Sky" five times daily. 25 retail shops. Three wedding chapels. "Scintas" stage show.

Riviera Hotel & Casino
2901 Las Vegas Blvd. South
Las Vegas, Nevada 89109
(702) 734-5110
Website: www.theriviera.com

Toll-Free Number: (800) 634-3420
Reservation Number: (800) 634-6753
Rooms: 2,100 Price Range: $29-$159
Suites: 154 Price Range: $195-$900
Restaurants: 5 (1 open 24 hours)
Buffets: B-$8.50/$9.95 (Sat-Sun)
      L-$9.50 D-$12.99
Casino Size: 109,800 Square Feet
Other Games: SB, RB, S21, MB, PGP,
      CSP, LIR, SIC, B6, K
Fun Book: Look for coupon in magazines
Special Features: Nondenominational worship services with chaplain. Burger King, Pizza Hut, Panda Express and Quizno's Subs. Three stage shows: "Splash," "An Evening at La Cage" and "Crazy Girls." Comedy Club.

Free Things To See In Las Vegas!

The Fountains at Bellagio

The Fountains at Bellagio is one of the most ambitious water features ever conceived in terms of choreography, complexity and scale.

More than one thousand fountains dance in front of the hotel, creating a marvelous union of water, music and light. The display spans more than 1,000 feet, with water soaring as high as 240 feet in the air. The fountains are choreographed to music ranging from classical and operatic pieces to songs from Broadway shows.

Showtimes are every 30 minutes from 3 p.m (starts at noon on Saturday and Sunday) until 8 p.m. After 8p.m. the shows start every 15 minutes until midnight.

Sahara Hotel & Casino
2535 Las Vegas Blvd. South
Las Vegas, Nevada 89109
(702) 737-2111
Website: www.saharahotelandcasino.com

Toll-Free Number: (800) 634-6645
Reservation Number: (800) 634-6666
Rooms: 1,949 Price Range: $29-$119
Suites: 100 Price Range: $105-$375
Restaurants: 5 (1 open 24 hours)
Buffets: B/L-$5.99/$8.99 (Sat-Sun) D-$6.99
Casino Size: 46,480 Square Feet
Other Games: SB, RB, S21, P, PGP, LIR, B6, K
Fun Book: Show out-of-state ID at cashier cage
Special Features: *NASCAR* Cafe. *Sahara Speedworld* with roller coaster, race car simulator and other attractions. "Magician Steve Wyrick" stage show.

Sam's Town Hotel & Gambling Hall
5111 Boulder Highway
Las Vegas, Nevada 89122
(702) 456-7777
Website: www.samstown.com

Toll-Free Number: (800) 897-8696
Reservation Number: (800) 634-6371
Rooms: 620 Price Range: $39-$125
Suites: 30 Price Range: $99-$275
Restaurants: 6 (1 open 24 hours)
Buffets: B-$8.99 (Sat-Sun) L-$6.99
   D-$9.99/$12.99 (Wed)/$15.99 (Fri)
Casino Size: 118,000 Square Feet
Other Games: SB, RB, S21, P, PGP, LIR, K, BG
Special Features: Indoor promenade with free laser-light show 4 times daily. 24-hour 56-lane bowling center. Two RV parks with 500 spaces. 18-theater movie complex. Childcare center.

Silver Saddle Saloon
2501 E.Charleston Boulevard
Las Vegas, Nevada 89104
(702) 474-2900

Restaurants: 1
Other Games: No Craps or roulette. Blackjack only played 4pm-4am (Fri)/9pm-4am (Sat)

Silverton Hotel Casino & RV Resort
3333 Blue Diamond Road
Las Vegas, Nevada 89139
(702) 263-7777
Website: www.silvertoncasino.com

Toll-Free Number: (800) 588-7711
Rooms: 292 Price Range: $35-$79
Suites: 8 Price Range: $59-$175
Restaurants: 5 (1 open 24 hours)
Buffets: B-$4.99/$5.99 (Sat)/$8.99 (Sun)
   L-$6.99 D-$8.99/$10.99 (Tue/Wed/Sat)/
   $9.99 (Thu/Sun)/$13.99 (Fri)
Casino Size: 32,134 Square Feet
Other Games: PGP, LIR, TCP, K
Fun Book: Given to slot club members
Senior Discount: Join Silver Seekers Club, if 55+
Special Features: 460-space RV park. 3 pools with Jacuzzi and water slides. 24-hour grocery store. Free shuttle to Strip.

Slots-A-Fun
2890 Las Vegas Blvd. South
Las Vegas, Nevada 89109
(702) 794-3814

Toll-Free Number: (800) 354-1232
Restaurants: 1 Snack Bar
Casino Size: 16,733 Square Feet
Other Games: CSP, LIR
Fun Book: Ask at cashier cage
Special Features: $1 Heinekens. 99-cent 1/4-pound hot dog. $1 blackjack. 25-cent roulette.

Stardust Resort & Casino
3000 Las Vegas Blvd. South
Las Vegas, Nevada 89109
(702) 732-6111
Website: www.stardustlv.com

Toll-Free Number: (800) 824-6033
Reservation Number: (800) 634-6757
Rooms: 1,552 Price Range: $49-$135
Suites: 195 Price Range: $95-$350
Restaurants: 6 (1 open 24 hours)
Buffets: B-$6.99 L-$7.99 D-$10.99
Casino Size: 53,538 Square Feet
Other Games: SB, RB, B, MB, P, PGP,
         CSP, LIR, TCP, B6, K
Fun Book: Ask at Logo shop
Special Features: "Wayne Newton" stage show.

Stratosphere Hotel & Casino
2000 Las Vegas Blvd. South
Las Vegas, Nevada 89117
(702) 380-7777
Website: www.stratospherehotel.com

Reservation Number: (800) 99-TOWER
Rooms: 2,444 Price Range: $39-$129
Suites: 250 Price Range: $114-$229
Restaurants: 5 (1 open 24 hours)
Buffets: B-$6.49 L-$7.49/$10.99 (Sun)
         D-$10.99/$14.99 (Fri-Sat)
Casino Size: 54,300 Square Feet
Other Games: SB, RB, MB, PGP, CSP,
         LIR, TCP, B6, K
Senior Discount: $1 off tower admission, 10% off room rate, if 55, or older
Fun Book: Given to hotel guests at check-in
Special Features: 135-story observation tower (admission charge). Two thrill rides. Revolving restaurant. 50 retail stores. Kid's Quest childcare center. Video arcade. "American Superstars" evening stage show. "Viva Las Vegas" afternoon stage show.

Terribles's Hotel and Casino
4100 Paradise Road
Las Vegas, Nevada 89156
(702) 733-7000
Website:www.terribleherbst.com

Reservation Number: (800) 640-9777
Rooms: 370 Price Range: $29-$49
Restaurants: 2 (one open 24 hours)
Buffets: B: $4.99/$8.99 (Sun)
         L-$6.99 D-$9.99/$12.99 (Thu)
Casino Size: 25,338 Square Feet
Other Games: SB, RB, BG
Special Features: McDonald's restaurant.

Treasure Island
3300 Las Vegas Blvd. South
Las Vegas, Nevada 89109
(702) 894-7111
Website: www.treasureislandlasvegas.com

Reservation Number: (800) 944-7444
Rooms: 2,665 Price Range: $69-$329
Suites: 220 Price Range: $129-$999
Restaurants: 8 (1 open 24 hours)
Buffets: B-$7.99/$12.99 (Sat-Sun)
      L-$8.99/$12.99 (Sat-Sun) D-$12.99
Casino Size: 67,629 Square Feet
Other Games: SB, RB, S21, B, MB, PG, PGP,
      CSP, LIR, TCP, B6, K
Special Features: Lagoon with live-action sea
battle between pirates and British sailors every 90 minutes from 5:30pm until 10pm/11:30
(Fri-Sat). Health spa/salon. Two wedding
chapels. Ben &Jerry's. Starbucks. Krispy
Kreme. Cirque du Soleil's "Mystere" stage
show.

Tropicana Resort & Casino
3801 Las Vegas Blvd. South
Las Vegas, Nevada 89109
(702) 739-2222
Website: www.tropicanalv.com

Reservation Number: (888) 826-8767
Rooms: 1,877 Price Range: $39-$159
Suites: 115 Price Range: $160-$240
Restaurants: 5 (1 open 24 hours)
Buffets: B-$7.95 L-$7.95
      D-$9.95/$14.95 (Wed)
Casino Size: 60,700 Square Feet
Other Games: SB, RB, PGP, CSP, LIR, TCP
Senior Discount: Various, if 65 or older
Special Features: Wedding chapel. Swim-up
blackjack table. Free wildlife walk and bird
show Fri-Wed at 11am, 12:30pm and 2pm.
"The Best of the Folies Bergere" evning stage
show. "The Illusionary Magic of Rick Thomas" afternoon stage show. Comedy club.

The Venetian Resort Hotel Casino
3355 Las Vegas Blvd. South
Las Vegas, Nevada 89109
(702) 414-1000
Website: www.venetian.com

Reservation Number: (888) 283-6423
Suites: 3,036 Price Range: $129-$10,000

Restaurants: 15
Casino Size: 105,344 Square Feet
Other Games: SB, RB, S21, B, MB, PG,
      PGP, CSP, LIR, TCP, B6
Special Features: Recreates city of Venice with
canals, gondoliers and replica Campanile
Tower, St. Mark's Square, Doge's Palace and
Rialto Bridge. 90 retail stores. Madame
Tussaud's Wax Museum. "Melinda-First Lady
of Magic" stage show.

Western Hotel & Casino
899 East Fremont Street
Las Vegas, Nevada 89101
(702) 384-4620

Reservation Number: (800) 634-6703
Rooms: 116 Price Range: $17-$22
Restaurants: 1 (open 24 hours)
Casino Size: 15,125
Other Games: K, BG, P, No Craps

Westward Ho Hotel & Casino
2900 Las Vegas Blvd. South
Las Vegas, Nevada 89109
(702) 731-2900
Website: www.westwardho.com

Reservation Number: (800) 634-6803
Rooms: 777 Price Range: $27-$80
Suites: 60 Price Range: $71-$111
Restaurants: 2 (1 open 24 hours)
Buffets: B/L-$6.95 D-$8.95
Casino Size: 34,457 Square Feet
Other Games: LIR
Special Features: Room-front parking. Some
3-bedroom apartments available.

Wild Wild West Casino
3330 West Tropicana Avenue
Las Vegas, Nevada 89103
(702) 736-8988

Reservation Number: (800) 634-3488
Rooms: 305 Price Range: $35-$55
Restaurants: 1 (open 24 hours)
Casino Size: 6,314 Square Feet
Other Games: SB
Special Features: Part of Station Casinos
group.

Laughlin

Map location: **#2** (on the Colorado River, 100 miles south of Las Vegas and directly across the river from Bullhead City, Arizona).

Laughlin is named after Don Laughlin, who owns the Riverside Hotel & Casino and originally settled there in 1966. The area offers many water sport activities on the Colorado River as well as at nearby Lake Mojave. If you are planning an overnight visit it is recommended that you make advance reservations because if the casino hotels are fully booked there are no other rooms in the city. For Laughlin tourism information call: (800) 4-LAUGHLIN. You can also visit their Website at: http://www.visitlaughlin.com.

Here's information, as supplied by Nevada's State Gaming Control Board, showing the slot machine payback percentages for all of Laughlin's casinos for the fiscal year beginning July 1, 2001 and ending June 30, 2002:

Denomination	Payback %
5¢ Slots	90.53
25¢ Slots	94.65
$1 Slots	95.39
$1 Megabucks	87.64
$5 Slots	96.95
All Slots	94.20

These numbers reflect the percentage of money returned to the players on each denomination of machine. All electronic machines including slots, video poker and video keno are included in these numbers.

Optional games in the casino listings include: sports book (SB), race book (RB), baccarat (B), mini-baccarat (MB), poker (P), pai gow poker (PGP), Caribbean stud poker (CSP), let it ride (LIR), keno (K), big 6 wheel (B6) and bingo (BG).

Colorado Belle Hotel Casino & Microbrewery
2100 S. Casino Drive
Laughlin, Nevada 89029
(702) 298-4000
Website: www.coloradobelle.com

Reservation Number: (800) 477-4837
Rooms: 1,176 Price Range: $19-$95
Suites: 48   Price Range: $125-$175

Restaurants: 6
Buffets: B-$5.99 L-$6.99
　　　　 D-$7.99/$14.99 (Fri)
Casino Size: 48,205 Square Feet
Other Games: SB, S21, P, CSP, LIR, K
Special Features: Children's arcade. Sand beach. Microbrewery. Krispy Kreme doughnut shop.

Don Laughlin's
Riverside Resort Hotel & Casino
1650 S. Casino Drive PMB 500
Laughlin, Nevada 89029
(702) 298-2535
Website: www.riversideresort.com

Reservation Number: (800) 227-3849
Rooms: 1,404 Price Range: $22-$49
Executive Rooms: 93 Price Range: $69-$99
Restaurants: 6
Buffets: B-$5.99 L-$6.99
　　　　 D-$6.99/$12.95 (Fri)
Casino Size: 80,763 Square Feet
Other Games: SB, RB, P, CSP, LIR, K, BG
Senior Discount: 10% AARP room discount
Fun Book: Given to seniors, if 55, or older
Special Features: 840-space RV park. Six-plex cinema. Classic car exhibit. 34-lane bowling center. Childcare center.

Edgewater Hotel Casino
2020 S. Casino Drive
Laughlin, Nevada 89029
(702) 298-2453
Website: www.edgewater-casino.com

Reservation Number: (800) 677-4837
Rooms: 1,420 Price Range: $25-$65
Suites: 23 Price Range: $75-$220
Restaurants: 4
Buffets: B-$5.99 L-$6.99
　　　　 D-$7.99/$8.99 (Fri/Sat)
Casino Size: 53,729 Square Feet
Other Games: SB, RB, S21, P, B6, TCP
　　　　　　　 PGP, CSP, LIR, K, BG
Casino Marketing: (800) 289-8777
Senior Discount: Room discount, if 55, or older
Fun Book: Look in brochure racks for coupon
Special Features: Video arcade. 99¢ shrimp cocktail. 99¢ hot dog. Free airport shuttle. Krispy Kreme donut shop.

Flamingo Laughlin
1900 S. Casino Drive
Laughlin, Nevada 89029
(702) 298-5111
Website: www.flamingolaughlin.com

Reservation Number: (888) 662-5825
Rooms: 1,900 Price Range: $22-$100
Suites: 90 Price Range: $85-$350
Restaurants: 6 (1 open 24 hours)
Buffets: B-$3.49 L-$4.49 D-$5.99
Casino Size: 57,155 Square Feet
Other Games: SB, RB, S21, MB, P, PGP,
          CSP, LIR, TCP, B6, K
Fun Book: Ask at Magic Club booth
Special Features: Burger King. Colorado River tour cruises. $1 off buffet for slot club members.

Golden Nugget Laughlin
2300 S. Casino Drive
Laughlin, Nevada 89029
(702) 298-7111
Website: www.gnlaughlin.com

Reservation Number: (800) 237-1739
Rooms: 300 Price Range: $29-$85
Suites: 4 Price Range: $150-$300
Restaurants: 5 (1 open 24 hours)
Buffets: B-$3.99 L-$4.99 D-$7.99
Casino Size: 32,600 Square Feet
Other Games: SB, RB, CSP, K
Casino Marketing: (800) 955-7568
Special Features: 10% room discount for AAA and AARP members. Suites must be booked through the casino. Gift shop.

Harrah's Laughlin Casino & Hotel
2900 S. Casino Drive
Laughlin, Nevada 89029
(702) 298-4600
Website: www.harrahs.com

Reservation Number: (800) HARRAHS
Rooms: 1,656 Price Range: $25-$95
Suites: 39 Price Range: Casino Use Only
Restaurants: 5
Buffets: B/L-$7.99 D-$10.99
Casino Size: 47,000 Square Feet
Other Games: SB, RB, PGP, LIR, TCP, K
Special Features: Beach and health club. McDonalds. Baskin-Robbins.

Pioneer Hotel & Gambling Hall
2200 S. Casino Drive
Laughlin, Nevada 89029
(702) 298-2442
Website: www.pioneerlaughlin.com

Reservation Number: (800) 634-3469
Rooms: 395 Price Range: $25-$80
Suites: 20 Price Range: $48-$100
Restaurants: 2 (1 open 24 hours)
Buffets: B-$5.95 L/D-$7.95/$12.95 (Fri)
Casino Size: 19,500 Square Feet
Other Games: LIR, TCP, K

Ramada Express Hotel & Casino
2121 S. Casino Drive
Laughlin, Nevada 89029
(702) 298-4200
Website: www.ramadaexpress.com

Toll-Free Number: (800) 243-6846
Rooms: 1,501 Price Range: $39-$69
Suites: 55 Price Range: $89-$119
Restaurants: 5 (1 open 24 hours)
Buffets: B-$5.99 D-$7.99/$11.99
Casino Size: 52,000 Square Feet
Other Games: SB, RB, CSP, LIR, K
Casino Marketing: (800) 343-4533
Fun Book: Given at slot club booth
Special Features: $1 million display of railroad antiques and memorabilia. Free ride on steam train. Train-shaped swimming pool. Arcade.

River Palms Resort Casino
2700 S. Casino Drive
Laughlin, Nevada 89029
(702) 298-2242
Website: www.rvrpalm.com

Reservation Number: (800) 835-7903
Rooms: 995 Price Range: $31-$60
Suites: 8 Price Range: $70-$350
Restaurants: 7 (1 open 24 hours)
Buffets: B-$4.99/$7.99 (Sun) L-$5.99 D-$7.99
Casino Size: 71,300 Square Feet
Other Games: SB, RB, P, PGP, CSP, TCP,
          LIR, B6, K, BG
Casino Marketing: (800) 835-7904
Senior Discount: Various specials Fri, if 50+

Lovelock

Map Location: **#19** (92 miles N.E. of Reno on I-80)

Sturgeon's Casino
1420 Cornell Avenue
Lovelock, Nevada 89419
(775) 273-2971
Website: www.ramada.com

Toll-Free Number: (888) 234-6835
Rooms: 74   Price Range: $40-$69
Spa Rooms: 2   Price Range: $75-$100
Restaurants: 1
Casino Size: 5,625 Square Feet
Other Games: No Craps or Roulette
Special Features: Hotel is Ramada Inn. Room discount for AAA and AARP members.

McDermitt

Map Location: **#20** (Just S. of the Oregon border on Hwy. 95)

Say When
P.O. Box 375
McDermitt, Nevada 89421
(775) 532-8515

Restaurants: 1
Casino Size: 5,940 Square Feet
Other Games: No Craps or Roulette

Mesquite

Map Location: **#21** (77 miles N.E. of Las Vegas on I-15 at the Arizona border)

Here's information, as supplied by Nevada's State Gaming Control Board, showing the slot machine payback percentages for all of the Mesquite area casinos for the fiscal year beginning July 1, 2001 and ending June 30, 2002:

Denomination	Payback %
5¢ Slots	92.92
25¢ Slots	95.32
$1 Slots	95.50
$1 Megabucks	89.00
$5 Slots	95.66
All Slots	94.67

These numbers reflect the percentage of money returned on each denomination of machine and encompass all electronic machines including slots, video poker and video keno.

CasaBlanca Hotel-Casino-Golf-Spa
950 W. Mesquite Boulevard
Mesquite, Nevada 89027
(702) 346-7259
Website: www.casablancaresort.com

Reservation Number: (800) 459-7529
Rooms: 500 Price Range: $39-$89
Suites: 18 Price Range: $99-$249
Restaurants: 3 (1 open 24 hours)
Buffets: B-$5.49 L-$6.49/$9.99 (Sun)
          D-$8.49/$12.99 (Fri-Sat)
Casino Size: 27,775 Square Feet
Other Games: SB, RB, P, PGP, LIR, TCP, K
Special Features: 45-space RV park. 18-hole golf course. Health spa offers massages, body care, facials and mud treatments.

Eureka Casino & Hotel
275 Mesa Boulevard
Mesquite, Nevada 89027
Website: www.eurekamesquite.com
(702) 346-4600

Reservation Number: (800) 346-4611
Rooms: 192 Price Range: $29-$59
Suites: 18 Price Range: $59-$129
Restaurants: 2 (1 open 24 hours)
Buffets: B-$4.75 L-$5.50/$5.95 (Fri-Sat)
          D-$6.95/$7.95 (Fri-Sat)
Casino Size: 31,100 Square Feet
Other Games: SB, RB, P, PGP, BG
Fun Book: Given to new slot club members.

Oasis Resort•Casino•Golf•Spa
P.O. Box 360
Mesquite, Nevada 89024
(702) 346-5232
Website: www.oasisresort.com

Reservation Number: (800) 21-OASIS
Rooms: 1,000 Price Range: $28-$69
Suites: 100   Price Range: $69-$139
Restaurants: 3 (1 open 24 hours)
Buffets: B-$5.45/$6.99 (Sun) L-$6.45
          D-$8.99/$11.49 (Fri)
Casino Size: 33,557 Square Feet

Other Games: SB, RB, P, PGP, LIR, K
Fun Book: Only given to hotel guests
Special Features: 50-space RV park. 18-hole
golf course. Wagon trail rides. Shotgun sports
club. Health club and spa. 2-for-1 breakfast
and lunch buffets Sun-Thu.

Virgin River Hotel/Casino/Bingo
100 Pioneer Boulevard
Mesquite, Nevada 89027
(702) 346-7777
Website: www.virginriver.com

Reservation Number: (800) 346-7721
Rooms: 720 Price Range: $25-$45
Suites: 2   Price Range: $250
Restaurants: 2 (1 open 24 hours)
Buffets: B-$4.49/$5.49 (Sat-Sun)
          L-$5.49/$6.49 (Sat-Sun)
          D-$8.49/$10.49 (Tue/Fri/Sat)
Casino Size: 49,000 Square Feet
Other Games: SB, RB, P, K, BG
Special Features: 24-lane bowling center. Four
movie theaters. Lagoon pool with waterfall and
slide. Video arcade.

Minden

Map Location: **#15** (42 miles S. of Reno on
Hwy. 395)

Carson Valley Inn
1627 Highway 395 N.
Minden, Nevada 89423
(775) 782-9711
Website: www.cvinn.com

Reservation Number: (800) 321-6983
Rooms: 220 Price Range: $49-$99
Suites: 9   Price Range: $119-$169
Restaurants: 3 (1 open 24 hours)
Casino Size: 11,600 Square Feet
Other Games: SB, RB, TCP, K
Senior Discount: Get Senior Inn Club card if
            50 or older for various discounts
Fun Book: Given to lodge/hotel/RV park guests
Special Features: 60-space RV park. 24-hour
convenience store. Wedding chapel. Golf,
hunting and ski packages offered. Childcare
center.

N. Las Vegas

Map Location: **#22** (5 miles N.E. of the Las
Vegas Strip on Las Vegas Blvd. N.)

Bighorn Casino
3016 E. Lake Mead Boulevard
N. Las Vegas, Nevada 89030
(702) 642-1940

Restaurants: 1
Casino Size: 3,694 Square Feet
Other Games: No Craps or Roulette

Cannery Hotel & Casino
2121 E. Craig Road
N. Las Vegas, Nevada 89030

EXPECTED TO OPEN BY JANUARY 2003
Rooms: 201 Price Range: Not Set at Press Time
Restaurants: 4 (1 open 24 hours)
Casino Size: 50,000 Square Feet
Other Games: SB, RB, PGP, KIR, TCP

Fiesta Casino Hotel
2400 N. Rancho Drive
Las Vegas, Nevada 89130
(702) 631-7000
Website: www.stationcasinos.com

Reservation Number: (800) 731-7333
Rooms: 100 Price Range: $39-$139
Restaurants: 7
Buffets: B-$4.99/$8.99 (Sun) L-$6.99
          D-$8.99/$11.99 (Mon)/$13.99 (Wed)/
          $10.99 (Fri)
Casino Size: 59,951 Square Feet
Casino Marketing: (800) 731-7333
Other Games: SB, RB, PGP, LIR, TCP, K, BG
Special Features: Drive-through sports/race
book. Coffee bar.

Jerry's Nugget
1821 Las Vegas Blvd. North
N. Las Vegas, Nevada 89030
(702) 399-3000
Website: www.jerrysnugget.com

Restaurants: 2
Casino Size: 33,101 Square Feet
Other Games: SB, RB, PGP, K, BG
Special Features: European Bakery.

Mahoney's Silver Nugget
2140 Las Vegas Blvd. North
N. Las Vegas, Nevada 89030
(702) 399-1111
Website: www.mahoneyscasino.com

Restaurants: 1
Casino Size: 18,100 Square Feet
Other Games: SB, P, K, BG, No Roulette
Special Features: 24-lane bowling center.

Opera House Saloon & Casino
2542 Las Vegas Blvd. North
N. Las Vegas, Nevada 89030
(702) 649-8801

Restaurants: 1
Casino Size: 4,420 Square Feet
Other Games: BG, No Craps or Roulette

The Poker Palace
2757 Las Vegas Blvd. North
N. Las Vegas, Nevada 89030
(702) 649-3799

Restaurants: 1
Casino Size: 14,350 Square Feet
Other Games: SB, RB, P, BG, No Craps/Roulette

Ramada Inn Speedway Casino
3227 Civic Center Drive
N. Las Vegas, Nevada 89030
(702) 399-3297
Website: www.ramada.com

Reservation Number: (877) 333-9291
Rooms: 92 Price Range: $39-$79
Suites: 3   Price Range: $119
Restaurants: 1
Casino Size: 15,540 Square Feet
Other Games: RB, SB, TCP
Special Features: Closest hotel/casino to Las Vegas Motor Speedway.

Rampart Casino
221 N. Rampart Boulevard
Las Vegas, Nevada 89128
(702) 869-7777

Toll-Free Number: (877) 869-8777
Rooms: 216 Price Range: $119-$149
Suites: 70 Price Range: $209-$299
Restaurants: 11
Buffets: L-$7.95/$10.95 (Sun) D-$10.95
Casino Size: 56,320 Square Feet
Other Games: SB, RB, PGP, LIR, TCP
Special Features: Hotel is JW Marriott. Golf course. Spa.

Santa Fe Station Hotel & Casino
4949 North Rainbow Drive
N. Las Vegas, Nevada 89130
(702) 658-4900
Website: www.stationcasinos.com

Toll Free Number: (866) 767-7770
Reservation Number: (800) 678-2846
Rooms: 200 Price Range: $39-$99
Restaurants: 3 (1 open 24 hours)
Casino Size: 93,400 Square Feet
Other Games: SB, RB, PGP, LIR, TCP, K, BG
Special Features: Ice skating arena. 24-hour 60-lane bowling center. Iguana Bar and Sports Bar.

Suncoast Hotel and Casino
9090 Alta Drive
Las Vegas, Nevada 89145
(702) 636-7111
Website: www.suncoastcasino.com

Toll-Free Number: (877) 677-7111
Rooms: 400 Price Range: $49-$99
Suites: 40 Price Range: $199-$399
Restaurants: 6 (1 open 24 hours)
Buffets: B-$4.95 L-$6.95 D-$9.95
Casino Size: 92,000 Square Feet
Other Games: SB, RB, MB, PGP, LIR, TCP, BG
Funbook: Given to hotel guests at check-in
Special Features: 64-lane bowling center. 16-screen movie theater. Travel agency. Free shuttle to airport and Strip. Childcare center.

Texas Station
2101 Texas Star Lane
N. Las Vegas, Nevada 89102
(702) 631-1000
Website: www.texasstation.com

Reservation Number: (800) 654-8888
Rooms: 200 Price Range: $39-$109
Restaurants: 5 (1 open 24 hours)
Buffets: B-$4.99/$8.99 (Sat-Sun)
L-$6.99 D-$9.99/$10.99 (Fri-Sat)
Casino Size: 123,045 Square Feet
Other Games: SB, RB, MB, P, PGP,
LIR, TCP, K, BG
Special Features: 18 movie theaters. 60-lane
bowling center. Kids Quest childcare center.

Pahrump

Map Location: **#23** (59 miles W. of Las Vegas
on Hwy. 160)

Mountain View Recreation Center
1750 S. Pahrump Valley Boulevard
Pahrump, Nevada 89048
(775) 727-7777

Restaurants: 1
Buffets: B-$2.95 L-$3.95 D-$5.95
Casino Size: 18,000 Square Feet
Other Games: No Craps or Roulette
Senior Discount: 10% off Sat-Thu dinner buf-
fets, if 55 or older

Pahrump Nugget Hotel & Gambling Hall
681 S. Highway 160
Pahrump, Nevada 89048
(775) 751-6500
Website: www.pahrumpnugget.com

Toll Free Number: (866) 751-6500
Rooms: 75 Price Range: $49-$89
Restaurants: 3 (1 open 24 hours)
Buffets: B/L-$3.99 D-$5.99/$6.99 (Fri)
Casino Size: 20,371 Square Feet
Other Games: SB, P, BG
Senior Discount: 2-for-1 dinner buffet
Mon-Thu if 55 or older
Special Features: Video arcade. Supervised
children's play area. Food court with
McDonalds, Dairy Queen and sub shop.

Saddle West Hotel/Casino & RV Park
1220 S. Highway 160
Pahrump, Nevada 89048
(775) 727-1111
Website: www.saddlewest.com

Reservation Number: (800) 433-3987
Rooms: 148 Price Range: $39-$85
Suites: 10 Price Range: $60-$125
Restaurants: 2 (1 open 24 hours)
Buffets: B-$4.99/$6.99 (Sat-Sun) L-$5.99
D-$6.99/$8.99 (Fri)/$7.99 (Sat)
Casino Size: 18,457 Square Feet
Other Games: SB, RB, BG
Senior Discount: 80-space RV park. Room dis-
count for AARP and AAA members. Closest
casino to Death Valley National Park.

Terrible's Lakeside Casino & RV Park
5870 S. Homestead Road
Pahrump, Nevada 89048
(775) 751-7770
Website: www.terribleherbst.com

Toll Free Number: (888) 558-LAKE
Restaurants: 1
Buffets: B-$2.99 L-$3.99 D-$5.95
Casino Size: 8,300 Square Feet
Other Games: SB, BG, No Craps or Roulette
Senior Discount: 10% off buffets, if 55 or older
Special Features: 160-space RV park.
Terrible's general store and Chevron gas sta-
tion.

Terrible's Town
771 Frontage Road
Pahrump, Nevada 89048
(775) 751-7777
Website: www.terribleherbst.com

Toll Free Number: (888) 837-7425
Restaurants: 1
Casino Size: 10,100 Square Feet
Other Games: SB, RB, BG
Funbook: Ask in casino
Special Features: Blimpie's, Pizza Hut and
Baskin-Robbins food outlets. General store
and Chevron gas station.

Primm

Map Location: **#6** (25 miles S.W. of Las Vegas on I-15; 9 miles from the California border)

Buffalo Bill's Resort & Casino
I-15 South
Primm, Nevada 89019
(702) 382-1212
Website: www.primadonna.com

Toll-Free Number: (800) FUN-STOP
Rooms: 1,242 Price Range: $25-$60
Suites: 15   Price Range: $205
Restaurants: 5 (1 open 24 hours)
Buffets: B-$6.25 L-$6.70 D-$7.45
Casino Size: 62,130 Square Feet
Other Games: SB, RB, S21, P, PGP, CSP
            LIR, TCP, B6, K, BG
Fun Book: Look for coupon in brochure racks
Special Features: Roller coaster. Flume ride. Two water slides. Movie theater. Train shuttle connects to Whiskey Pete's and Primm Valley.

Primm Valley Resort & Casino
I-15 South
Primm, Nevada 89019
(702) 382-1212
Website: www.primadonna.com

Reservation Number: (800) FUN-STOP
Rooms: 661 Price Range: $32-$70
Suites: 4   Price Range: $205
Restaurants: 3 (1 open 24 hours)
Buffets: B-$5.63 (Sat-Sun) L-$6.70 D-$7.45
Casino Size: 38,049 Square Feet
Other Games: SB, RB, S21, MB, PGP,
            CSP, LIR, TCP, K, BG
Fun Book: Look for coupon in brochure racks
Special Features: 199-space RV park. Free monorail to Whiskey Pete's.

Whiskey Pete's Hotel & Casino
I-15 South
Primm, Nevada 89019
(702) 382-1212
Website: www.primadonna.com

Reservation Number: (800) FUN-STOP
Rooms: 777 Price Range: $20-$50
Suites: 4   Price Range: $205
Restaurants: 4 (1 open 24 hours)
Buffets: B-$6.25(Sat-Mon) L-$6.38 D-$6.97
Casino Size: 36,400 Square Feet
Other Games: SB, RB, S21, PGP, CSP,
            LIR, TCP, K
Fun Book: Look for coupon in brochure racks
Special Features: Al Capone's car and Bonnie & Clyde's "death" cars on display. Free monorail service to Primm Valley.

Reno

Map Location: **#4** (near the California border, 58 miles N.E. of Lake Tahoe and 32 miles N. of Carson City).

Reno may be best known for its neon arch on Virginia Street which welcomes visitors to "The Biggest Little City in the World." The current arch is actually the fourth one since the original arch was built in 1927. The area also houses the nation's largest car collection at the National Automobile Museum. For Reno information call the Reno/Sparks Convention & Visitors Authority at (800) FOR-RENO.

Here's information, as supplied by Nevada's State Gaming Control Board, showing the slot machine payback percentages for all of the Reno area casinos for the fiscal year beginning July 1, 2001 and ending June 30, 2002:

Denomination	Payback %
5¢ Slots	93.11
25¢ Slots	94.37
$1 Slots	95.90
$1 Megabucks	88.57
$5 Slots	96.71
All Slots	95.01

These numbers reflect the percentage of money returned on each denomination of machine and encompass all electronic machines including slots, video poker and video keno. For the 5¢ slot player Reno's casinos offer slightly better

The arch in downtown Reno that welcomes visitors to
"The Biggest Little City in the World" is the city's most famous landmark.

returns than the Las Vegas Strip casinos and are among the highest in the state in that denomination.

Optional games in the casino listings include: sports book (SB), race book (RB), baccarat (B), mini-baccarat (MB), Spanush 21 (S21), pai gow (PG), poker (P), pai gow (PG), pai gow poker (PGP), Caribbean stud poker (CSP), let it ride (LIR), big 6 wheel (B6), keno (K) and bingo (BG).

Atlantis Casino Resort
3800 S. Virginia Street
Reno, Nevada 89502
(775) 825-4700
Website: www.atlantiscasino.com

Reservation Number: (800) 723-6500
Rooms: 1,000 Price Range: $29-$169
Suites: 30 Price Range: $129-$425
Restaurants: 7 (1 open 24 hours)
Buffets: B-$6.99/$8.99 (Sat)/$15.99 (Sun)
 L-$8.99/$9.99 (Sat) D-$11.99/$20.99 (Fri-Sat)
Casino Size: 51,000 Square Feet
Other Games: SB, RB, P, PGP, LIR, TCP, K
Casino Marketing: (800) 994-5900
Senior Discount: 10% off food, if 55 or older

Bonanza Casino
4720 N. Virginia Street
Reno, Nevada 89506
(775) 323-2724
Website: www.bonanzacasino.com

Restaurants: 2 (1 open 24 hours)
Buffets: B-$7.95 (Sat)/$6.95 (Sun)
 L-$5.95 D-$7.95
Casino Size: 12,583 Square Feet
Other Games: SB, RB, K
Senior Discount: 10% off food, if 60, or older
Fun Book: Show out-of-town ID
Special Features: $1 single-deck BJ. 25¢ craps and roulette.

Bordertown Casino RV Resort
19575 Highway 395
N. Reno, Nevada 89506
(775) 972-1309
Website: www.bordertowncasinorv.com

Toll-Free Number: (800) 443-4383
RV Reservations: (800) 218-9339
Restaurants: 1
Casino Size: 4,650 Square Feet
Other Games: No Craps or Roulette
Fun Book: Ask at cashier's cage
Special Features: 50-space RV park.

Circus Circus Hotel Casino/Reno
500 N. Sierra Street
Reno, Nevada 89503
(775) 329-0711
Website: www.circusreno.com

Reservation Number: (800) 648-5010
Rooms: 1,464 Price Range: $39-$199
Suites: 108 Price Range: $69-$239
Restaurants: 6 (1 open 24 hours)
Buffets: B-$6.99/$9.99 (Sat-Sun) L-$7.99
        D-$9.99/$13.99 (Fri-Sat)
Casino Size: 61,380 Square Feet
Other Games: SB, RB, MB, P, PGP, CSP, LIR, K
Fun Book: Only given to hotel guests
Special Features: Free circus acts. Carnival
games. 24-hour gift shop/liquor store.

Club Cal-Neva/Virginian Hotel and Casino
38 E. Second Street
Reno, Nevada 89505
(775) 323-1046
Website: www.clubcalneva.com

Toll-Free Number (877) 777-7303
Rooms: 303 Price Range: $29-$119
Suites: 6 Price Range: $99-$450
Restaurants: 5 (1 open 24 hours)
Buffets: L-$5.95/$6.95 (Sat-Sun)
        D-$8.95/$14.95 (Sat-Sun)
Casino Size: 43,260 Square Feet
Other Games: SB, RB, B, P, PGP, LIR, K, BG

Diamond's Casino at Holiday Inn
1010 E. 6th Street
Reno, Nevada 89512
(775) 323-4183

Reservation Number: (800) 648-4877
Rooms: 280 Price Range: $69-$109
Suites: 6 Price Range: $99-$175
Restaurants: 2 (1 open 24 hours)
Casino Size: 10,000 Square Feet
Other Games: SB, RB, No Roulette or Craps
Fun Book: Only given to hotel guests
Special Features: Located next to Holiday Inn.
Free airport and downtown shuttle.

Eldorado Hotel Casino
345 N. Virginia Street
Reno, Nevada 89501
(775) 786-5700
Website: www.eldoradoreno.com

Reservation Number: (800) 648-5966
Rooms: 817 Price Range: $49-$119
Suites: 127 Price Range: $110-$750
Restaurants: 9 (1 open 24 hours)
Buffets: B-$5.99/$9.99 (Sat-Sun)
    L-$6.99 D-$10.99/$24.99 (Fri)/$19.99 (Sat)
Casino Size: 76,500 Square Feet
Other Games: SB, RB, S21, MB, PG, P, PG,
        PGP, LIR, TCP, B6, K
Casino Marketing: (800) 648-4597
Special Features: In-house coffee roasting.
Pasta shop. Microbrewery. Bakery. Butcher
shop. Gelato factory. Video arcade.

Fitzgeralds Casino/Hotel - Reno
255 N. Virginia Street
Reno, Nevada 89504
(775) 785-3300
Website: www.fitzgeraldsreno.com

Toll-Free Number: (800) 535-LUCK
Room Reservations: (800) 648-5022
Rooms: 351 Price Range: $24-$150
Suites: 8 Price Range: $100-$240
Restaurants: 3 (1 open 24 hours)
Buffets: B-$5.49/$6.49 (Sat-Sun)
        L-$6.49/$7.49 (Fri-Sat)
        D-$10.88/$11.88 (Sat)
Casino Size: 26,380 Square Feet
Other Games: SB, RB, LIR, TCP, K
Special Features: Irish-themed casino. Room
discount for AAA members.

Golden Phoenix Hotel & Casino
255 N. Sierra Street
Reno, Nevada 89501
(775) 785-7100
Website: www.phoenixreno.com

Reservation Number: (800) 648-1828
Rooms: 604 Price Range: $33-$89
Restaurants: 3 (1 open 24 hours)
Casino Size: 40,000 Square Feet
Other Games: SB, RB, CSP, LIR
Special Features: Formerly the Flamingo
Reno. Benihana Steak House.

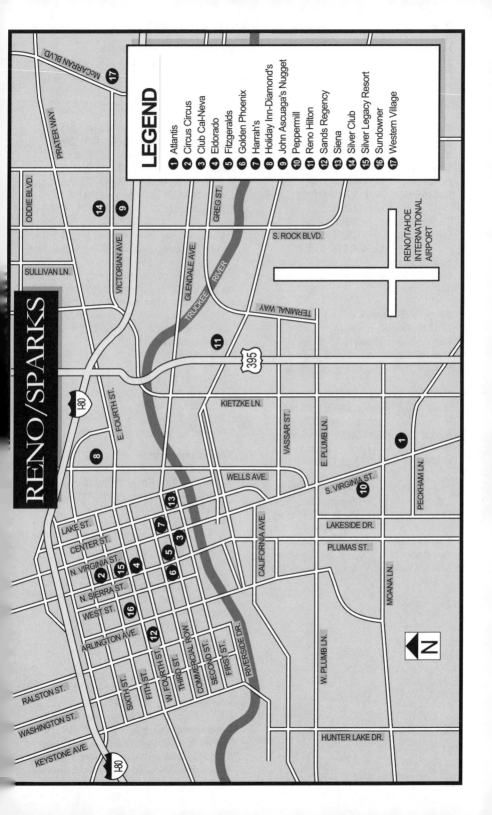

Harrah's Reno
219 N. Center Street
Reno, Nevada 89501
(775) 786-3232
Website: www.harrahsreno.com

Toll-Free Number: (800) 423-1121
Reservation Number: (800) HARRAHS
Rooms: 456 Price Range: $39-$149
Suites: 60 Price Range: $69-$195
Restaurants: 7 (1 open 24 hours)
Buffets: B-$6.99 L-$7.99/$10.99 (Sat-Sun)
      D-$10.99/$22.99 (Sat)
Casino Size: 53,100 Square Feet
Other Games: SB, RB, S21, B, MB,
      PG, PGP, LIR, TCP, K
Special Features: Some rooms are at Hampton Inn which is connected to Harrah's.

Peppermill Hotel Casino Reno
2707 S. Virginia Street
Reno, Nevada 89502
(775) 826-2121
Website: www.peppermillcasinos.com

Toll-Free Number: (800) 648-6992
Reservation Number: (800) 282-2444
Rooms: 1,070 Price Range: $39-$149
Suites: 185 Price Range: $79-$399
Restaurants: 6 (1 open 24 hours)
Buffets: B-$7.99/$15.99 (Sun)
     L-$9.99/$12.99 (Sat)
     D-$14.99/$24.99 (Fri)/$22.99 (Sat)
Casino Size: 48,510 Square Feet
Other Games: SB, RB, B, PG, P, PGP,
     CSP, LIR, TCP, B6, K
Casino Marketing: (800) 648-5555
Fun Book: Only given to hotel guests
Senior Discount: Various discounts if 55+

Reno Hilton Casino Resort
2500 E. Second Street
Reno, Nevada 89595
(775) 789-2000
Website: www.renohilton.com

Reservation Number: (800) 648-5080
Rooms: 1,847 Price Range: $69-$209
Suites: 154 Price Range: $275-$1,000
Restaurants: 10 (1 open 24 hours)
Buffets: B-$6.49 L-$6.99 D-$10.99
Casino Size: 117,400 Square Feet
Other Games: SB, RB, B, MB, PG, P, PGP,
     LIR, TCP, B6, K
Fun Book: Only given to hotel guests
Senior Discount: Join Club Magic/Club 55 if
     55+ for various discounts
Special Features: Largest hotel in Reno. Two movie theaters. 265-space RV park. KOA campground. 50-lane bowling center. Health club. Shopping mall. 8 tennis courts. Family amusement center. Laketop golf driving range. Indoor simulated golf.

The Sands Regency Hotel Casino
345 North Arlington Avenue
Reno, Nevada 89501
(775) 348-2200
Website: www.sandsregency.com

Reservation Number: (800) 648-3553
Rooms: 811 Price Range: $69-$109
Suites: 27 Price Range: $89-$159
Restaurants: 3 (1 open 24 hours)
Casino Size: 29,000 Square Feet
Other Games: SB, PGP, LIR, TCP, K, BG
Special Features: Arby's, Tony Roma's and Pizza Hut Express.

Siena Hotel Spa Casino
1 S. Lake Street
Reno, Nevada 89501
(775) 337-6260
Website: www.sienareno.com

Toll-Free Number: (877) 743-6233
Rooms: 214 Price Range: $49-$69
Suites: 27 Price Range: $199-$575
Restaurants: 3 (1 open 24 hours)
Casino Size: 23,000 Square Feet
Other Games: SB, RB, MB, PGP, LIR, TCP, K
Fun Book: Given with initial slot club sign-up
Special Features: Business center. Health spa. Wine cellar. AAA and AARP room discounts.

The Best Places To Play in Reno/Tahoe

Roulette - The best roulette game in the Reno/Tahoe area can be found at Club Cal-Neva in downtown Reno which offers a single-zero roulette wheel but only on the weekends. Single-zero roulette has only a 2.70% edge as compared to the usual 5.26% edge on a double-zero roulette wheel. Club Cal-Neva has three roulette wheels in the casino but only one of them is single-zero. The minimum bet is $2.

Craps - Almost all Reno/Tahoe area casino offer double odds on their crap games. The casinos offering the highest odds are the Sands Regency in Reno and the Lakeside Inn in Lake Tahoe which both offer 10 times odds.

Blackjack - There's good news and bad news for blackjack players in Northern Nevada. The good news is that there is an abundance of single-deck and double-deck games available. The bad news though is that unlike Las Vegas, where many Strip-area casinos stand on soft 17 in their blackjack games, virtually all casinos in the Reno/Tahoe area hit soft 17. This results in a slightly higher advantage (.20%) for the casinos. Additionally, some casinos may also restrict your double-downs to two-card totals of 9, 10 or 11 only. The following recommendations apply to basic strategy players.

For single-deck players the best game is in Sparks at Baldini's which is the only casino to offer a game where the dealer stands on soft 17. Additional rules are: double down on any first two cards, split any pair and resplit any pair. The casino edge in this game is actually in favor of the player by .01%.

Next best is the Alamo Travel Center in Sparks which has similar rules to Baldini's, except they hit soft 17, they allow late surrender and they will also count a Six-Card Charlie as an automatic winner. The casino edge here is .10%.

Following those two is the game at the Sundowner where they will only allow you to double down on two-card-totals of 9, 10 or 11 but they will give you a "push" if your cards total 21 and the dealer has a blackjack with an ace in the hole. The casino edge in this game is .15%.

Next best are nine casinos that offer single-deck with the basic Northern Nevada rules: double down on any first two cards, split any pair and resplit any pair (except aces): Baldini's, Peppermill, Atlantis, Siena, Rail City, John Ascuaga's Nugget, Western Village, Boomtown and Silver Club. The casino edge here is .18%.

John Ascuaga's Nugget in Sparks is the best place to play double-deck blackjack. Their two-deck game has the following rules: double down on any first two cards, split any pair, resplit any pair (except aces) and double down after split. This works out to a casino edge of .40%

Next best are five casinos in Reno that offer those same basic rules, except for doubling after splitting: Silver Legacy, Eldorado, Atlantis, Reno Hilton and Club Cal-Neva. John Ascuaga's Nugget in Sparks also offers the same game.

For six-deck shoe games the best place is John Ascuaga's Nugget in Sparks which offers the following rules: double down on any number of cards, split any pair, resplit any pair (including aces) and double down after splitting. The casino edge in this game is .31%.

The next best places to play six-deck games are all in Lake Tahoe: Caesars, Harrah's, and Lakeside Inn. The game's edge is .56% with these rules: double down on any two cards, split any pair, resplit any pair (including aces) and double allowed after split.

If you take away resplitting of aces from the above game you have a game with a casino edge of .63% that's offered in Reno at the Eldorado, Reno Hilton, Siena and Circus Circus. It's also offered in Lake Tahoe at Horizon, Bill's and Harvey's.

Video Poker - Smart video poker players know that the three best varieties of machines to look for are: 9/6 Jacks or Better, 10/7 Double Bonus and full-pay Deuces Wild. By only playing these three kinds of machines, playing the maximum coin and using perfect strategy you can achieve, theoretically, the following payback percentages: 99.54% on 9/6 Jacks or Better, 100.17% on 10/7 Double Bonus and 100.76% on full-pay Deuces Wild.

Fortunately, excellent video poker opportunities are available in Northern Nevada with nickel, quarter and dollar 9/6 Jacks or Better games available at almost every casino in Reno. John Ascuaga's Nugget, Atlantis and the Horizon in Lake Tahoe, also offer some quarter 9/6 games with 4,700 coin (rather than the standard 4,000) for the royal flush jackpot. In Lake Tahoe only Harrah's and Horizon offer quarter 9/6 games, while many casinos offer the game at the $1 level. Fifty-play 9/6 at denominations from nickel to quarters is offered at Circus Circus, Atlantis, Hilton, Peppermill and Silver Legacy.

10/7 Double Bonus in quarters (some with progressive jackpots) is widely available in Reno and Sparks. $1 10/7 Double Bonus can be found at: Atlantis, John Ascuaga's Nugget, Cal-Neva, Eldorado, Silver Legacy, Siena, Peppermill, Hilton and Western Village.

Full-pay Deuces Wild is offered in quarter denominations in Reno at Circus-Circus, Hilton and Silver Legacy (progressive) but is not available anywhere in Lake Tahoe.

Another popular video poker game - Pick'em - is offered in quarters and dollars at Harrah's, Boomtown, Hilton and John Ascuaga's Nugget. Pick'em is also offered in Lake Tahoe at Harvey's (quarters) and Harrah's ($1 and $5).

Slots - For slot players it pays to play where the machines are set to return the most. According to the Nevada Gaming Control Board, for the fiscal year ending June 30, 2002 the average north Lake Tahoe slot machine returned 93.21% while the average south Lake Tahoe machine returned 94.39%. In Reno the average return was 95.01% but the highest return of all was 95.40% in Sparks. Additionally, Sparks seems to be an especially good spot for low limit players because the city's nickel machines had the highest returns in the state: 94.44%.

Silver Legacy Resort Casino
407 N. Virginia Street
Reno, Nevada 89501
(775) 325-7401
Website: www.silverlegacy.com

Reservation Number: (800) 687-8733
Rooms: 1,720 Price Range: $55-$169
Suites: 150 Price Range: $100-$260
Restaurants: 5 (1 open 24 hours)
Buffets: B-$6.99/$9.99 (Sat-Sun)
        L-$7.99 D-$10.99/$14.99 (Fri-Sat)
Casino Size: 88,400 Square Feet
Other Games: SB, RB, S21, B, PG, PGP,
        CSP, LIR, TCP, B6, K
Casino Marketing: (800) 215-7721
Special Features: Automated mining machine
above casino floor. Comedy club. Rum bar.

Sundowner Hotel Casino
450 N. Arlington Avenue
Reno, Nevada 89503
(775) 786-7050
Website: www.sundowner-casino.com .

Reservation Number: (800) 648-5490
Rooms: 583 Price Range: $35-$69
Suites: 10 Price Range: $109-$200
Restaurants: 3 (1 open 24 hours)
Buffets: B-$5.95 (Sat-Sun) D-$6.95/$9.95 (Fri)
Casino Size: 19,640 Square Feet
Other Games: SB, RB, K
Casino Marketing: (800) 648-5490

Searchlight

Map Location: **#25** (58 miles S. of Las Vegas
on Hwy. 95)

Searchlight Nugget Casino
100 N. Highway 95
Searchlight, Nevada 89046
(702) 297-1201

Room Reservations: (702) 297-1144
Rooms: 20 Price Range: $35-$50
Casino Size: 3,260 Square Feet
Other Games: P, No Craps or Roulette

Sparks

Map Location: **#4** (Sparks is a suburb of Reno
and is located one mile east of Reno on I-80)

Here's information, as supplied by Nevada's
State Gaming Control Board, showing the slot
machine payback percentages for all of the
Sparks area casinos for the fiscal year beginning July 1, 2001 and ending June 30, 2002:

Denomination	Payback %
5¢ Slots	94.44
25¢ Slots	95.40
$1 Slots	96.21
$1 Megabucks	87.41
$5 Slots	97.04
All Slots	95.40

These numbers reflect the percentage of money
returned on each denomination of machine and
encompass all electronic machines including
slots, video poker and video keno. For nickel
slot players Sparks' casinos offer the highest
returns in the state.

Alamo Travel Center
1959 East Greg Street
Sparks, Nevada 89431
(775) 355-8888
Website: www.thealamo.com

Reservation Number: (800) 800-8000
Rooms: 71 Price Range: $57-$80
Restaurants: 1
Casino Size: 7,150 Square Feet
Other Games: SB, RB, K, No Craps or Roulette
Special Features: Motel is Super 8. Truck stop.
Video arcade. Post office and service station.

Baldini's Sports Casino
865 South Rock Boulevard
Sparks, Nevada 89431
(775) 358-0116
Website: www.baldinissportscasino.com

Restaurants: 4 (1 open 24 hours)
Buffets: B-$3.99/$6.99 (Sat/Sun)
⠀⠀⠀⠀⠀L-$5.99 D-$6.99
Casino Size: 17,340 Square Feet
Other Games: SB, RB, K, TCP, No Roulette
Senior Discount: 15% off food, if 55 or older
Special Features: Convenience store. Gas station. Free six-pack of Pepsi awarded with natural 4-of-a-kind, or better, in video poker with maximum coins bet.

John Ascuaga's Nugget
1100 Nugget Avenue
Sparks, Nevada 89431
(775) 356-3300
Website: www.janugget.com

Toll-Free Number: (800) 648-1177
Rooms: 1,600 Price Range: $36-$155
Suites: 150 Price Range: $99-$295
Restaurants: 8 (1 open 24 hours)
Buffets: B-$9.50 (Sat)/$11.50 (Sun) L-$7.99
⠀⠀⠀⠀D-$11.50 (Wed/Sun)/$13.50 (Tue/Thu)/
⠀⠀⠀⠀$17.95 (Fri/Sat)/$14.95 (Mon)
Casino Size: 82,600 Square Feet
Other Games: SB, RB, P, PGP,
⠀⠀⠀⠀⠀⠀⠀⠀LIR, TCP, K, BG
Special Features: Wedding chapel. Video arcade. Health club.

Rail City Casino
2121 Victorian Avenue
Sparks, Nevada 89431
(775) 359-9440

Restaurants: 1
Buffets: L-$5.95 D-$6.95/$9.95 (Fri)
Casino Size: 16,620 Square Feet
Other Games: SB, RB, K
Senior Discount: 20% off buffet, if 50 or older

Silver Club Hotel/Casino
1040 Victorian Avenue
Sparks, Nevada 89432
(775) 358-4771
Website: www.silverclub.com

Reservation Number: (800) 905-7774
Rooms: 204 Price Range: $39-$79
Suites: 8 Price Range: $85-$225
Restaurants: 4 (1 open 24 hours)
Buffets: B-$4.95 L-$5.95 D-$7.99/$9.99 (Fri)
Casino Size: 17,502 Square Feet
Other Games: SB, RB, LIR, TCP, K
Senior Discount: 10% off food, if 55 or older

Western Village Inn & Casino
815 Nichols Boulevard
Sparks, Nevada 89432
(775) 331-1069

Reservation Number: (800) 648-1170
Rooms: 280 Price Range: $22-$50
Suites: 5 Price Range: $110-$135
Restaurants: 3 (1 open 24 hours)
Casino Size: 26,973 Square Feet
Other Games: SB
Fun Book: Given to hotel guests, or
⠀⠀⠀⠀⠀⠀⠀⠀at cage after cashing a check
Senior Discount: Room discount, if 55 or older

Tonopah

Map Location: **#26** (200 miles N.W. of Las Vegas on Hwy. 95 where it meets Hwy. 6)

The Station House
P.O. Box 1351
Tonopah, Nevada 89049
(775) 482-9777

Rooms: 75 Price Range: $60-$80
Suites: 3 Price Range: $136
Restaurants: 1
Casino Size: 4,800 Square Feet
Other Games: No Roulette
Special Features: 20-space RV park.

Verdi

Map Location: **#4** (4 miles W. of Reno on I-80 at the California border)

Boomtown Hotel & Casino
P.O. Box 399
Verdi, Nevada 89439
(775) 345-6000
Website: www.boomtownreno.com

Reservation Number: (800) 648-3790
Rooms: 318 Price Range: $49-$150
Suites: 20 Price Range: $99-$279
Restaurants: 4 (1 open 24 hours)
Buffets: B-$7.49/$10.99 (Sat-Sun) L-$7.99
          D-$9.99/$23.99 (Fri-Sun)
Casino Size: 39,650 Square Feet
Other Games: SB, RB, P, PGP, LIR, K
Special Features: 203-space RV park. 24-hour mini-mart. Indoor family fun center with rides and arcade games. Free shuttle to/from Reno.

Wells

Map Location: **#27** (338 miles N.E. of Reno on I-80)

Four Way Bar/Cafe & Casino
U.S. 93 & Interstate 80
Wells, Nevada 89835
(775) 752-3344

Restaurants: 1
Casino Size: 4,500 Square Feet
Other Games: No Craps or Roulette
Fun Book: Ask at cage

Lucky J's Casino
PO Box 515/U.S. 93 & Interstate 80
Wells, Nevada 89835
(775) 752-2252

Restaurants: 1
Casino Size: 900 Square Feet
Other Games: No Craps or Roulette
Special Features: Located in Flying J Truck Stop. Blackjack open 7:30am-11:30 pm.

W. Wendover

Map Location: **#28** (Just W. of the Utah border on I-80)

Peppermill Inn & Casino
680 Wendover Boulevard
W. Wendover, Nevada 89883
(775) 664-2255
Website: www.peppermillwendover.com

Reservation Number: (800) 648-9660
Rooms: 198 Price Range: $31-$90
Suites: 26 Price Range: $60-$215
Restaurants: 1 (open 24 hours)
Buffets: B-$7.95/$10.95 (Sun) L-$8.95
          D-$11.95/$18.95 (Fri)
Casino Size: 24,880 Square Feet
Other Games: SB, PGP, LIR, TCP, K
Fun Book: Given to hotel guests at check-in
Special Features: Single-zero roulette.

Rainbow Hotel Casino
1045 Wendover Boulevard
W. Wendover, Nevada 89883
(775) 664-4000
Website: www.rainbowwendover.com

Toll-Free Number: (800) 217-0049
Rooms: 298 Price Range: $28-$100
Suites: 71 Price Range: $70-$250
Restaurants: 2
Buffets: B-$7.95 L-$8.95/$9.95 (Sat-Sun)
          D-$15.95/$18.95 (Fri-Sat)
Casino Size: 47,560 Square Feet
Other Games: SB, PGP, P, LIR, TCP
Senior Discount: $2 off buffet, if 65 or older

Red Garter Hotel & Casino
P.O. Box 2399
W. Wendover, Nevada 89883
(775) 664-3315
Website: www.fh-inc.com

Toll-Free Number: (800) 982-2111
Rooms: 46 Price Range: $22-$65
Restaurants: 1
Casino Size: 13,600 Square Feet
Other Games: SB
Fun Book: Ask at Welcome Center

Silver Smith Casino Resort
101 Wendover Boulevard
W. Wendover, Nevada 89883
(775) 664-2231
Website: www.statelinenv.com

Toll-Free Number: (800) 648-9668
Reservation Number: (800) 848-7300
Rooms: 498 Price Range: $25-$90
Suites: 50 Price Range: $99-$199
Restaurants: 8 (1 open 24 hours)
Buffets: B-$9.95 (Sat-Sun) D-$7.95
Casino Size: 25,538 Square Feet
Other Games: PGP, LIR, TCP, K
Special Features: 56-space RV Park. Connected by sky bridge to State Line Casino. Gift shop. Liquor Store. Video arcade. Golf packages.

State Line Hotel & Casino
100 Wendover Boulevard
W. Wendover, Nevada 89883
(775) 664-2221
Website: www.statelinenv.com

Toll-Free Number: (800) 648-9668
Reservation Number: (800) 848-7300
Rooms: 498 Price Range: $25-$90
Suites: 50 Price Range: $99-$199
Restaurants: 1 (open 24 hours)
Buffets: B-$8.95 (Sat-Sun) D-$10.95/$14.95 (Fri)
Casino Size: 47,358 Square Feet
Other Games: SB, MB, PGP, LIR,TCP, B6, K
Special Features: Connected by sky bridge to Silver Smith Casino. Gift shop. Golf packages

Winnemucca

Map Location: **#29** (164 miles N.E. of Reno on I-80)

Model T Hotel/Casino/RV Park
1130 W. Winnemucca Blvd.
Winnemucca, Nevada 89446
(775) 623-2588
Website: www.modelt.com

Reservation Number: (800) 645-5658
Rooms: 75 Price Range: $45-$75
Restaurants: 4 (1 open 24 hours)
Casino Size: 9,535 Square Feet
Other Games: LIR, TCP, K, No Craps or Roulette
Fun Book: Given to hotel and RV park guests
Special Features: 58-space RV park. Food court with Baskin-Robbins, A&W, Taco Bell Express and coffee shop. Country store.

Red Lion Inn & Casino
741 W. Winnemucca Boulevard
Winnemucca, Nevada 89445
(775) 623-2565
 Website: www.redlionwinn.com

Reservation Number: (800) 633-6435
Rooms: 100 Price Range: $55-$94
Suites: 7 Price Range: $105-$165
Restaurants: 1
Casino Size: 3,050 Square Feet
Other Games: SB, RB, No Craps or Roulette
Fun Book: Given to hotel guests and also distributed by local motels

Winners Hotel/Casino
185 W. Winnemucca Boulevard
Winnemucca, Nevada 89445
(775) 623-2511
Website: www.winnerscasino.com

Reservation Number: (800) 648-4770
Rooms: 125 Price Range: $35-$60
Suites: 3 Price Range: $70-$80
Restaurants: 2
Buffets: B-$5.49 (Sat-Sun) D-$9.95 (Fri)
Casino Size: 11,340 Square Feet
Other Games: LIR, TCP, BG
Fun Book: Need coupon from local motels
Senior Discount: $1 off buffet, if 55 or older
Special Features: Courtesy car service to other motels, local businesses and airport/transportation facilities. Gift shop. Video arcade.

Yerington

Map Location: **#30** (60 miles S.E. of Reno on Hwy. Alt. 95)

Casino West
11 N. Main Street
Yerington, Nevada 89447
(775) 463-2481
 Website: www.casino-west.net

Reservation Number: (800) 227-4661
Rooms: 79 Price Range: $44-$56
Restaurants: 1
Buffets: B-$5.50 (Sun)
        D-$6.50/$12.95 (Fri)/$5.50 (Sun)
Casino Size: 4,550 Square Feet
Other Games: K, No Craps or Roulette
Senior Discount: Room discounts, if 55+
Special Features: Movie theater. 12-lane bowling alley. Slot club members get $1 off buffets.

Indian Casino

Avi Hotel & Casino
10000 Aha Macav Parkway
Laughlin, Nevada 89029
(702) 535-5555
Website: www.avicasino.com
Map Location: **#2**

Toll-Free Number: (800) AVI-2-WIN
Rooms: 301 Price Range: $19-$119
Suites: 29 Price Range: $59-$175
Restaurants: 3 (1 open 24 hours)
Buffets: B-$4.49/$5.49 (Sat-Sun)
        L-$5.49/$5.99 Sat-Sun)
        D-$6.99/$7.49 (Sat)/$9.99 (Fri)
Casino Size: 25,000 Square Feet
Other Games: SB, P, CSP, TCP, LIR, K, BG
Special Features: 300-space RV park. On Colorado River with boat dock, launch and private beach. Baskin-Robbins. Subway. Gas station. Smoke shop. Kid's Quest childcare center.

NEW JERSEY

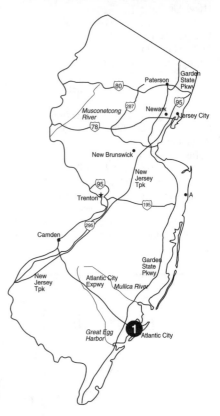

Map Location: **#1** (on the Atlantic Ocean in southeast New Jersey, 130 miles south of New York City and 60 miles southeast of Philadelphia)

Once a major tourist destination that was world-famous for its steel pier and boardwalk attractions, Atlantic City fell into decline and casino gambling was seen as its salvation when voters approved it there in 1976.

The first casino (Resorts International) opened to "standing-room-only crowds" in 1978. Since then 11 more casinos have opened and all but two are located along the boardwalk. The other two (Harrah's and Trump Marina) are located in the marina section.

MGM-Mirage Resorts and Boyd Gaming Corp. are partners in a $1 billion, 40-story, 2,010-room resort that will be built on a 25-acre site in the city's Marina district directly across from Harrah's. Construction for the new *Borgata Resort and Spa* began in mid-2000 and the property is expected to open in mid-2003. For more current information on the project you can visit their website at www.theborgata.com

Following is information from the New Jersey Casino Control Commission regarding average slot payout percentages for the 12-month period from July 1, 2001 through June 30, 2002:

CASINO	PAYBACK %
Sands	92.8
Trump Taj Mahal	92.1
Resorts	92.1
Tropicana	92.0
Harrah's	92.0
Caesars	92.0
Trump's Marina	92.0
Trump Plaza	91.9
A.C. Hilton	91.9
Bally's A.C.	91.8
Showboat	91.4
Claridge	91.3

These figures reflect the total percentages returned by each casino for all of their electronic machines which includes slot machines, video poker, etc.

All Atlantic City casinos are open 24 hours and, unless otherwise noted, the games offered at every casino are: slots, video poker, big six, craps, blackjack, roulette, baccarat, mini-baccarat, Caribbean stud poker, let it ride, pai gow poker and keno. Additional games offered include: simulcasting (S), poker (P), pai gow (PG), sic bo (SB), double exposure blackjack (DE), Spanish 21 (S21), three-card poker (TCP) and casino war (W). The minimum gambling age is 21.

For more information on visiting New Jersey you can contact the state's Travel & Tourism Department at (800) 537-7397. For information only on Atlantic City call (800) 262-7395.

The Best Places To Play in Atlantic City

Blackjack: The blackjack games offered at Atlantic City casinos are pretty much all the same: eight-deck shoe games with double down on any first two cards, dealers stands on soft 17, pairs can be split up to three times and doubling after splitting is allowed. This works out to a casino edge of .44% against a player using basic strategy.

There are 11 casinos that deal an eight-deck game with the standard rules shown above: Bally's, Wild Wild West, Caesars, Harrah's, Hilton, Resorts, Sands, Showboat, Tropicana, Trump Plaza and Trump Marina.

If you're willing to make higher minimum bets you can find slightly better games. Most casinos offer six-deck games with minimum bets of $25 per hand. A six-deck game, with the standard rules in place, lowers the casino edge from .44% to .42% The casinos offering this game are: Bally's, Caesars, Claridge, Hilton, Resorts, Showboat, Tropicana and all three Trump casinos.

Roulette: When choosing roulette games it's usually best to play in a casino offering a single-zero wheel because the casino advantage is 2.70% versus a double-zero wheel which has a 5.26% advantage. However, that situation is somewhat different in Atlantic City because of certain gaming regulations. On double-zero wheels the casinos can only take one-half of a wager on even-money bets (odd/even, red/black, 1-18/19-36) when zero or double-zero is the winning number. This lowers the casino edge on these particular bets to 2.63%, while the edge on all other bets remains at 5.26%. This rule is not in effect on single-zero wheels and virtually all bets on that game have a 2.70% house edge.

There are nine casinos that have single-zero roulette wheels: Harrah's, Trump Marina, Bally's, Showboat, Trump Taj Mahal, Hilton, Tropicana, Trump Plaza and Caesars. You should be aware, however, that almost all of these games are only open on weekends and they also require $25 minimum bets ($50 at Plaza, $100 at Caesars).

Craps: In craps it's best to play at casinos that allow you to bet the maximum amount of "free odds" in which the casino has no advantage. Additionally, field bettors should find casinos that pay triple (rather than double) on 12 because this lowers the casino edge from 5.6% to 2.8%. Unfortunately, there are no casinos in Atlantic City that pay triple on 12 in the field.

There are five casinos that offer five times odds on all of their crap games: Claridge, Resorts, Tropicana, Trump Taj Mahal and Hilton. Additionally, Trump Marina offers one table with 10 times odds but they require a $25 minimum bet.

Video Poker: One of the best video poker games available in Atlantic City is a Double Joker machine with a 99.97% payback. The paytable to look for is one that offers 9-for-1 on 4-of-a-kind (rather than 8-for-1 which lowers the payback to 98.10%). Other good games to look for are: 9/6 Jacks or Better (99.5%) and Pick'em (99.99%).

Quarter Games - Very few 9/6 Jacks or Better games can be found. The Claridge has about five and Trump Plaza has a couple. At the 50-cent level some 9/6 games can be found at the Sands and Tropicana. The most 9/5 Double Joker games are at Showboat which has about six. The Claridge has a few and Tropicana has one. Quarter Pick'em can be found at Bally's, Resorts, Claridge and Trump Plaza. Trump Marina has some All American in their Gamemakers.

Dollar Games - There are quite a few casinos offering 9/6 Jacks or Better: Caesars, Harrah's, Resorts (one machine), Sands, Taj Mahal, Tropicana, Trump Marina. Additionally, Bally's has it with a progressive. Claridge has two 9/5 Double Joker games. Pick'em can be found at Bally's. Atlantic City's only 10/7 Double Bonus machine can be found at Trump Plaza (#P-036) and $5 9/6 games are available at Bally's, Caesars, Harrah's, Tropicana, Trump Marina, Taj Mahal and the Sands.

Unlike video poker games, when it comes to slot machines you really can't tell what they're set to pay back. Therefore, you need to rely on statistics from the state's gaming regulators to see where the best-paying machines are located. Just take a look at the statistics on page 298 to see which casinos offer the best returns on their machines.

Atlantic City Hilton Casino Resort
Boston & The Boardwalk
Atlantic City, New Jersey 08401
(609) 347-7111
Website: www.hiltonac.com

Reservation Number: (800) 257-8677
Rooms: 675 Price Range: $99-$375
Suites: 54 Price Range: $220-$600
Restaurants: 6 (1 open 24 hours)
Buffets: L/D-$15.99/$16.99 (Sat-Sun)
Casino Size: 59,440 Square Feet
Other Games: S, PG, SB, DE
Casino Marketing: (800) THE-GRAND
Special Features: Spa facilities with indoor pool. Unisex salon. AARP room discount.

Bally's Atlantic City
Park Place and the Boardwalk
Atlantic City, New Jersey 08401
(609) 340-2000
Website: www.ballysac.com

Reservation Number: (800) 225-5977
Rooms: 1,162 Price Range: $99-$400
Suites: 92 Price Range: $279-$620
Restaurants: 15 (1 open 24 hours)
Buffets (Bally's): B-$11.99 L/D-$13.99
Buffets (W.W. West): L-$14.95 D-$17.95
Casino Size (P. Place): 80,809 Square Feet
Casino Size: (W.W. West) 73,935 Square Feet
Other Games: S, PG, SB, TCP, S21
Special Features: Walkway connects to Wild Wild West-a themed casino with mountain, waterfalls, 17 animated robotic figures, three western restaurants and three retail shops. Spa offers package plans and body treatments.

The Borgata
One Borgata Way
Atlantic City, NJ 08401
(609) 667-1000
Website: www.the borgata.com

EXPECTED TO OPEN SUMMER 2003
Toll-Free Number: (800) 443-0104
Reservation Number: (800) 524-2867
Rooms: 1,600 Prices: Not set at press time
Suites: 400 Prices: Not set at press time
Restaurants: 11
Buffets: Prices not set at press time
Casino Size: 135,000 Square Feet
Other Games: S, P, PG, SB
Special Features: Health spa. Outdoor pool.

Caesars Atlantic City
2100 Pacific Avenue
Atlantic City, New Jersey 08401
(609) 348-4411
Website: www.caesarsac.com

Toll-Free Number: (800) 443-0104
Reservation Number: (800) 524-2867
Rooms: 1,479 Price Range: $75-$375
Suites: 198 Price Range: $175-$700
Restaurants: 12 (1 open 24 hours)
Buffets: B-$10.95 L-$16.95
         D-$16.95/$19.95 (Fri-Sun)
Casino Size: 120,231 Square Feet
Casino Marketing: (800) 367-3767
Other Games: S, P, PG, SB
Special Features: Roman theme throughout hotel and casino. Smoke-free sections. Planet Hollywood restaurant. Health spa. Shopping arcade. Outdoor pool. Rooftop tennis. Unisex beauty salon.

Claridge Casino Hotel
Boardwalk & Park Place
Atlantic City, New Jersey 08401
(609) 340-3400
Website: www.claridge.com

Reservation Number: (800) 257-8585
Rooms: 449 Price Range: $110-$200
Suites: 53 Price Range: $210-$540
Restaurants: 5 (1 open 24 hours)
Casino Size: 58,565 Square Feet
Other Games: SB, DE
Casino Marketing: (800) 847-LUCK
Special Features: Indoor pool and health spa. Unisex salon. Gift shop.

Harrah's Casino Hotel
777 Harrah's Boulevard
Atlantic City, New Jersey 08401
(609) 441-5000
Website: www.harrahs.com

Reservation Number: (800) 2-HARRAH
Rooms: 1,300 Price Range: $99-$269
Suites: 326 Price Range: Casino Use Only
Restaurants: 8 (1 open 24 hours)
Buffets: B-$11.99 D-$19.99
Casino Size: 89,617 Square Feet
Other Games: P, W
Casino Marketing: (800) 2-HARRAH
Special Features: Largest hotel in New Jersey. 65-slip marina. Fitness center with indoor swimming pool. Two retail shops. Beauty salon. Video arcade. Miniature golf course.

Resorts Casino Hotel
1133 Boardwalk
Atlantic City, New Jersey 08401
(609) 344-6000
Website: www.resortsac.com

Toll-Free Number: (800) 336-6378
Reservation Number: (800) 334-6378
Rooms: 644 Price Range: $89-$250
Suites: 30 Price Range: $150-$500
Restaurants: 10 (1 open 24 hours)
Buffets: B-$9.95 L-$10.95 D-$14.95
Casino Size: 77,000 Square Feet
Other Games: S, P, PG, 3-Card Poker
Casino Marketing: (800) 438-7424
Special Features: Health Spa with Nautilus equipment. Squash club. Game room. 1133 Nightclub. Beachfront shops.

Sands Hotel & Casino
Indiana Avenue & Brighton Park
Atlantic City, New Jersey 08401
(609) 441-4000
Website: www.acsands.com

Reservation Number: (800) 257-8580
Rooms: 476 Price Range: $105-$275
Suites: 58 Price Range: $300-$600
Restaurants: 5 (1 open 24 hours)
Buffets (Boardwalk): B-$7.95 L/D-$14.95
Buffets (Gourmet): B: $32.95(Sun) D: $26.95
Casino Size: 57,296 Square Feet
Other Games: S, P, PG, SB
Casino Marketing: (800) AC-SANDS

Showboat Casino-Hotel
801 Boardwalk
Atlantic City, New Jersey 08401
(609) 343-4000
Website: www.harrahs.com

Reservation Number: (800) 621-0200
Rooms: 731 Price Range: $109-$199
Suites: 69 Price Range: Casino Use Only
Restaurants: 8 (1 open 24 hours)
Buffets: L-$14.99 D-$17.99
Casino Size: 80,707 Square Feet
Other Games: S, P, PG
Special Features: 60-lane Bowling Center.
Video arcade.

Tropicana Casino & Resort
Brighton Avenue and the Boardwalk
Atlantic City, New Jersey 08401
(609) 340-4000
Website: www.tropicana.net

Reservation Number: (800) THE-TROP
Rooms: 1,370 Price Range: $78-$275
Suites: 254 Price Range: $148-$355
Restaurants: 8 (1 open 24 hours)
Buffets: B/L-$11.95 D-$16.95
Casino Size: 114,320 Square Feet
Other Games: S, P, PG, DE
Casino Marketing: (800) 338-5553
Special Features: Single-zero roulette game offered on weekends ($50 minimum bet).

Trump Marina Hotel Casino
Huron Avenue & Brigantine Boulevard
Atlantic City, New Jersey 08401
(609) 441-2000
Website: www.trumpmarina.com

Reservation Number: (800) 365-8786
Rooms: 568 Price Range: $85-$399
Suites: 160 Price Range: $175-$450
Restaurants: 7 (1 open 24 hours)
Buffets: B-$7.50 L/D-$12.50
Casino Size: 73,734 Square Feet
Other Games: P, PG, SB
Casino Marketing: (800) 777-8477
Special Features: Adjacent to state marina with 640 slips. 3-acre recreation deck with pools, jogging track, tennis courts, miniature golf course and health club.

Trump Plaza Hotel and Casino
The Boardwalk at Mississippi Avenue
Atlantic City, New Jersey 08401
(609) 441-6000
Website: www.trumpplaza.com

Reservation Number: (800) 677-7378
Rooms: 1,331 Price Range: $105-$400
Suites: 73 Price Range: $325
Restaurants: 11 (1 open 24 hours)
Buffets: L-$12.95 D-$14.95
Casino Size: 138,295 Square Feet
Other Games: PG, SB
Casino Marketing: (800) 677-0711
Special Features: Health spa with massage, herbal wraps and salt-glo loofah cleansing. Indoor pool. East Side Lounge offers live entertainment nightly with no cover and one drink minimum.

Trump Taj Mahal Casino Resort
1000 Boardwalk at Virginia Avenue
Atlantic City, New Jersey 08401
(609) 449-1000
Website: www.trumptaj.com

Reservation Number: (800) 825-8888
Rooms: 1,013 Price Range: $125-$395
Suites: 237 Price Range: $300-$550
Restaurants: 9 (1 open 24 hours)
Buffets: L/D-$15.95
Casino Size: 116,199 Square Feet
Casino Marketing: (800) 234-5678
Other Games: S, P, PG, SB, S21, TCP
Senior Discount: Room discount if 50, or older, with Trump Card. 50% off buffets.
Special Features: Health spa and indoor Olympic-size pool. Hard Rock cafe.

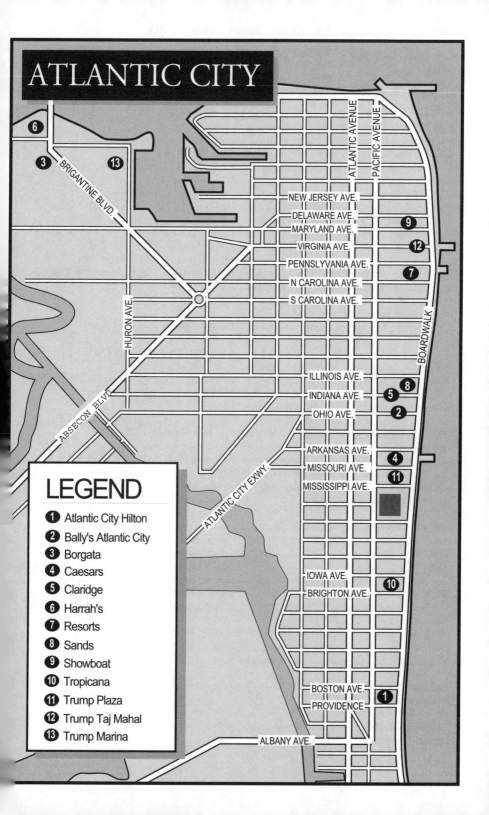

NEW MEXICO

New Mexico's Indian casinos offer an assortment of table games and electronic gaming machines. Additionally, slot machines are allowed at four of the state's race tracks as well as at about 30 various fraternal and veterans clubs.

New Mexico gaming regulations require that electronic machines at racetracks and fraternal/veterans organizations be set to return a minimum of 80% and a maximum of 96%.

New Mexico's Indian tribes do not make their slot machine payback percentages a matter of public record but the terms of the compact between the state and the tribes require all electronic gaming machines to return a minimum of 80%.

Unless otherwise noted, all New Mexico Indian casinos are open 24 hours and offer: blackjack, craps, roulette, video slots and video poker. Some casinos also offer: mini-baccarat (MB), poker (P), pai gow poker (PGP), three-card poker (TCP), Caribbean stud poker (CSP), let it ride (LIR), big 6 wheel (B6), keno (K), bingo (BG) and Simulcasting (S). The minimum gambling age is 21 but some casinos will allow you to play bingo if you are 18 or older.

For information on visiting New Mexico call the state's tourism department at (800) 733-6396.

Big Rock Casino Bowl
419 N. Riverside Drive
Espanola, New Mexico 87532
(505) 747-3100
Website: www.bigrockcasino.com
Map Location: **#7** (25 miles N. of Santa Fe)

Toll-Free Number: (866) 244-7625
Restaurants: 2 Liquor: Yes
Hours: 8am-4am/24 hours (Fri-Sat)
Other Games: No roulette
Special Features: 24-lane bowling center.

Camel Rock Casino
17486-A Highway 84/285
Santa Fe, New Mexico 87504
(505) 984-8414
Website: www.camelrockcasino.com
Map Location: **#2**

Toll-Free Number: (800) GO-CAMEL
Restaurants: 1 Liquor: No
Buffets: B-$4.95 L-$7.95 D-$7.95/$9.95 (Fri)
Casino Size: 60,000 Square feet
Other Games: CSP, BG (Thu-Mon)
Senior Discount: Bingo discount on Thursday, if 55, or older

Casino Apache
P.O Box 205
Mescalero, New Mexico 88340
(505) 630-4100
www.innofthemountaingods.com/casino.htm
Map Location: **#4** (90 miles N.E. of Las Cruces)

Toll-Free Number: (877) 277-5677
Room Reservations: (800) 545-9011
Rooms: 240 Price Range: $110-$135
Rooms: 20 Price Range: $120-$165
Restaurants: 3 Liquor: Yes
Buffets: B-$5.95 L-$10.95
　　　　　D-$10.95/$12.95 (Wed)
Hours: 7am-2:30am/24 hours (Thu-Sat)
Casino Size: 45,000 Square Feet
Other Games: P, CSP, K
Senior Discount: 20% off buffet, if 62, or older
Special Features: Casino is located in Inn of the Mountain Gods. Hotel offers golf, swimming, horseback riding and tennis.

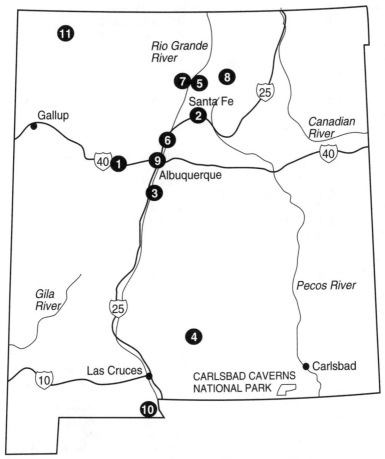

Cities of Gold Casino Hotel
10-B Cities of Gold Road
Santa Fe, New Mexico 87501
(505) 455-3313
Website: www.citiesofgold.com
Map Location: **#2**

Toll-Free Number: (800) 455-3313
Room Reservations: (877) 455-0515
Rooms: 122 Price Range: $65-$95
Suites: 2 Price Range: $136
Restaurants: 2 Liquor: Yes
Buffets: B-$3.95 (Fri-Sun) L/D-$6.95
Hours: 8am-4am/24 hours (Fri-Sat)
Casino Size: 40,000 Square Feet
Other Games: P, LIR, BG, S
Fun Book: Given when you first get club card
Special Features: They also operate Pojoaque
Sports Bar which is one block away from main
casino. Liquor is served there but they only
have slots. AAA/AARP room discounts.

Dancing Eagle Casino
P.O. Box 520
Casa Blanca, New Mexico 87007
(505) 552-0942
Website: www.dancingeaglecasino.com
Map Location: **#1** (40 miles W. of Albuquerque)

Toll-Free Number: (877) 440-9969
Restaurants: 1 Liquor: No
Hours: 8am-4am/24 hours (Thu-Sun)
Casino Size: 21,266 Square Feet

Isleta Casino Resort
11000 Broadway S.E.
Albuquerque, New Mexico 87105
(505) 869-2614
Website: www.isletacasinoresort.com
Map Location: **#3**

Toll-Free Number: (877) 7-ISLETA
Restaurants: 5 Liquor: Yes
Buffets: B-$3.95 (Sat-Sun) L-$4.95
      D-$6.13/$12.95 (Fri)/$9.95 (Sat)
Hours: 8am-4am/24 hours (Fri-Sat)
Casino Size: 30,000 Square Feet
Other Games: P, BG, K
Senior Discount: 13% buffet discount, if 55+
Special Features: Convenience store. Gas station. 27-hole golf course. Alcohol is only served at sports bar in casino.

Ohkay Casino Resort
P.O. Box 1270
San Juan Pueblo, New Mexico 87566
(505) 747-1668
Website: www.ohkay.com
Map Location: **#5** (24 miles N. of Santa Fe)

Toll-Free Number: (800) PLAY-AT-OK
Room Reservation (877) 829-2865
Rooms: 101 Price Range: $65-$95
Suites: 24 Price Range: $95-$135
Restaurants: 2 (1 open 24 hours) Liquor: Yes
Buffets: B-$5.99 L-$6.99 D-$7.99
Casino Size: 35,000 Square Feet
Senior Discount: 10% off room, if 55 or older
Special Features: Hotel is Best Western.

San Felipe Casino Hollywood
25 Hagan Road
Algodones, New Mexico 87001
(505) 867-6700
Website: www.sanfelipecasino.com
Map Location: **#6** (17 miles N. of Albuquerque)

Toll-Free Number: (877) 529-2946
Restaurants: 2 Liquor: No
Buffets: B-$4.25 L-$6.25 D-$7.50
Hours: 8am-4am/24 hours (Thu-Sun)
Other Games: PGP

Sandia Casino
30 Rainbow Road
Albuquerque, New Mexico 87113
(505) 796-7500
Website: www.sandiacasino.com
Map Location: **#9**

Toll-Free Number: (800) 526-9366
Restaurants: 3 Liquor: Yes
Buffets: B-$4.95 L-$5.95
  D-$7.95/$6.95(Thu)/$14.95 (Fri)/$9.95 (Sat)
Hours: 8am-4am/24 hours (Thu-Sun)
Casino Size: 65,000 Square feet
Other Games: P, CSP, LIR, K, BG, TCP
Senior Discount: Bingo discounts, if 65, or older
Special Features: Largest poker room in New Mexico. Subway sandwich shop.

Santa Ana Star Casino
54 Jemez Dam Canyon Road
Bernalillo, New Mexico 87004
(505) 867-0000
Website:www.santaanastar.com
Map Location: **#6** (17 miles N. of Albuquerque)

Restaurants: 4 Liquor: No
Buffets: B-$3.95 (Sat)/$7.25 (Sun)
     L-$6.95 D-$7.95/$19.95(Thu)
Hours: 8am-4am/24 hours (Fri-Sat)
Casino Size: 19,000 Square Feet
Other Games: P, LIR
Special Features: 36-lane bowling alley. New 288-room hotel expected to open by mid-2003.

Sky City Casino
P.O. Box 519
San Fidel, New Mexico 87049
(505) 552-6017
Website: www.skycitycasino.com
Map Location: **#1** (50 miles W. of Albuquerque)

Toll-Free Number: (888) SKY-CITY
Rooms: 134 Price Range: $50-$70
Suites: 15 Price Range: $75-$135
Restaurants: 1 Liquor: No
Buffets: B-$6.95 (Sat-Sun) L-$7.95 D-$9.95
Hours: 8am-4am/24 hours (Thu-Sat)
Casino Size: 30,000 Square Feet
Other Games: P, BG, S
Senior Discount: 10% off buffet, if 55, or older

Taos Mountain Casino
P.O. Box 1477
Taos, New Mexico 87571
(505) 758-4460
Website:www.taosmountaincasino.com
Map Location: **#8** (50 miles N.E. of Santa Fe)

Toll-Free Number: (888) WIN-TAOS
Restaurants: 1 Deli Liquor: No
Hours: 8am-2am/3am (Fri/Sat)
Other Games: No craps
Special Features: Entire casino is non-smoking.

Pari-Mutuels

Downs at Albuquerque
P.O. Box 8510
Albuquerque, NM 87198
(505) 266-5555
Website: www.abqdowns.com
Map Location: **#9**

Restaurants: 1
Buffets: B-$3.99 L-$4.95 D-$7.95
Hours: Noon-Midnight Daily
Other Games: Only gaming machines
Senior Discount: $2 off weekend buffets, if 55+
Special Features: Live horse racing late March through early June and during New Mexico State Fair in September. Horse race simulcasting all year.

Ruidoso Downs & Billy The Kid Casino
P.O. Box 449
Ruidoso Downs, NM 88346
(505) 378-4431
Website: www.btkcasino.com
Map Location: **#4** (90 miles N.E. of Las Cruces)

Restaurants: 1
Buffets: B-$6.50 (Sun) L-$6.50 D-$7.95
Hours: 11am-11pm/12pm-12am (Fri)
Other Games: Only gaming machines
Senior Discount: 10% off buffets, if 55 or older
Special Features: Live horse racing (Thu-Sun) during season which runs from late May through early September. Horse race simulcasting all year.

Sunland Park
1200 Futurity Drive
Sunland Park, NM 88063
(505) 874-5200
Website: www.sunland-park.com
Map Location: **#10** (5 miles W. of El Paso, TX)

Restaurants: 1
Buffets: L-$7.95 D-$9.95
Hours: Noon-Midnight
Other Games: Only gaming machines
Senior Discount: Special coupon book, if 55+
Special Features: Live thoroughbred and quarter-horse racing during season which runs from November through April. Simulcasting of horse racing all year.

SunRay Park and Casino
#39 Road 5568
Farmington, NM 87401
(505) 566-1200
Website: www.sunraygaming.com
Map Location: **#11** (150 miles N.W. of Santa Fe)

Restaurants: 1
Hours: Noon-Midnight
Other Games: Only gaming machines
Special Features: Live horse racing during season which runs from September through November. Simulcasting of horse racing all year.

NEW YORK

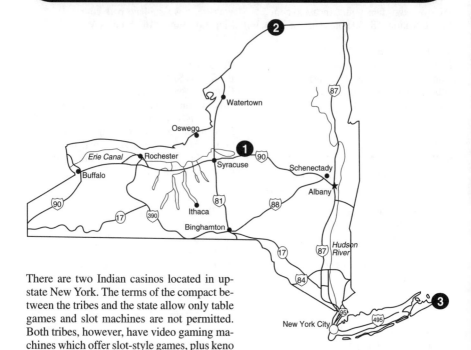

There are two Indian casinos located in up-state New York. The terms of the compact be-tween the tribes and the state allow only table games and slot machines are not permitted. Both tribes, however, have video gaming ma-chines which offer slot-style games, plus keno and poker. These machines do not pay out in cash. Instead, they print out a receipt which must be exchanged for cash.

The two New York casinos are open 24 hours and offer the following games: blackjack, craps, roulette, pai gow poker, mini-baccarat, Caribbean stud poker, let it ride, money (big six) wheel and poker. The minimum gambling age at both casinos is 18.

In October 2001 the New York Assembly passed legislation to expand gambling within the state by allowing up to six new Indian ca-sinos. Three of the casinos would be located in the western half of the state and the other three would be located in the Catskills (about a three-hour drive from mid-town Manahattan). Additionally, the law allowed for the introduction of slot-machine-type video lottery terminals (VLTs) at eight racetracks: Aqueduct, Yonkers, Monticello, Finger Lakes, Vernon Downs, Saratoga Springs, Buffalo and Batavia.

As of August 2002 the required tribal-state compacts for the new Indian casinos had not been neogtiated and details for the VLT's were still being worked out. It will probably be late 2003 before any VLT's or casinos are operat-ing.

For more information on visiting New York call the state's travel information center at (800) 225-5697.

Akwesasne Mohawk Casino
Route 37, Box 670
Hogansburg, New York 13655
(518) 358-2222
Web Site: www.mohawkcasino.com
Map Location: **#2** (65 miles W. of Champlain)

Toll-Free Number: (888) 622-1155
Restaurants: 2   Liquor: Yes
Buffets: B-$3.95 (Sat-Sun) L-$7.95 D-$11.95
Casino Size: 40,000 Square Feet

Turning Stone Casino Resort
5218 Patrick Road
Verona, New York 13478
(315) 361-7711
Web Site: www.turning-stone.com
Map Location: **#1** (adjacent to NY State Thruway exit 33 at Verona, off Route 365, 30 miles E. of Syracuse)

Toll-Free Number: (800) 771-7711
Rooms: 277 Price Range: $96-$175
Suites: 28 Price Range: $126-$395
Restaurants: 9 Liquor: No
Buffets: B-$6.95 (Sat-Sun) L-$8.95/$9.95 (Fri)
    D-$8.95/$12.95 (Fri/Sat)
Casino Size: 100,000 Square Feet
Other Games: Baccarat, Mini-Baccarat,Sic Bo, Double-deck BJ, Acey-Deucey, Bingo, Keno
Special Features: Three golf courses. Gift shop. Discount smoke shop. AAA and AARP room discounts. 800-seat showroom.

New York has one casino boat which travels three miles out into international waters where gambling is permitted. The boat offers: blackjack, craps, roulette, Caribbean stud poker, let it ride, slots and video poker.

Freeport Casino Cruises
361 Woodcleft Avenue
Freeport, New York 11520
(516) 377-7400
Map Location **#3**

Reservation Number: (516) 377-7400
Gambling Age: 21
Ship's Registry: U.S.A.
Food Service: Free Snacks
Schedule:
    11:30am - 4:30pm/5:00pm (Fri-Sat)
    7:00pm - 11:30pm/12:30am (Fri-Sat)
Price: Free   Port Charges: Included
Parking: Free
Special Features: 500-passenger, *Midnight Gambler II* departs from Freeport's Nautical Mile. You must be 21 or older to board.

NORTH CAROLINA

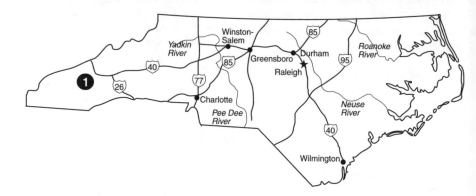

North Carolina has one Indian casino. In August, 1994 the state's Eastern Band of Cherokee Indians signed a compact with the governor to allow some form of video gambling with jackpots of up to $25,000. According to the terms of the compact the video machines must be games of skill and they are required to return a minimum of 83% and a maximum of 98%.

No table games are offered at the Cherokee Casino, only video slots, video poker, and video versions of craps and blackjack. The slots are different than slots you will find in other casinos because of the required "skill" factor. With these "skill" slots you have two opportunities to spin the reels. The "skill" factor comes into play because after seeing the results of your first spin you then have to decide whether to keep none, one, two, or all three of the symbols on each reel before you spin them again.

The casino is open 24 hours and the minimum gambling age is 21. For more information on visiting North Carolina call the state's division of travel & tourism at (800) 847-4862.

Harrah's Cherokee Casino
P.O. Box 1959
Cherokee, North Carolina 28719
(828) 497-7777
Website: www.harrahs.com
Map Location: **#1** (55 miles S.W. of Asheville)

Toll-Free Number: (800) HARRAHS
Rooms 252 Price Range: $129-$179
Restaurants: 5 Liquor: No
Buffets: B-$8.00 L-$10.00 D-$14.50
Special Features: Offers $77 "Play and Stay" packages at five nearby hotels. Planet-4-Kidz childcare center. 1,500-seat entertainment pavilion.

NORTH DAKOTA

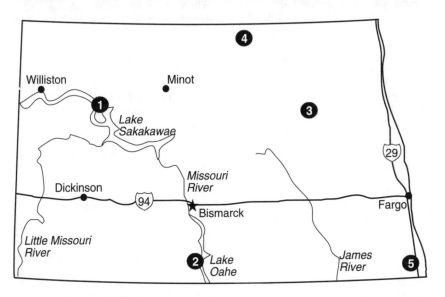

North Dakota has more than 800 sites throughout the state that offer blackjack, with a $25 maximum bet, for the benefit of charities.

There are also six Indian casinos which, although not restricted to that same $25 amount, are limited by law to the following maximum bets: blackjack-$100 (two tables in a casino may have limits up to $250), craps-$60, roulette-$50, slots/video poker-$25 and poker-$50 per bet, per round with a maximum of three rounds.

The terms of the state's compact with the tribes require gaming machines to return a minimum of 80% and a maximum of 100%. However, if a machine is affected by skill, such as video poker or video blackjack, the machines must return a minimum of 83%.

All casinos are open 24 hours and offer: blackjack, craps, roulette, poker, slots, video poker, video keno and video blackjack. Optional games include: Caribbean stud poker (CSP), let it ride (LIR), keno (K), bingo (BG), big-6 wheel (B6) and simulcasting (S). The minimum gambling age is 21.

For information on visiting North Dakota call the state's tourism office at (800) 437-2077

Dakota Magic Casino
16849 102nd Street SE
Hankinson, North Dakota 58041
(701) 634-3000
Website: www.dakotamagic.com
Map Location: **#5** (50 miles S. of Fargo)

Toll-Free Number: (800) 325-6825
Rooms: 76 Price Range: $40-$50
Suites: 8 Price Range: $80-$85
Restaurants: 1 Liquor: Yes
Buffets: B-$4.95 L-$5.95 D-$5.95/$9.95(Fri)
Casino Size: 24,000 Square Feet
Other Games: P, K
Funbook: Given to hotel guests
Senior Discount: Various on Mon, if 55 or older

Four Bears Casino & Lodge
HC 3, Box 2-A
New Town, North Dakota 58763
(701) 627-4018
Website: www.4bearscasino.com
Map Location: **#1** (150 miles N.W. of Bismarck)

Toll-Free Number: (800) 294-5454
Rooms: 97 Price Range: $55-$70
Suites: 3 Price Range: $99
Restaurants: 2 Liquor: Yes
Buffets: B-$6.95 (Sat-Sun) L-$4.95 (Mon-Fri)
    D-$5.95/$6.95 (Wed)/$7.95 (Sun/Mon)/
    $9.95 (Fri)/$11.95 (Sat)
Other Games: P, BG
Casino Marketing: (800) 294-5454 ext 303
Funbook: Inquire at slot club desk
Senior Discount: Various on Wed/Thu, if 55+
Special Features: 80-space RV park with laundry and shower facilities. Nearby marina.

Prairie Knights Casino & Resort
7932 Highway 24
Fort Yates, North Dakota 58538
(701) 854-7777
Website: www.prairieknights.com
Map Location: **#2** (60 miles S. of Bismarck)

Toll-Free Number: (800) 425-8277
Rooms: 96 Price Range: $60-$75
Suites: 4 Price Range: $85-$130
Restaurants: 2 Liquor: Yes
Buffets:L/D-$9.25/$13.95 (Sun)
Casino Size: 42,000 Square Feet
Other Games: S21, TCP, LIR
Casino Marketing: (701) 854-7777
Senior Discount: $5.75 buffet from 11am - 3pm
                (Mon-Sat), if 55 or older
Special Features: Marina with boat slips and 32 RV sites. $45 rooms for slot club members.

Sky Dancer Hotel & Casino
Highway 5 West
Belcourt, North Dakota 58316
(701) 244-2400
Website: www.skydancercasino.com
Map Location: **#4** (120 miles N.E. of Minot)

Toll-Free Number: (866) 244-9467
Rooms: 70 Price Range: $45-$55
Suites: 27 Price Range: $75-$85
Restaurants: 2 Liquor: Yes
Buffets: B-$3.95 L-$5.95 D-$6.95
Casino Size: 25,000 Square Feet
Other Games: LIR, TCP, BG, S,
                P, No Roulette
Special Features: Gift shop. 12 Free RV hookups.

Spirit Lake Casino & Resort
Highway 57
Spirit Lake, North Dakota 58370
(701) 766-4747
Website: www.spiritlakecasino.com
Map Location: **#3** (6 miles S. of Devil's Lake)

Toll-Free Number: (800) WIN-U-BET
Rooms: 124 Price Range: $70
Suites: 16 Price Range: $80-$125
Restaurants: 3 Liquor: No
Buffets: B-$4.50/$7.95 (Sun) L-$5.95
                D-$9.95/$14.95 (Wed)
Casino Size: 45,000 Square Feet
Other Games: P, LIR, BG
Senior Discount: 10% off room, if 55 or older
Special Features: 15-space RV park. Gift shop. Discount smoke shop. 10% room discount for AAA members. Marina.

Turtle Mountain Chippewa Mini-Casino
Highway 5 West
Belcourt, North Dakota 58316
(701) 477-6438
Map Location: **#4** (120 miles N.E. of Minot)

Restaurants: 1 Liquor: Yes
Other Games: Only Machines - No Table Games
Special Features: Located four miles east of Sky Dancer Hotel and Casino.

OREGON

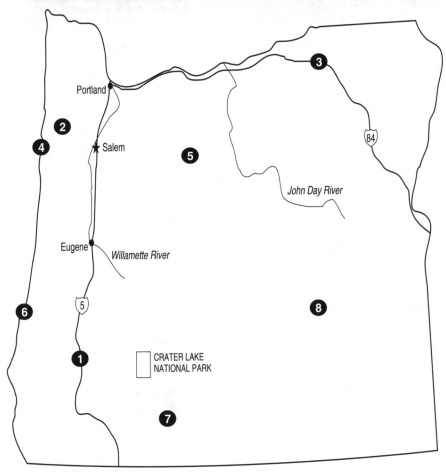

Oregon law permits bars and taverns to have up to five video lottery terminals that offer various versions of video poker. The maximum bet allowed is $2 and the maximum payout on any machine is capped at $600. These machines are the same as regular video gaming devices but are called lottery terminals because they are regulated by the state's lottery commission which receives a share of each machine's revenue. The machines accept cash but do not pay out in cash; instead, they print out a receipt which must be taken to a cashier.

During the Oregon Lottery's fiscal year from July 1, 2001 through June 30, 2002, the VLT's had an actual return of 93.78%.

There are eight Indian casinos in operation in Oregon and according to the governor's office which regulates the Tribe's compacts, "there is no minimum payback percentage required on the Tribe's machines. Each Tribe is free to set their own limits on their machines."

All casinos offer blackjack, video slots, video poker, video keno, video blackjack and pull tabs. Some casinos also offer: craps (C), roulette (R), poker (P), Pai Gow Poker (PGP), let it ride (LIR), big 6 wheel (B6), bingo (BG), keno (K) and simulcasting. Unless otherwise noted, all casinos are open 24 hours and the minimum gambling age is 21. For Oregon tourism information call (800) 547-7842.

Chinook Winds Gaming Center
1777 N.W. 44th Street
Lincoln City, Oregon 97367
(541) 996-5700
Website: www.chinookwindscasino.com
Map Location: **#4** (45 miles W. of Salem)

Toll-Free Number: (888) CHINOOK
Restaurants: 3   Liquor: Yes
Buffets: B-$5.99 L-$10.99
              D-$10.99/$13.99 (Fri/Sat)
Other Games: P, BG, K, LIR, CSP, PGP
Funbook: Given with slot club membership.
Senior Discount: Buffet discount, if 55, or older
Special Features: Smoke-free area. Childcare
center. Video arcade. Gift shop.

Kah-Nee-Ta Resort & Casino
6823 Highway 8
Warm Springs, Oregon 97761
(541) 553-1112
Website: www.kahneeta.com
Map Location: **#5** (100 miles E. of Portland)

Toll-Free Number: (800) 238-6946
Reservation Number: (800) 554-4786
Rooms: 139 Price Range: $139-$260
Restaurants: 2   Liquor: Yes
Buffets: B-$7.95 L-$9.95 D-$18.95
Casino Size: 25,000 Square Feet
Hours: 8:30am-2am
Other Games: P
Funbook: Given to lodge guests, bus groups,
    seniors on Monday, ladies on Wednesdays
6pm-9pm and men on Tuesdays 6pm-9pm
Senior Discount: Free funbook Mon, if 55+
Special Features: 18-hole golf course. Horse-
back riding. European spa. Campground.

Kla-Mo-Ya Casino
34333 Hwy 97 North
Chiloquin, Oregon 97624
(541) 783-7529
Website: www.klamoya.com
Map Location: **#7** (20 miles N. of Klamath
Falls)

Toll-Free Number: (888) 552-6692
Restaurants: 2   Liquor: No
Buffets: L/D-$7.95
Hours: 7am-1am/24 Hours (Fri-Sat)
Other Games: P
Senior Discount: $2 buffet discount. Various
promotions on Mondays, if 55 or older

The Mill Resort & Casino
3201 Tremont Avenue
North Bend, Oregon 97459
(541) 756-8800
Website: www.themillcasino.com
Map Location: **#6** (75 miles S.W. of Eugene)

Toll-Free Number: (800) 953-4800
Rooms: 112 Price Range: $69-$99
Suites: 3 Price Range: $125-$185
Restaurants: 4 Liquor: Yes
Buffets: B-$9.95 (Sun) L-$8.95 D-$14.95
Other Games: P, BG
Senior Discount: 10% off food, if 55 or older
Funbook: Given when you join slot club
Special Features: $1 blackjack tables. Free
shuttle bus from local motels. Video arcade.
Room and food discounts for club members.

The Old Camp Casino
2205 W. Monroe Street
Burns, Oregon 97720
(541) 573-1500
Map Location: **#8** (250 miles S. of Pendleton)

Restaurants: 1 Liquor: Yes
Hours: 11am-11pm/2am (Fri-Sat)
Other Games: P, BG
Special Features: Liquor sold in lounge and
restaurant only. RV park.

Seven Feathers Hotel & Casino Resort
146 Chief Miwaleta Lane
Canyonville, Oregon 97417
(541) 839-1111
Website: www.sevenfeathers.com
Map Location: **#1** (80 miles S. of Eugene)

Toll-Free Number: (800) 548-8461
Rooms: 145 Price Range: $89-$109
Suites: 1 Price Range: $175-$225
Restaurants: 3 Liquor: Yes
Buffets: B-$16.50 (Sun) D-$10.95
Casino Size: 27,300 Square Feet
Other Games: C, R, P, K, BG
Funbook: Ask during birth month
Senior Discount: 10% off room, if 55, or older
Special Features: RV park. 18-hole golf course.
10% room discount for AAA/AARP members.

Spirit Mountain Casino
P.O. Box 39
Grand Ronde, Oregon 97347
(503) 879-2350
Website: www.spiritmountain.com
Map Location: **#2** (85 miles S.W. of Portland)

Toll-Free Number: (800) 760-7977
Rooms: 94 Price Range: $89-$109
Suites: 6 Price Range: $159
Restaurants: 5 Liquor: Yes
Buffets: B-$5.75 L-$6.75 D-$9.75/$11.95 (Wed)
Funbook: Ask Tue. at Player Services Desk
Other Games: C, R, P, PGP, LIR, B6, K, BG, S
Special Features: Separate nonsmoking casino
and bingo area. Liquor sold in lounge only.
Childcare center. Video arcade.

Wildhorse Resort & Casino
72777 Highway 331
Pendleton, Oregon 97801
(541) 278-2274
Website: www.wildhorseresort.com
Map Location: **#3** (211 miles E. of Portland)

Toll-Free Number: (800) 654-9453
Rooms: 100 Price Range: $65-$95
Suites: 5 Price Range: $175
Restaurants: 2 Liquor: No
Casino Size: 40,000 Square Feet
Other Games: P, K, BG, S
Senior Discount: 10% off room, if 55, or older
Special Features: RV park. 18-hole golf course.
Health spa. Cultural Institute. 10% hotel dis-
count for AAA or tribal members.

RHODE ISLAND

Rhode Island has two pari-mutuel facilities which both feature video lottery terminals (VLT's). These machines are the same as regular video gaming devices but are called lottery terminals because they are regulated by the state's lottery commission which receives a share of each machine's revenue. The machines accept cash but don't pay out in cash; instead, they print out a receipt which must be taken to a cashier.

All VLT's are programmed to play at least six different games: blackjack, keno, slots and three versions of poker (jacks or better, joker poker and deuces wild).

The Rhode Island Lottery does not provide figures to determine the actual paybacks on its VLT's, however, according to Dennis Tripodi, finance administrator for the Rhode Island Lottery, the VLT's are programmed to pay back the following amounts over time:

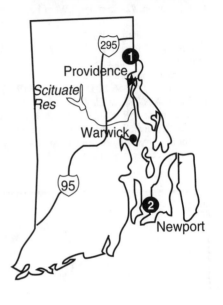

Blackjack - 99.1%
5¢, 10¢, 25¢ Video Poker - 95%
50¢ Video Poker - 96.5%
$1 Video Poker - 98%
5¢, 10¢, 25¢ Slots - 92%
50¢ Slots - 94%
$1 Slots - 96%
25¢ Keno - 92%
50¢ Keno - 94%
$1 Keno - 96%.

The minimum gambling age is 18. For information on visiting Rhode Island call the state's tourism division at (800) 556-2484.

Lincoln Park
1600 Louisquisset Pike
Lincoln, Rhode Island 02865
(401) 723-3200
Web Site: www.lincolnparkri.com
Map Location: **#1** (10 miles N. of Providence)

Toll-Free Number: (800) 720-7275
Restaurants: 3
Hours: 9am-1am Daily
Admission: Free
Valet Parking: Free
Special Features: Live dog racing (Mon/Wed/Fri/Sat) throughout the year. Daily simulcasting of horse and dog racing.

Newport Grand Jai-Alai
150 Admiral Kalbfus Road
Newport, Rhode Island 02840
(401) 849-5000
Web Site: www.newportgrand.com
Map Location: **#2**

Toll-Free Number: (800) 451-2500
Restaurants: 1
Hours: 10am-1am Daily
Admission: Free
Valet Parking: $1.50
Special Features: Live jai-alai games (Thu-Sun) from early March through October. Daily (except Tuesday) simulcasting of horse and dog racing.

SOUTH CAROLINA

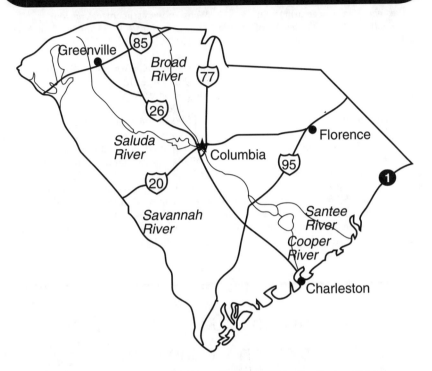

South Carolina has three gambling cruise ships which sail three miles out into international waters where casino gambling is permitted.

All boats offer: blackjack, craps, roulette, caribbean stud poker, slots and video poker.

For more information on visiting South Carolina call the state's tourism department at (800) 872-3505.

Southern Elegance Casino Cruises
4491 Waterfront Avenue
Little River, South Carolina 29566
(843) 249-9811
Website: www.southernelegancecasino.com
Map Location: **#1** (35 miles N. of Myrtle Beach)

Reservation Number: (877) 250-5825
Meal Service: Deli
Schedule:
    11:00am - 4:30pm (Mon-Thu)
    7:00pm-12:30am   (Daily)
    12:00pm-5:30pm   (Sat-Sun)
Prices: Free
Port Charges: None   Parking: Free
Other Games: Aces Poker
Senior Discount: Mon/Tue/Thur receive $10
    in tokens and complimentary food, if 55+
Special Features: 500-passenger boat sails from Little River waterfront. Free shuttle available from Myrtle Beach. Must be 21, or older, to board.

Stardancer Casino Cruises
1180 Hwy 17 North
Little River, South Carolina 29566
(843) 280-7731
Website: www.stardancercasino.com
Map Location: **#1** (35 miles N. of Myrtle Beach)

Reservation Number: (800) 2345-WIN
Gambling Age: 21
Buffets: $3 Day/$3 Eve
Schedule:
   11:30am - 5:00pm (Tue-Sat)
    7:00pm - 12:30am (Mon-Sat)
    1:00pm - 7:00pm (Sun)
Prices: Free
Port Charges: None   Parking: Free
Other Games: Let It Ride
Senior Discount: $5 free tokens for $10, if 50+
Special Features: 506-passenger boat sails from N. Myrtle Beach Marina. Must be 21, or older, to board.

SunCruz Casino - Myrtle Beach
4491 Waterfront Drive
Little River, South Carolina 29566
(843) 280-2933
Website: www.suncruzcasino.com
Map Location: **#1** (35 miles N. of Myrtle Beach)

Reservation Number: (800) 474-DICE
Gambling Age: 18
Meal Service: A la carte menu
Schedule:
   11:00am - 4:15pm (Mon-Fri)
    Noon - 5:15pm (Sat-Sun)
    7:00pm - 12:15am (Sun-Thu)
    7:00pm - 1:00am (Fri/Sat/Holidays)
Prices: Free
Port Charges: Included   Parking: Free
Other Games: Mini-Baccarat, Let It Ride
Special Features: 600-passenger *SunCruz VII* sails from Little River waterfront. Must be 18, or older, to board.

SOUTH DAKOTA

South Dakota's bars and taverns are allowed to have up to 10 video lottery terminals (VLT's) that offer the following games: poker, keno, blackjack and bingo. These machines are the same as regular video gaming devices but are called lottery terminals because they are regulated by the state's lottery commission which receives a share of each machine's revenue. The machines accept cash but don't pay out in cash; instead, they print out a receipt which must be taken to a cashier. Slot machines, as well as blackjack and poker are only permitted at Indian casinos and in Deadwood.

Deadwood was once most famous for being the home of Wild Bill Hickok who was shot to death while playing cards in the No. 10 Saloon. The hand he held at the time was two pairs: black aces and eights, which is now commonly referred to as a "dead man's hand." Wild Bill is buried in the local cemetery along with another local celebrity: Calamity Jane.

The first casinos in Deadwood opened on November 1, 1989. All of the buildings in the downtown area are required to conform with the city's authentic 1880's architecture. Many of the casinos are located in historic structures but there are also some new structures which were designed to be compatible with the historic theme of the town. The old No. 10 Saloon is still operating and you can actually gamble in the same spot where old Wild Bill bit the dust! One of the casinos, Midnight Star, is owned by movie actor Kevin Costner and his brother, Dan.

South Dakota law limits each casino licensee to a maximum of 30 slot machines and no one person is allowed to hold more than three licenses. Some operators combine licenses with other operators to form a cooperative which may look like one casino but in reality it's actually several licensees operating under one name.

The state's gaming laws originally limited blackjack, poker, let it ride and three-card poker bets to a maximum of $5, however, in late 2000 the law was changed to allow maximum bets of $100.

In addition to the Deadwood casinos, there are also nine Indian casinos in South Dakota. These casinos are also subject to the $100 maximum bet restrictions.

Here are statistics from the South Dakota Commission on Gaming for the payback percentages on all of Deadwood's slot machines for the one-year period from July 1, 2001 through June 30, 2002:

Denomination	Payback %
5¢ Slots	91.02
25¢ Slots	91.02
$1 Slots	92.06
$5 Slots	93.48

Some of the larger casinos are open 24 hours but most of the smaller ones are open from 8am until midnight Sunday through Thursday and 8am until 2am on the weekends.

There is a scheduled shuttle service to all of the casinos that operates from 8am to midnight weekdays and 7am to 3 am weekends. (During the summer months the weekday hours are extended to 7am to 1:30am). The cost is 50 cents per ride.

Unless otherwise noted, all casinos offer slot machines and video poker. Some casinos also offer: blackjack (BJ), let it ride (LIR), three-card poker (TCP), Caribbean stud poker and poker (P). Most of the Indian casinos also offer bingo (BG).

The minimum gambling age is 21 (18 at Indian casinos that don't serve alcohol). South Dakota's casinos have very liberal rules about allowing minors into casinos and virtually all of the casinos will allow children to enter with their parents until about 8 p.m. Additionally, South Dakota is the only jursidiction that will allow children to stand next to their parents while they are gambling.

For South Dakota tourism information call (800) 732-5682. For information on visiting Deadwood call the city's Chamber of Commerce at (800) 999-1876, or visit their website at www.deadwood.org.

Deadwood

Map Location: **#1** (in the Black Hills, 41 miles N.W. of Rapid City. Take I-90 W. Get off at the second Sturges exit and take Hwy. 14-A into Deadwood)

B. B. Cody's
681 Main Street
Deadwood, SD 57732
(605) 578-2209

Restaurants: 2 (1 open 24 hours)
Other Games: BJ
Special Features: Video arcade. Pizza Hut Express. $7.99 prime rib dinner.

Best Western Hickok House
137 Charles Street
(605) 578-1611

Best Western Reservations: 800-528-1234
Rooms: 38   Price Range: $39-$109
Restaurants: 1
Special Features: Hot tub and sauna. AAA and AARP room discount.

Bodega Bar
662 Main Street
(605) 578-1996

Restaurants: 1
Other Games: BJ

Buffalo Saloon
658 Main Street
(605) 578-9993

Hours: 24 hours daily
Other games: BJ (Thu-Sat)

Bullock Express
68 Main Street
(605) 578-3476

Reservation Number: 800-526-8277
Rooms: 38   Price Range: $65-$95
Restaurants: 1
Hours: 6am-2am
Special Features: Room discount for AARP members.

Bullock Hotel
633 Main Street
(605) 578-1745
Website: www.bullockhotel.com

Reservation Number: 800-336-1876
Rooms: 29   Price Range: $75-$99
Suites: 7   Price Range: $135-$159
Restaurants: 1
Hours: 24 hours daily
Special Features: Deadwood's oldest hotel. 10% room discount for AAA members.

Cadillac Jacks's Gaming Resort
360 Main Street
(605) 578-1500
Website: www.cadillacjacksgaming.com

Toll Free Number: (866) 332-3966
Rooms: 103 Price Range: $47-$99
Suites: 11 Price Range: $99-$189
Restaurants: 1
Hours: 24 hours daily
Casino Size: 10,000 Square Feet
Other Games: BJ, TCP
Senior Discount: Free meal Mon-Sat, if 50+
　　　　　　　　and slot club member
Special Features: Hotel is AmericInn. Denny's restaurant.

Celebrity Hotel & Casino
629 Main Street
(605) 578-1909
Website: www.celebritycasinos.com

Toll-Free Number: (888) 399-1886
Rooms: 9 Price Range: $49-$99
Suites: 3 Price Range: $79-$139
Hours: 24 Hours Daily
Special Features: Car and motorcycle museum. Free to hotel guests, otherwise $2.50 for adults and $1.50 for seniors (55 or older) and children (6-12). 10% AAA room discount.

Dakota Frontier/Deadwood Stage
670 Main Street
(605) 578-1515

Dakota Territory Saloon
652 Main Street
(605) 578-3566

Nestled in the Black Hills of South Dakota, the entire city of Deadwood has been designated a national historic landmark. Free historic walking tours are offered daily.

Deadwood Dick's Saloon/Nickel Dick's
51-55 Sherman Street
(605) 578-3224
Website: www.deadwooddicks.com

Toll Free Number: (877) 882-4990
Rooms: 5 Price Range: $59-$69
Suites: 6 Price Range: $85-$125
Restaurants: 1
Special Features: Antiques mall. 30% room discount for stays of over 3 days.

Deadwood Gulch Resort
Highway 85 South/P.O. Box 643
(605) 578-1294
Website: www.deadwoodgulch.com

Reservation Number: (800) 695-1876
Rooms: 95 Price Range: $62-$109
Suites: 3 Price Range: $85-$145
Restaurants: 2
Hours: 24 hours daily
Casino Size: 7,000 Square Feet
Other Games: BJ
Special Features: Property is Days Inn. 10% room discount to AAA and AARP members. Convenience store and gas station. Family fun park with go-carts, bumper boats, miniature golf, batting cages, kiddie playland and arcade.

Deadwood Gulch Saloon
560 Main Street
(605) 578-1207

Deadwood Inn
27 Deadwood Street
(605) 578-7700

Toll Free Number: (877) 815-7974
Rooms: 19 Price Range: $59-$99
Suites: 4 Price Range: $89-$175
Casino Size: 1,000 Square Feet
Special Features: 10% room discount if 65+

Elk's Lodge
696 Main Street #508
(605) 578-1333

First Gold Hotel & Gaming
270 Main Street
(605) 578-9777
Website: www.firstgold.com

Reservation Number: (800) 274-1876
Rooms: 132 Price Range: $39-$149
Suites: 2 Price Range: $89-$199
Restaurants: 1
Hours: 24 hours daily
Casino Size: 7,000 Square Feet
Other Games: BJ, TCP
Senior Discount: 10% off room, if 60, or older
Special Features: 79¢ breakfast and $1.99 lunch specials. RV park located next door. Also contains the **Horseshoe** and **Blackjack** casinos.

Four Aces
531 Main Street
(605) 578-2323
Website: www.fouracesdeadwood.com

Toll Free Number: (800) HAMPTON
Rooms: 59 Price Range: $99-$119
Suites: 5 Price Range: $150-$350
Restaurants: 1
Buffets: B-$6.54 (Sun) L-$3.74
      D-$6.54/$8.41 (Fri-Sat)
Hours: 24 hours daily
Casino Size: 24,000 Square Feet
Other Games: BJ, LIR, TCP

Gold Country Inn
801 Main Street
Deadwood, SD 57732
(605) 578-2393

Reservation Number: (800) 287-1251
Rooms: 53 Price Range: $45-$59
Restaurants: 1

Gold Dust Gaming & Entertainment Complex
688 Main Street
(605) 578-2100
Website: www.golddustgaming.com

Toll-Free Number: 800-456-0533
Rooms: 56 Price Range: $69-$150
Suites: 22 Price Range: $150-$250
Restaurants: 1
Buffets: B-$4.99 L-$5.99
      D-$9.99/$10.99 (Sat)/$11.95 (Fri)
Hours: 24 hours Daily
Casino Size: 30,000 Square Feet
Other Games: BJ, P
Funbook: Call or write to request in advance
Senior Discount: $1 off buffets, if 55, or older
Special Features: Hotel is Holiday Inn Express. Largest gaming complex in Deadwood with nine casinos including: **Legends, French Quarter and Silver Dollar.** AARP discount, free continental breakfast, indoor pool, gym, whirlpool, arcade.

Hickok's Saloon
685 Main Street
(605) 578-2222

Other Games: BJ
Special Features: Video arcade.

Historic Franklin Hotel
700 Main Street
(605) 578-2241
Website: www.deadwood.net/franklin

Reservation Number: 800-688-1876
Rooms: 80 Price Range: $39-$97
Suites: 15 Price Range: $90-$175
Restaurants: 1
Other Games: BJ, P
Senior Discount: 10% off room, if 65, or older
Special Features: Historic old hotel. Three lounges. Wedding chapel.

Lady Luck
660 Main Street
(605) 578-1162

Lucky 8 Gaming Hall/Super 8 Lodge
196 Cliff Street
(605) 578-2535
Website: www.deadwoodsuper8.com

Reservation Number: (800) 800-8000
Rooms: 51 Price Range: $40-$90
Suites: 4 Price Range: $80-$130
Restaurants: 1
Hours: 24 hours daily
Funbook: Given to guests at check-in
Senior Discount: 10% AARP room discount
Special Features: Casino claims highest percentage payback chips are installed on their games. Video arcade.

McKenna's Gold
470 Main Street
(605) 578-3207

Midnight Star
677 Main Street
(605) 578-1555
Website: www.themidnightstar.com

Toll-Free Number: (800) 999-6482
Restaurants: 2
Other Games: BJ, LIR, TCP
Funbook: Call to receive by mail
Special Features: Kevin Costner is part-owner and the property features a museum with authentic costumes and memorabilia from his movies. Sports Bar & Grill.

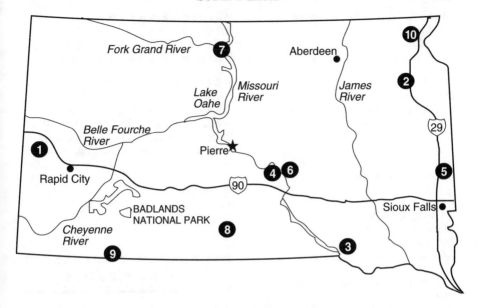

Mineral Palace Hotel & Gaming Complex
601 Main Street
(605) 578-2036
Website: www.mineralpalace.com

Reservation Number: (800) 84-PALACE
Rooms: 63 Price Range: $69-$109
Suites: 4 Price Range: $89-$225
Restaurants: 1
Hours: 24 hours daily
Other Games: BJ
Special Features: Contains **Cousin Jack's**, **Carrie Nation's** and **Deadwood Livery** casinos. Cappuccino/espresso bar. Liquor store.

Mint Casino
638 Main Street
(605) 578-1201

Miss Kitty's Gaming Emporium
647 Main Street
(605) 578-1811

Restaurants: 2
Hours: 24 Hours Daily
Other Games: BJ, P
Special Features: Chinese and Mexican restaurants.

Mustang Sally's
634 Main Street
(605) 578-2025

Old Style Saloon #10
657 Main Street
(605) 578-3346
Website: www.saloon10.com

Toll-Free Number: (800) 952-9398
Restaurants: 1
Casino Size: 4,000 Square Feet
Other Games: BJ, P, TCP
Special Features: During summer there is a re-enactment of the "Shooting of Wild Bill Hickok" at 1, 3, 5 and 7 p.m. Wild Bill's chair and other Old West artifacts on display.

Oyster Bay/Fairmont Hotel
628 Main Street
(605) 578-2205

Restaurants: 1
Special Features: Historic restoration of 1895 brothel and spa. Features first-class oyster bar.

Silverado Gaming & Restaurant
709 Main Street
(605) 578-3670
Website: www.silveradocasino.com

Toll-Free Number: (800) 584-7005
Restaurants: 1
Buffets: B-$5.95 (Sat-Sun) L-$5.95
    D-$10.95/$11.95 (Fri-Sat)
Hours: 24 hours daily
Casino Size: 20,000 Square Feet
Other Games: BJ, LIR, TCP, CSP
Funbook: Call or write for information

Thunder Cove Inn
Highway 85 South
(605) 578-3045
Website: www.thunder-cove.com

Toll-Free Number: (800) 209-7361
Rooms: 30 Price Range: $33-$54
Suites: 4 Price Range: $55-$80
Special Features: All nonsmoking rooms. 10%
off room for AAA/AARP and seniors 55+.

Tin Lizzie Gaming
555 Main Street
(605) 578-1715
Web Sit: www.tinlizzie.com

Toll-Free Number: (800) 643-4490
Restaurants: 1
Buffets: B-$1.99 L-$1.99
Hours: 24 hours daily
Casino Size: 8,300 Square Feet
Other Games: BJ
Funbook: Request online or write
Senior Discount: Various, if 50 or older
Special Features: Also contains **Casey's** and
Mustang casinos. Stay and win packages
available for lodging at several local hotels.
Free food specials Fri-Sun (call for details).

Veteran's Of Foreign War
10 Pine Street
(605) 578-9914

Wild West Winners Casino
608-622 Main Street
(605) 578-1100
Website: www.wildwestwinners.com

Toll-Free Number: (800) 873-1876
Restaurants: 1
Funbook: Call or write for information
Special Features: Also contains **Miss P.J.'s
Parlor** casino and **Wild Bill Bar and Gam-
bling Hall**. Steakhouse restaurant.

Wooden Nickel
9 Lee Street
(605) 578-1952

Indian Casinos

Dakota Connection
RR 1, Box 177-B
Sisseton, South Dakota 57262
(605) 698-4273
Website: www.dakotaconnection.net
Map Location: **#10** (165 miles N. of Sioux
Falls)

Toll-Free Number: (800) 542-2876
Restaurants: 1 Liquor: No
Buffets: B-$5.95 (Sat-Sun) L-$6.95 (Sat-Sun)
Hours: 24 Hours Daily
Other Games: BJ, BG
Senior Discount: Various on Tue, if 55 or older

Dakota Sioux Casino
16415 Sioux Conifer Road
Watertown, South Dakota 57201
(605) 882-2051
Website: www.dakotasioux.com
Map Location: **#2** (104 miles N. of Sioux Falls)

Toll-Free Number: (800) 658-4717
Restaurants: 1 Liquor: Yes
Buffets: B-$4.95 (Fri-Sun)
Hours: 24 Hours Daily
Other Games: BJ, P, BG (Fri-Tue)
Senior Discount: Specials on Mon, if 55+

Fort Randall Casino Hotel

West Hwy. 46/RR 1, Box 46
Wagner, South Dakota 57380
(605) 487-7871
Website: www.fortrandall.com
Map Location: **#3** (100 miles S.W. of Sioux Falls)

Room Reservations: (800) 362-6333
Rooms: 57 Price Range: $49.80
Suites: 2 Price Range: $71.80
Restaurants: 1 Liquor: Yes
Buffets: B-$4.95 L-$5.95 D-$8.95/$10.95 (Fri)
Hours: 24 hours daily
Other Games: BJ, P, BG

Golden Buffalo Casino

P.O. Box 204
Lower Brule, South Dakota 57548
(605) 473-5577
Map Location: **#4** (45 miles S.E. of Pierre)

Room Reservations: (605) 473-5506
Rooms: 38 Price Range: $48-$55
Restaurants: 1 Liquor: Yes
Hours: 8am-1am Daily
Other Games: BJ, P, TCP, BG (Wed)

Grand River Casino

P.O. Box 639
Mobridge, South Dakota 57601
(605) 845-7104
Website: www.grandrivercasino.com
Map Location: **#7** (240 miles N.E. of Rapid City)

Toll-Free Number: (800) 475-3321
Restaurants: 1 Liquor: Yes
Hours: 8am-3am/24 hours (Fri-Sat)
Other Games: BJ, P

Lode Star Casino

P.O. Box 140
Fort Thompson, South Dakota 57339
(605) 245-6000
Website: www.lodecasino.com
Map Location: **#6** (150 miles N.W. of Sioux Falls)

Room Reservations: (605) 245-2176
Restaurants: 1 Liquor: Yes
Rooms: 50 Price Range: $55-$62
Hours: 8am-2am/7am-4am (Fri-Sat)
Other Games: BJ, P
Senior Discount: 10% off room, if 50 or older

Prairie Wind Casino

HC 49, Box 10
Pine Ridge, South Dakota 57770
(605) 867-6300
Website: www.prairiewindcasino.net
Map Location: **#9** (85 miles S.E. of Rapid City)

Toll-Free Number: (800) 705-9463
Restaurants: 1 Liquor: No
Hours: 24 Hours Daily
Other Games: BJ, P, TCP
Special Features: Casino is located 12 miles East of Oelrichs off Hwy. 385 and 8 miles West of Oglala on Hwy. 18.

Rosebud Casino

Highway 83 (on SD/NE stateline)
Mission, South Dakota 57555
(605) 378-3800
Website: www.rosebudcasino.com
Map Location: **#8** (22 miles S. of Mission)

Toll-Free Number: (800) 786-7673
Room Reservations: (877) 521-9913
Rooms: 60 Price Range: $50-$79
Suites: 2 Price Range: $79-$99
Restaurants: 2 Liquor: Yes
Buffets: D-$7.99
Hours: 24 hours daily
Other Games: BJ, P, BG
Senior Discount: Various, if 55 or older
Funbook: Ask at marketing office
Special Features: Hotel is a Quality Inn. AAA, AARP and Internet discounts available.

Royal River Casino Bingo & Motel

607 S. Veterans Street
Flandreau, South Dakota 57028
(605) 997-3746
Website: www.royalrivercasino.com
Map Location: **#5** (35 miles N. of Sioux Falls on I-29)

Toll-Free Number: (800) 833-8666
Rooms: 60 Price Range: $55-$60
Suites: 6 Price Range: $90-$95
Restaurants: 2 Liquor: Yes
Hours: 24 Hours Daily
Casino Size: 15,000 Square Feet
Other Games: BJ, P, BG
Special Features: $3 buffet discount if you have a Player's Club Card. RV parking for $10 per day. AAA and AARP room discounts.

TEXAS

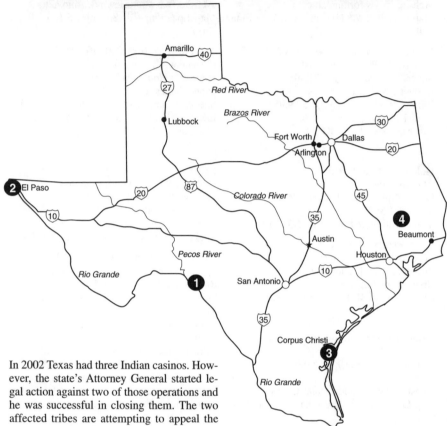

In 2002 Texas had three Indian casinos. However, the state's Attorney General started legal action against two of those operations and he was successful in closing them. The two affected tribes are attempting to appeal the state's decision or to work out some other arrangement with the state in order to allow them to re-open.

If you would like to check the status of those two casinos you can call them directly:

Speaking Rock Casino
122 S. Old Pueblo Road
El Paso, Texas 79907
(915) 860-7777
Website: www.speakingrockcasino.com
Map Location: **#2**

Alabama-Coushatta Entertainment Center
710 State Park Road
Livingston, Texas 77351
(936) 563-1500
Map Location: **#4**

The one remaining Texas Indian casino offers poker, pull tab machines, bingo and a player-pool-banked blackjack game where each player must pay a commission to the house for each bet that is made. The minimum gambling age is 21 and the casino is open 24 hours daily.

For more information on visiting Texas call (800) 888-8TEX.

Kickapoo Lucky Eagle Casino
Rt 1, Box 7777
Eagle Pass, Texas 78852
(830) 758-1995
Website: www.kickapooluckyeaglecasino.com
Map Location: **#1** (150 miles S.W. of San Antonio)

Toll-Free Number: (888) 255-8259
Restaurants: 1 Liquor: Yes
Casino Size: 16,000 Square Feet
Special Features: Blackjack commission is 50¢ per $25 bet.

Texas has one casino boat which sails nine miles out into the Gulf of Mexico where casino gambling is permitted. The boat offers: blackjack, craps, roulette, Caribbean stud poker, mini-baccarat, let it ride, casino war, slots and video poker.

Texas Treasure Casino Cruises
1401 W. Wheeler Avenue
Aransas Pass, Texas 78336
(361) 758-4444
Website: www.txtreasure.com
Map Location: **#3** (10 miles N.E. of Corpus Christi)

Reservation Number: (800) 472-5215
Gambling Age: 21   Ship's Registry: Panama
Meal Service: Buffet Included
Schedule:
  11:30pm-5:00pm (Daily)
  6:30pm-12:00am/12:30am (Thu)/1am (Fri/Sat)
Prices: $24.95/$29.95 (Fri Eve-Sun)
Port Charges: None   Parking: Free
Senior Discount: $5 off any cruise, if 55+
Special Features: 1,224-passenger *Texas Treasure* sails from dock near ferry in Aransas Pass. Restaurant upgrade is available for $15 per person. 50% off for ladies on Friday evenings. 50% off for men on Thursday evenings. Slot club members sail for $10 on Tuesdays. Must be 21 or older to board.

WASHINGTON

There are 25 Indian casinos operating in Washington and 17 of these casinos are affiliated with tribes that have compacts with the state that allow them to offer table games, as well as special video poker and video slot machines which aren't allowed to accept cash. Instead, a cashless system is used whereby you have to go to a cashier cage, or a kiosk, and buy a smart card which then deducts losses from, or credits wins to, your account.

Of the state's remaining eight casinos, four are affiliated with the Spokane Tribe, three are operated by the Colville Confederated Tribes and one is affiliated with the Shoalwater Tribe. All of these Tribes have an ongoing dispute with the state and are operating without compacts. All eight of these casinos offer regular spinning-reel slots that accept cash, plus an assortment of table games.

Most Washington casinos are not open on a 24-hour basis and the hours of operation are noted in each casino's listing. All casinos offer slots, video poker, blackjack, craps, roulette and pull tabs. Optional games offered include: baccarat (B), mini-baccarat (MB), poker (P), pai gow poker (PGP), Caribbean stud poker (CSP), three-card poker (TCP), Spanish 21 (S21), big 6 wheel (B6), keno (K) and bingo (BG). The minimum gambling age is 18 (21 if liquor is served).

Although most of the casinos have toll-free numbers many of these numbers will only work for calls made within Washington. For more information on visiting Washington call the tourism department at (800) 544-1800.

Chewelah Casino
2555 Smith Road
Chewelah, Washington 99109
(509) 935-6167
Website: www.chewelahcasino.com
Map Location: **#13** (50 miles N. of Spokane)

Toll-Free Number: (800) 322-2788
Restaurants: 1 Deli Liquor: No
Buffets: D-$13.95 (Thu)/$7.95 (Sun)
Hours: 9am-2am/24 Hours (Fri-Sat)
Casino Size: 22,000 Square Feet

Other Games: BG
Senior Discount: Various on Wed if 55 or older
Funbook: Given out on Fridays
Special Features: Regular slots. One block from Double Eagle Casino.

Clearwater Casino
15347 Suquamish Way N.E./Box 1210
Suquamish, Washington 98392
(360) 598-6889
Website: www.clearwatercasino.com
Map Location: **#14** (15 miles W. of Seattle via Bainbridge Ferry)

Toll-Free Number: (800) 375-6073
Restaurants: 2 Liquor: Yes
Buffets: L-$6.00 D-$5.00 (Mon/Wed)
 $8.00 (Tue)/$9.00 (Thu/Sun)/$13.00 (Fri-Sat)
Hours: 10am-4am Daily
Other Games: MB, P, PGP, CSP, LIR, K, BG
Senior Discount: 50% off Sun buffets,if 55+
Special features: Cashless video slots. Closest casino to Seattle. Free shuttle service.

Coulee Dam Casino
515 Birch Street
Coulee Dam, Washington 99155
(509) 633-0766
Website: www.colvillecasinos.com/couleedam
Map Location: **#11** (190 miles E. of Seattle)

Toll-Free Number: (800) 556-7492
Restaurants: 1 Deli Liquor: No
Hours: 9am-Mid/2am (Fri/Sat)
Other Games: No craps or roulette
Casino Marketing: (800) 648-2946
Special features: Cashless video slots. Gift shop. BJ tables open 4pm/2pm (Sun).

Double Eagle Casino
2539 Smith Road
Chewelah, Washington 99109
(509) 935-4406
Map Location: **#13** (50 miles N. of Spokane)

Restaurants: 1 Deli Liquor: No
Hours: 9am-1am/2am (Fri-Sat)
Other Games: PGP, No Craps
Special Features: Regular slots. One block from Chewelah Casino.

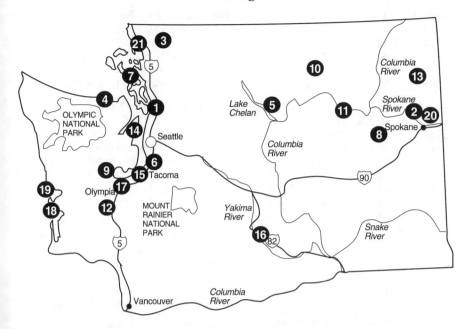

Emerald Queen Casino
2102 Alexander Avenue
Tacoma, Washington 98421
(206) 594-7777
Website: www.emeraldqueen.com
Map Location: **#15**

Toll-Free Number: (888) 831-7655
Restaurants: 3 Liquor: Yes
Buffets: L-$8.75 D-$14.95/$17.95 (Mon/Sat)
Hours: 10am-6am Daily
Other Games: MB, P, PGP, CSP, LIR, K, S21
Special Features: Cashless video slots. Property has two casinos. One is on a riverboat and the other is in a shoreside facility.

Li'l Chiefs Casino
P.O. Box 130
Wellpinit, Washington 99040
(509) 258-4544
Map Location: **#2** (25 miles N.W. of Spokane)

Restaurants: 1 Liquor: No
Hours: 9am-1/2am (Fri-Sat)
Other Games: Only Slots and Video Poker
Special Features: Regular slots. Casino is in city of Ford.

Little Creek Casino
West 91 Highway 108
Shelton, Washington 98584
(360) 427-7711
Website: www.little-creek.com
Map Location: **#9** (23 miles N. of Olympia off Hwy 101/108 interchange)

Toll-Free Number: (800) 667-7711
Restaurants: 2 Liquor: Yes
Buffets: L-$5.95 D-$8.95/ $13.95 (Thu-Sat)
Hours: 10am-4am/6am (Fri-Sat)
Casino Size: 49,000 Square Feet
Other Games: MB, P, PGP, CSP, LIR, K, BG
Senior Discount: Specials Tue/Wed, if 50+
Special Features: Cashless video slots. Gift shop.

Lucky Dog Casino
19330 N. Highway 101
Shelton, Washington 98584
(360) 877-5656
Map Location: **#9** (23 miles N. of Olympia)

Restaurants: 1 Deli Liquor: No
Hours: 10am-Midnite/2am (Fri-Sat)
Other Games: No table games
Special Features: Cashless video slots.

Lucky Eagle Casino
12888 188th Avenue SW
Rochester, Washington 98579
(360) 273-2000
Website: www.luckyeagle.com
Map Location: **#12** (26 miles S. of Olympia)

Toll-Free Number: (800) 720-1788
Restaurants: 5 Liquor: Yes
Buffets: L-$7.95 D-$13.95/$18.95 (Fri-Sat)
Hours: 10am-4am/10am-6am (Fri/Sat)
Casino Size: 75,000 Square Feet
Other Games: P, PGP, LIR, TCP, K, BG
Funbook: Given to new slot club members
Senior Discount: Various on Mondays if 55+
Special Features: Cashless video slots. 20-space RV park. Single and double-deck BJ.

Mill Bay Casino
455 E. Wapato Lake Road
Manson, Washington 98831
(509) 687-2102
Website: www.colvillecasinos.com/millbay
Map Location: **#5** (200 miles N.E. of Seattle on the N. shore of Lake Chelan)

Toll-Free Number: (800) 648-2946
Restaurants: 1 Liquor: No
Buffets: B-$8.50 (Sun)
Other Games: PGP
Senior Discount: Food discounts,if 55, or older
Funbook: Distributed by local motels
Special Features: Regular slots.

Muckleshoot Casino
2402 Auburn Way South
Auburn, Washington 98002
(206) 804-4944
Website: www.casino-fun.com
Map Location: **#6** (20 miles S. of Seattle)

Toll-Free Number (800) 804-4944
Restaurants: 3 Liquor: Yes
Buffets: L-$8.95 (Sat-Sun) D-$16.95
Hours: 10am-5:45am Daily
Other Games: B, P, PGP, CSP, LIR, TCP, S21,
　　　　　　K, BG, Simulcasting (seasonal)
Senior Discount: $3 off Sat lunch, if 55 or older
Special Features: Cashless video slots.

Nooksack River Casino
5048 Mt. Baker Highway
Deming, Washington 98244
(360) 592-5472
Website: www.nooksackcasino.com
Map Location: **#3** (14 miles E. of Bellingham)

Restaurants: 1 Liquor: Yes
Buffets: L-$7.95/$12.95 (Sun)
　　D-$13.95/$11.95 (Thu)/$12.95 (Sun)/$15.95 (Fri)
Hours: 10am-3am/6am (Fri-Sat)
Casino Size: 21,500 Square Feet
Other Games: MB, PGP, CSP, LIR
Senior Discount: $2 off buffets, if 55 or older
Special Features: Cashless video slots.

Northern Quest Casino
100 N. Hayford Road
Airway Heights, Washington 99001
(509) 242-7000
Website: www.northernquest.net
Map Location: **#20** (10 miles N. of Spokane)

Restaurants: 1 Liquor: Yes
Buffets: B-$5.95 L-$7.95 D-$10.95
Hours: 9am-5am
Casino Size: 21,500 Square Feet
Other Games: P, K, Simulcasting
Senior Discount: Buffet discounts, if 55+
Special Features: Cashless video slots.

Okanogan Bingo and Casino
41 Appleway Road
Okanogan, Washington 98840
Website: www.colvillecasinos.com/okanogan
(509) 422-4646
Map Location: **#10** (165 miles E. of Seattle)

Toll-Free Number: (800) 559-4643
Restaurants: 1 Snack Bar Liquor: No
Hours: 9am-Mid/2am (Fri/Sat)
Other Games: BG, No Craps or Roulette
Special Features: Regular slots. Bj opens 4pm.

Point No Point Casino
7989 Salish Lane NE
Kingston, Washington 98346
(360) 297-0070
Website: www.pointnopointcasino.com
Map Location: **#14** (18 miles W. of Seattle via Bainbridge Ferry)

Restaurants: 1 Liquor: Yes
Casino Size: 12,000 Square Feet

Hours: 10am-2am Daily
Other Games: PGP, S21
Special Features: Cashless video slots.

Quinault Beach Resort
78 Route 115
Ocean Shores, Washington 98569
(360) 289-9466
Website: www.quinaultbchresort.com
Map Location: **#19** (90 miles W. of Tacoma)

Toll-Free Number: (888) 461-2214
Rooms: 159 Price Range: $139-$159
Suite: 9 Price Range: $300-$750
Restaurants: 3   Liquor: Yes
Buffets: L-$7.95 D-$10.95
Casino Size: 16,000 Square Feet
Hours: 9am-2am/4:30am (Fri-Sat)
Other Games: B, PGP, LIR, CSP, S21, K
Senior Discount: Various on Wed, if 55 or older
Special Features: Cashless video slots. Full
service spa. AARP room discount.

Red Wind Casino
12819 Yelm Highway
Olympia, Washington 98513
(360) 412-5000
Website: www.redwindcasino.net
Map Location: **#17**

Toll-Free Number: (866) 946-2444
Restaurants: 1 Liquor: Yes
Hours: 9am-5am Daily
Casino Size: 12,000 Square Feet
Other Games: PGP, CSP, LIR, K, S21
Senior Discount: Free lunch Mon-Wed, if 55+
Fun Book: Ask at promotions booth
Special Features: Cashless video slots.

7 Cedars Casino
270756 Highway 101
Sequim, Washington 98382
(360) 683-7777
Website: www.7cedarscasino.com
Map Location: **#4** (70 miles N.W. of Seattle
via ferry)

Toll-Free Number: (800) 4-LUCKY-7
Restaurants: 1 Liquor: Yes
Buffets: D-$16.95 (Fri)/$10.95 (Sat)
Hours: 10am-1am/3am (Fri-Sat)
Other Games: BG
Special Features: Cashless video slots.

Shoalwater Bay Casino
4112 Highway 105
Tokeland, Washington 98590
(360) 267-2048
Map Location: **#18** (75 miles S.W. of Olympia)

Toll-Free Number: (888) 332-2048
Restaurants: 1 Liquor: No
Hours: 10am-12am/2am (Fri-Sat)
Casino Size: 10,000 Square Feet
Other Games: P, No Craps or Roulette
Senior Discount: Various on Tue, if 55 or older
Special Features: Regular slots.

Silver Reef Casino
4876 Haxton Way
Ferndale, Washington 98248
(360) 383-0777
Website: www.silverreefcasino.com
Map Location: **#21** (7 miles N. of Bellingham)

Toll-Free Number: (866) 383-0777
Restaurants: 2 Liquor: Yes
Casino Size: 28,000 Square Feet
Hours: 10am-4am/6am (Fri-Sat)
Other Games: TCP, PGP, S21
Special Features: Cashless video slots.

Skagit Valley Casino
590 Dark Lane
Bow, Washington 98232
(360) 724-7777
Website: www.svcasinoresort.com
Map Location: **#7** (75 miles N. of Seattle)

Toll-Free Number: (877) 275-2448
Room Reservations: (800) 895-3423
Rooms: 86 Price Range: $79-$109
Rooms: 23 Price Range: $159-$185
Restaurants: 4 Liquor: Yes
Buffets: B-$5.75 (Sat)/$12.95 (Sun) L-$7.95
D-$10.95/$15.95 (Wed/Fri-Sat)
Hours: 9am-2am/4am (Fri-Sat)
Casino Size: 26,075 Square Feet
Other Games: MB, PGP, CSP, LIR, BG, K
Senior Discount: Various on Mon, if 55 or older
Special Features: Cashless video slots.

Swinomish Northern Lights Casino
837 Casino Drive
Anacortes, Washington 98221
(360) 293-2691
Website: www.swinomishcasino.com
Map Location: **#7** (70 miles N. of Seattle, between I-5 and Anacortes on Hwy. 20)

Restaurants: 2 Liquor: Yes
Buffets: B-$8.95 (Sun) L-$7.49
          D-$10.95/$16.95 (Fri)/$15.95 (Sat)
Hours: 11am-4am/6am (Fri-Sat)
Casino Size: 73,000 Square Feet
Other Games: P, PGP, LIR, TCP, BG, K,
          Red Dog, Simulcasting
Senior Discount: $1 off buffet, if 60 or older
Special Features: Cashless video slots. Gift shop.

Tulalip Casino
6410 33rd Avenue N.E.
Marysville, Washington 98271
(360) 651-1111
Website: www.tulalipcasino.com
Map Location: **#1** (30 miles N. of Seattle)

Toll-Free Number: (888) 272-1111
Restaurants: 2 Liquor: Yes
Buffets: B-$8.95 (Sun)
Hours: 10am-6am Daily
Casino Size: 45,000 Square Feet
Other Games: MB, P, PGP, K, BG
Special Features: Cashless video slots. Two hotels across from casino. Gift shop.

Two Rivers Casino & Resort
6828-B Highway 25 South
Davenport, Washington 99122
(509) 722-4000
Website: www.tworiverscasinoandresort.com
Map Location: **#8** (60 miles W. of Spokane)

Toll-Free Number: (877) 7-COME-11
Restaurants: 1 Liquor: No
Hours: 9am-1am/24 Hours (Fri/Sat)
Casino Size: 10,000 Square Feet
Other Games: No Craps or Roulette
Special Features: Regular slots. 35-space RV park. 200-slip marina.

Yakama Nation Legends Casino
580 Fort Road
Toppenish, Washington 98948
(509) 865-8800
Map Location: **#16** (20 miles S. of Yakima)

Toll-Free Number: (877) 7-COME-11
Restaurants: 2 Liquor: No
Buffets: B-$8.99 L-$5.99
          D-$7.99/$16.99 (Fri)/$10.99 (Sat)
Hours: 9am-3am/4am (Fri-Sat)
Casino Size: 45,000 Square Feet
Other Games: P, LIR, CSP, K, No Roulette
Funbook: Given to out-of-state visitors, Birthday Club members and for special events
Senior Discount: 10% off buffets, if 55 or older and Funbook on Tuesdays
Special Features: Cashless video slots. Childcare center. Indoor waterfall. Gift shop.

Card Rooms

Card rooms have been legal in Washington since 1974. Initially limited to just five tables per location, the law was changed in 1996 to allow up to 15 tables. Then, one year later, a provision was added to allow house-banked games. Permissible games include: blackjack, Caribbean stud poker, pai gow poker, let it ride and casino war. The games of baccarat, craps, roulette and keno are not allowed.

The maximum bet at each card room is dependant on certain licensing requirements and is capped at either $3, $25 or $100. Additionally, the rooms can be open no more than 20 hours per day. These card rooms are now commonly called "mini-casinos."

Each city and county has the option to ban the card rooms so they are not found in every major city (Seattle has none). Due to space limitations we don't list all of the Washington card rooms in this book but we do list them on our website: www.americancasinoguide.com

When you get to the American Casino Guide website look on the left side for "U.S. Casino Directory," click on that and when you get to the next page just click on "Washington."

WEST VIRGINIA

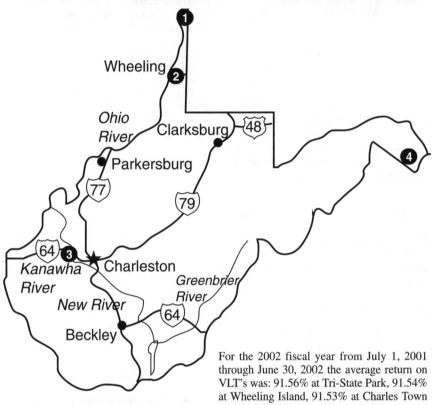

For the 2002 fiscal year from July 1, 2001 through June 30, 2002 the average return on VLT's was: 91.56% at Tri-State Park, 91.54% at Wheeling Island, 91.53% at Charles Town Races and 91.14% at Mountaineer Park.

For West Virginia tourism information call (800) 225-5982.

West Virginia has four pari-mutuel facilities that feature video lottery terminals. The VLT's are the same as regular video gaming devices but are called lottery terminals because they are regulated by the state's lottery commission which receives a share of each machine's revenue.

The maximum allowable bet on a machine is $2. Most of the gaming machines pay out coins or tokens but there are also some machines which will only print out a receipt which must be taken to a cashier. West Virginia law requires that VLT's return a minimum of 80% to a maximum of 95%. VLT games include: slots, blackjack, keno and numerous versions of poker. The minimum gambling age is 18.

Charles Town Races & Slots
P.O. Box 551
Charles Town, West Virginia 25414
(304) 725-7001
Website: www.ctownraces.com
Map Location: **#4**

Toll-Free Number: (800) 795-7001
Restaurants: 4
Buffets: L-$8.95
  D-$8.95/$14.95 (Mon/Fri/Sat)/$22.95 (Wed)
Hours: 7am-3:30am/3am (Sat)
       10am-3:30am (Sun)
Special Features: Live horse racing Wed-Sun. Daily simulcasting of horse and dog racing. Food court with five fast-food outlets.

Mountaineer Race Track & Gaming Resort
State Route #2
Chester, West Virginia 26034
(304) 387-2400
Website: www.mtrgaming.com
Map Location: **#1** (35 miles N. of Wheeling)

Toll-Free Number: (800) 804-0468
Room Reservations: (800) 489-8192
Rooms: 337 Price Range: $75-$119
Suites: 22 Price Range: $155-$185
Restaurants: 8
Buffets: B-$4.95 L-$7.95 D-$9.95
Hours: 7:30am-3:30am/3am (Sat)
       10am-3:30am (Sun)
Special Features: 18-hole golf course. Health
spa. Live horse racing Thur-Mon. Daily simul-
casting of horse and dog racing.

Wheeling Island
Racetrack & Gaming Center
1 S. Stone Street
Wheeling, West Virginia 26003
(304) 232-5050
Website: www.wheelingdowns.com
Map Location: **#2**

Toll-Free Number: (877) WIN-HERE
Restaurants: 2
Buffets: L-$8.95 D-$12.95
Hours: 9am-3am/10am-3am (Sun)
Casino Size: 50,000 Square Feet
Special Features: Live dog racing Wed-Mon.
Daily simulcasting of horse and dog racing.

Tri-State Racetrack & Gaming Center
1 Greyhound Lane
Cross Lanes, West Virginia 25356
(304) 776-1000
Map Location: **#3** (10 miles N.W. of Charles-
ton)

Toll-Free Number: (800) 224-9683
Restaurants: 1
Hours: 11am-3am/1pm-3am (Sun)
Casino Size: 30,000 Square Feet
Special Features: Live dog racing Wed-Mon.
Daily simulcasting of horse and dog racing.

WISCONSIN

All Wisconsin casinos are located on Indian reservations and blackjack is the only table game permitted.

The Indian tribes are not required to release information on their slot machine percentage paybacks, but according to the terms of the compact between the state and the tribes "for games not affected by player skill, such as slot machines, the machine is required to return a minimum of 80% and a maximum of 100% of the amount wagered."

Unless otherwise noted, all casinos are open 24 hours and the only games offered are: blackjack, slots, video poker and video keno. The minimum gambling age is 21 at all casinos (18 for bingo).

For visitor information call the state's department of tourism at (800) 432-8747.

Bad River Lodge Casino and Convention Center
U.S. Highway 2
Odanah, Wisconsin 54861
(715) 682-7121
Website: www.badriver.com
Map Location: **#1** (halfway between Ironwood, MI and Ashland, WI; 45 miles east of Duluth, MN on US 2)

Toll-Free Number: (800) 777-7449
Lodge Reservations: (800) 795-7121
Rooms: 42 Price Range: $45-$77
Suites: 8 Price Range: $65-$97
Restaurants: 2 Liquor: Yes
Buffets: B-$4.95 L-$6.95 D-$8.95
Casino Size: 19,200 Square Feet
Hours: 8am-2am /4am (Fri-Sat)
Special Features: 20-space RV park. Gas station. Grocery store. AAA and AARP members get 10% room discount.

Grindstone Creek Casino
13767 West County Road B
Hayward, Wisconsin 54843
(715) 634-2430
Map Location: **#2**

Restaurants: 1 snack bar Liquor: No
Hours: 10am-10pm Daily
Other Games: Machines Only
Special Features: Located 2-1/2 miles south of LCO Casino.

Ho Chunk Casino Hotel and Convention Center
S3214 Highway 12
Baraboo, Wisconsin 53913
(608) 356-6210
Website: www.ho-chunk.com
Map Location: **#4** (40 miles N. of Madison. On Hwy. 12 just S. of Delton)

Toll-Free Number: (800) 746-2486
Rooms: 295 Price Range: $29-$150
Suites: 20 Price Range: $89-$305
Restaurants: 5 (1 open 24 hrs) Liquor: Yes
Buffets: B-$6.95 L-$8.95
            D-$11.95/$21.95 (Wed)
Casino Size: 90,000 Square Feet
Other Games: Bingo
Senior Discount: Bingo discount if 55+
Special Features: Gift shop. Discount smoke shop. Shuttle service from local area motels. Kid's Quest childcare center.

Hole In The Wall Casino & Hotel
P.O. Box 98, Highways 35 & 77
Danbury, Wisconsin 54830
(715) 656-3444
Map Location: **#5** (26 miles E. of Hinckley, MN)

Toll-Free Number: (800) BET-U-WIN
Rooms: 45 Price Range: $55-$100
Restaurants: 1 Liquor: Yes
Casino Size: 22,500 Square Feet
Hours: 8am-2am/4am (Fri/Sat)
Special Features: 35-space RV park. Gift shop. $10 off room for slot club members.

Isle Vista Casino
Highway 13 North, Box 1167
Bayfield, Wisconsin 54814
(715) 779-3712
Website: http://www.ncis.net/islvista/
Map Location: **#6** (70 miles E. of Duluth, MN
on Hwy. 13, 3 miles N. of Bayfield)

Toll-Free Number: (800) 226-8478
Restaurants: 1 Liquor: Yes
Hours: 10am-12am/2am (Thu-Sat)
Other Games: Bingo (Thu/Sat/Sun)

Lake of the Torches Resort Casino
510 Old Abe Road
Lac du Flambeau, Wisconsin 54538
(715) 588-7070
Website: www.180025torch.com
Map Location: **#7** (160 miles N.W. of Green
Bay. Heading N. on Hwy. 51, go left on Hwy.
47, 12 miles to casino)

Toll-Free Number: (800) 25-TORCH
Room Reservations: (888) 599-9200
Rooms: 88 Price Range: $100-$110
Suites: 13 Price Range: $107-$150
Restaurants: 2 Liquor: Yes
Buffets: B-$5.95/$6.95 (Sat-Sun) L-$7.95
D-$10.95/$11.95 (Thu)/$12.95 (Sun)/$16.50 (Fri)
Other Games: Bingo (Tue-Sun)
Special Features: Slot club members get 20%
off room and other discounts. Room rates in-
clude free breakfast and $20 match play.

LCO Casino, Lodge & Convention Center
13767 W County Road B
Hayward, Wisconsin 54843
(715) 634-5643
Website: www.lcocasino.com
Map Location: **#2** (55 miles S.E. of Duluth,
MN. 3 miles N.E. of Hayward on county trunk B)

Toll-Free Number: (800) LCO-CASH
Room Reservations: (800) LCO-LODGE
Rooms: 41 Price Range: $54-$74
Suites: 14 Price Range: $75-$105
Restaurants: 2 Liquor: Yes
Buffets: B-$4.95 L-$6.95 D-$7.95
Casino Size: 35,000 Square Feet
Hours: 9am-4am Daily
Other Games: Bingo (Sun-Fri)
Senior Discount: 5% discount at Lodge and
    free prize spin on Sundays if 55, or older
Special Features: Sports lounge. Gift shop.

Majestic Pines Casino, Bingo & Hotel
W9010 Highway 54 East
Black River Falls, Wisconsin 54615
(715) 284-9098
Website: www.ho-chunk.com
Map Location: **#8** (110 miles M.W. of Madi-
son on Hwy. 54, 4 miles E. of I-94)

Toll-Free Number: (800) 657-4621
Rooms: 60 Price Range: $59-$75
Suites: 6 Price Range: $95
Restaurants: 2 Liquor: Yes
Buffets: L-$7.95 D-$9.95/$21.95 (Thu)
Hours: 8am-2am/4am (Fri, Sat & All Summer)
Size: 75,000 Square Feet
Other Games: Bingo (Thu-Tue)
Senior Discount: Spin prize wheel Wed and
    $5 off bingo packs on Sundays, if 55 or older
Special Features: 10% off buffets with slot club
card. Heated pool.

Menominee Casino, Bingo & Hotel
P.O. Box 760, Highways 47 & 55
Keshena, Wisconsin 54135
(715) 799-3600
Website: www.menomineecasinoresort.com
Map Location: **#9** (40 miles N.W. of Green
Bay on Hwy. 47, 7 miles N. of Shawano)

Toll-Free Number: (800) 343-7778
Rooms: 100 Price Range: $60-$70
Suites: 8 Price Range: $80-$125
Restaurants: 1 Liquor: Yes
Buffets: L-$6.95/$8.95 (Sun)
    D-$9.95/$9.95 (Wed-Thu)/$14.50 (Fri/Sat)
Casino Size: 36,000 Square Feet
Other Games: Bingo
Senior Discount: $5 matchplay on Tues if 55+
Special Features: 60-space RV park. Gift shop.
Smoke shop. 10% room discount for AAA and
AARP members. $10 matchplay and free con-
tinental breakfast with rooms.

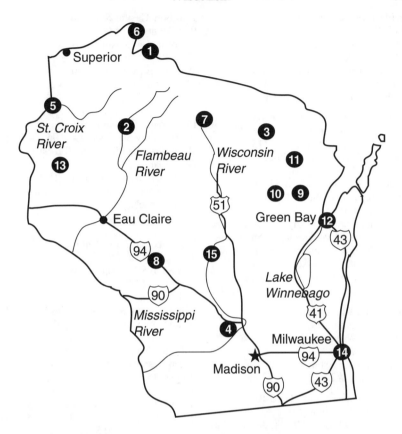

Mohican North Star Casino
W12180A County Road A
Bowler, Wisconsin 54416
(715) 787-3110
Website: www.mohicannorthstar.com
Map Location: **#10** (50 miles N.W. of Green Bay)

Toll-Free Number: (800) 952-0195
Restaurants: 1 Snack Bar Liquor: Yes
Hours: 8am-2am/24 Hours (Fri-Sat)
Other Games: Bingo (Sun-Mon/Wed-Fri)
Special Features: 57-space RV park. Smoke shop. Local motels offer casino packages.

Mole Lake/Regency Casino
Highway 55
Mole Lake, Wisconsin 54520
(715) 478-5290
Website: www.molelake.com
Map Location: **#3** (100 miles N.W. of Green Bay on Hwy. 55, 7 miles S. of Crandon)

Toll-Free Number: (800) 236-WINN
Motel Reservations: (800) 457-4312
Rooms: 25 Price Range: $46-$55
Restaurants: 1 Cafeteria Liquor: Yes
Hours: 10am-1am/3am (Fri/Sat)
Other Games: Bingo (Fri-Tue)
Senior Discount: $5 matchplay Wed if 50+
Special Features: Two casinos housed in separate buildings. Motel is two blocks from casino. Blackjack opens at 12 p.m. $10 match play given to hotel guests. 8-space RV park.

Oneida Bingo & Casino
2020/2100 Airport Drive
Green Bay, Wisconsin 54313
(414) 494-4500
Website: www.oneidabingoandcasino.net
Map Location: **#12** (across from Austin
Straubel Airport, take I-43 to Highway 172)

Toll-Free Number: (800) 238-4263
Reservation Number: (800) 333-3333
Rooms: 301 Price Range: $79-$159
Suites: 29 Price Range: $159-$229
Restaurants: 3 Liquor: No
Buffets (at Radisson Inn): B-$7.95 L-$7.95
Hours: 10am-4am (Tables)/24 Hours (Slots)
Other Games: Bingo
Senior Discount: Free early bird bingo pack
　　　　　　　on Wednesday, if 55, or older
Special Features: Features two casinos. One
is connected to Radisson Inn where hotel
rooms are located. Discount smoke shop.

Potawatomi Bingo Casino
1721 W. Canal Street
Milwaukee, Wisconsin 53233
(414) 645-6888
Website: www.paysbig.com
Map Location: **#14**

Toll-Free Number: (800) PAYS-BIG
Restaurants: 3 Liquor: No
Buffets: L-$9.99 D-$13.99/$15.99 (Fri-Sat)
Other Games: Bingo
Casino Size: 38,400 Square Feet
Special Features: Alcohol served in sports bar.

Potawatomi Bingo/Northern Lights Casino
Highway 32
Wabeno, Wisconsin 54566
(715) 473-2021
Website: www.cartercasino.com
Map Location: **#11** (85 miles N. of Green Bay
on Hwy. 32)

Toll-Free Number: (800) 487-9522
Lodge Reservations: (800) 777-1640
Rooms: 70 Price Range: $65-$85
Suites: 29 Price Range: $70-$105
Restaurants: 2 Liquor: Yes
Casino Size: 12,000 Square Feet
Hours: 9am-2am/4am (Fri/Sat)
Other Games: Bingo
Senior Discount: Specials on Wed if 55+
Special Features: Lodge is across parking lot
from casino and offers casino packages. 24-
hour gas station and convenience store.

Rainbow Casino & Bingo
949 County Road G
Nekoosa, Wisconsin 54457
(715) 886-4560
Website: www.rbcwin.com
Map Location: **#15** (50 miles S. of Wausau)

Toll-Free Number: (800) 782-4560
Restaurants: 2 Liquor: Yes
Buffets (only Sundays): L-$8.95 D-$9.95
Hours: 8am-2am/24 hours (Fri-Sat)
Other Games: Bingo
Senior Discount: Specials on Thu. if 55+
Special Features: Smoke and gift shop. Motel
and tour packages.

St. Croix Casino & Hotel
777 US Highway 8
Turtle Lake, Wisconsin 54889
(715) 986-4777
Website: www.stcroixcasino.com
Map Location: **#13** (105 miles S. of Duluth,
MN on Hwy. 8)

Toll-Free Number: (800) 846-8946
Room Reservations: (800) 782-9987
Rooms: 158 Price Range: $55-$67
Suites: 8 Price Range: $110-$135
Restaurants: 3   Liquor: Yes
Buffets: B-$4.20 L-$8.40 D-$11.60/$17 (Thu)
Casino Size: 95,000 Square Feet
Other Games: Bingo
Special Features: 20% off rooms for slot club
member.

Casino Index

FOXWOODS
RESORT ◆ CASINO

Route 2
Mashantucket, CT 06339
(860) 312-3000
(800) FOXWOODS

GREEKTOWN
CASINO
a Kewadin Casino™

555 E. Lafayette Avenue
Detroit, MI 48226
(313) 223-2999
(888) 771-4386
www.greektowncasino.com

195 Beach Boulevard
Biloxi, MS 39530
1-800-5-MAGIC-5
(228) 386-4600
www.casinomagic-biloxi.com

Players Club membership required to redeem this offer (membership is free). Offer is based on availability and valid on general admission seating only. Must be 21. No reproductions. No refunds. Not valid with any other offer. Management reserves the right to modify or cancel this promotion at any time. Offer valid at Casino Magic Biloxi only through December 25, 2003.

1980 Beach Boulevard
Biloxi, MS 39531
(800) PIRATE-9
(228) 385-6000

Subject to change or cancellation. Must be 21 or older with valid photo ID. Limit one per person. Not reponsible for lost or stolen coupons. Not valid with any other offer. Non-negotiable. Non-transferable. Non-refundable. Only valid November 1, 2002 through December 23, 2003.

ZF00000EXL1A7MB8

1980 Beach Boulevard
Biloxi, MS 39531
(800) PIRATE-9
(228) 385-6000

Subject to change or cancellation. Must be 21 or older with valid photo ID. Limit one per person. Not reponsible for lost or stolen coupons. Not valid with any other offer. Non-negotiable. Non-transferable. Non-refundable. Only valid November 1, 2002 through December 23, 2003.

ZF00000EXL1A7MB8

AMERICAN CASINO GUIDE

$15 Off!

alamo.com
1-800-354-2322
Alamo features GM vehicles

- Just reserve a midsize through a sport utility vehicle in the United States, Canada, Latin America or the Caribbean
- Valid for a rental of at least four days
- Valid through 12/31/03
- Book with your travel agent or Alamo at 1-800-354-2322. Or, book online at *alamo.com* Be sure to request ID #641394, Rate Code BY, and Coupon Code DB12 at time of reservation..

See terms and conditions on reserve side of this coupon.

DB12

CASINO COUPON

AMERICAN CASINO GUIDE

One FREE Upgrade!

Alamo

alamo.com
1-800-354-2322
Alamo features GM vehicles

- Just reserve a compact through midsize 4-door car in the U.S. or Canada, or an economy through fullsize car.in Europe
- Valid through 12/31/03
- Book with your travel agent or Alamo at 1-800-354-2322. Or, book online at *alamo.com*
- Be sure to request ID #641394, Rate Code BY and Coupon Code UB90 at time of reservations

See terms and conditions on reserve side of this coupon.

UB90

CASINO COUPON

AMERICAN CASINO GUIDE

Save on Your Car Rental with Alamo-Rent-A-Car!

alamo.com
1-800-354-2322

See the world one stop at a time with special rates from Alamo. As an American Casino Guide reader, you'll receive up up to 15% off our great rates year-round, unlimited mileage and no fee for the first additional driver. We'll always go that extra mile to make your car rental experince a fun part of your trip. Book with your travel agent or Alamo. Be sure to request ID #641394 and Rate Code BY. Alamo features GM vehicles. This is not a coupon.

See terms and conditions on reserve side.

CASINO COUPON

Terms and Conditions

- One coupon per Alamo rental and void once redeemed.
- Original coupon must be presented at counter upon arrival.
- Discount applies to basic rate, which does not include taxes (including GST), governmentally-authorized or imposed surcharges, concession and license recoupment/air tax recovery fees, airport and airport facility fees, or optional items.
- Offer is subject to standard rental conditions.
- Blackout dates may apply.
- Not valid with any other discount or promotional rate.
- Subject to availability and good only at participating Alamo locations.
- **In the United States, offer valid only at airport-serving locations.**
- Offer not valid in San Jose, California.
- Travel Agents GDS:ID-XA641394/RC-BY/SI-C-DB12

alamo.com
1-800-354-2322

Terms and Conditions

- One coupon per Alamo rental and void once redeemed.
- Original coupon must be presented at counter upon arrival.
- Upgrade is subject to availability at time of rental pick up.
- Offer is subject to standard rental conditions.
- Not valid with any other discount or promotional rate.
- Offer is good only at participating Alamo locations.
- In the United States, offer valid only at airport-serving locations.
- Blackout dates may apply.
- Certificate is valid for one free upgrade to the next car category (in Euope to the next car category with the same transmission)
- Travel Agents GDS:/ID-XA641394/RC-BY/SI-C-UB90

alamo.com
1-800-354-2322

Terms and Conditions

Discount applies to basic rate, which does not include taxes (including GST/VAT), governmentally-authorized or imposed surcharges, license recoupment/air tax recovery and concession recoupment fees, vehicle license fee, road fee, premium location charges, airport and airport facility fees, fuel, one-way rental charge and optional items. Renter must meet standard age, driver and credit requirements (may vary by country). 24-hour advance reservation required (up to 72 hours for licensee locations). May not be combined with other discounts. Availability is limited. Subject to change without notice. Black out dates may apply. In United States, offer valid only at airport-serving locations. This is not a coupon. Percentage discount is reflected in the reserved rate.

Alamo

alamo.com
1-800-354-2322

AMERICAN CASINO GUIDE

WORLD CHAMPIONSHIP BINGO TOURNAMENTS

Sponsor

BINGO BUGLE Newspapers®

1-800-326-0373

$100 Off Per Person

This coupon entitles the bearer to a $100 discount, per person, on the regular registration fee for the 15th Annual World Championship Bingo Tournament & Gaming Cruise, a spectacular 8-day Caribbean adventure aboard Carnival Cruise Line's *Glory* sailing from Port Canaveral, November 1st through 8th, 2003. Call 1-800-326-0373 for a free full-color brochure. Offer expires 10/1/03

CASINO COUPON

AMERICAN CASINO GUIDE

Go Greyhound.
Lucky Streak®

$5 Discount on a Greyhound Casino Ticket

This coupon entitles the bearer to a $5 discount on the purchase of a round-trip Greyhound casino ticket at any Greyhound office in California or Arizona. For more information on Greyhound travel call (800) 231-2222

CASINO COUPON

AMERICAN CASINO GUIDE

Go Greyhound.
Lucky Streak®

$5 Discount on a Greyhound Casino Ticket

This coupon entitles the bearer to a $5 discount on the purchase of a round-trip Greyhound casino ticket at any Greyhound office in California or Arizona. For more information on Greyhound travel call (800) 231-2222

CASINO COUPON

Reno Hilton

Buy One Buffet Get One FREE

Buy one breakfast, lunch or dinner at the Grand Canyon Buffet and receive the second for FREE. See back for full details

CASINO COUPON

Reno Hilton

$10 Room Discount

Save $10 on our prevailing daily room rate with this coupon. See reverse for full details.

CASINO COUPON

HYATT REGENCY LAKE TAHOE
A HYATT RESORT AND CASINO

Free Casino Fun Money

Please present this coupon at the Casino Cashier Cage to receive a FREE Casino Fun Money sheet loaded with valuable offers. See reverse side for full details.

CASINO COUPON

2500 E. Second St.
Reno, NV 89595
(702) 789-2000
(800) 648-5080

Present this coupon to the cashier at the Grand Canyon Buffet. Not valid in conjunction with any other offer or discounts. Must be 21 years or older.

Management reserves the right to change or cancel this offer at any time. Offer expires 12/24/03.

D-53

2500 E. Second St.
Reno, NV 89595
(702) 789-2000
(800) 648-5080

Call 1-800-648-5080 to make your ADVANCE reservations. Ask for reservation code ACG. Coupon must be presented on arrival. Promotional offer not available for groups or conventions. Must be 21 years or older. Limited availability. Excludes special events & holiday periods. Management reserves the right to change or cancel this offer at any time. Offer expires 12/24/03.

A HYATT RESORT AND CASINO

P.O. Box 3239
Incline Village, NV 89450
(775) 832-1234
(800) 233-1234

Limit one coupon per guest. Must be 21 years of age, or older. No cash value. Not valid with any other offer. Management reserves the right to cancel or modify this offer. Expires 12/30/03.

CIRCUS CIRCUS®
R E N O
A Mandalay Resort Group Property
www.circusreno.com

500 North Sierra Street • Reno, NV 89503
1-800-648-5010

Present coupon to Main Casino Cage. Must be 21. One Fun Book per coupon, per day.
Management reserves all rights. Subject to promotional availability. Not valid with any other offers. Expires 12/18/03.

CIRCUS CIRCUS®
R E N O
A Mandalay Resort Group Property
www.circusreno.com

500 North Sierra Street • Reno, NV 89503
1-800-648-5010

*Present coupon to front desk upon check-in. Must be 21. Requires 14 days advanced booking. Valid for Sky Tower room with 2 adults
and up to 3 children, 12 or under through 12/18/03. Holiday, convention and special event periods excluded.
Management reserves all rights. Subject to promotional availability. Not valid with any other offers.   **Code: RCG**

CIRCUS CIRCUS®
R E N O
A Mandalay Resort Group Property
www.circusreno.com

500 North Sierra Street • Reno, NV 89503
1-800-648-5010

AMERICAN CASINO GUIDE

SPORTS CASINO

Free Buffet!

Present this coupon to the cashier at Baldini's Buffet to buy one buffet at regular price and receive another FREE!

CASINO COUPON

AMERICAN CASINO GUIDE

Buy one adult admission and get one FREE!

Present this coupon at the Liberace Museum and get one free admission with the puchase of each adult admission. See back for full details.

CASINO COUPON

AMERICAN CASINO GUIDE

GUINNESS WORLD RECORDS MUSEUM

Two-For-One Admission

Present this coupon and get one free admission when a second admission of equal or greater value is purchased.

CASINO COUPON

Double Game Play Up To $50!

Present this coupon at the GameWorks location in Las Vegas and when you purchase from $10 to $50 of game play it will be matched with an equal amount of game play for FREE! See reverse for complete details.

CASINO COUPON

MADAME TUSSAUD'S
LAS VEGAS

2-For-1 General Admission
After 5:00 p.m.

Receive one FREE ticket with the purchase of a full-price general admission ticket at Madame Tussaud's Interactive Wax Museum located in front of the Venetian Resort on Las Vegas Boulevard. **Valid after 5:00 p.m. only.**

CASINO COUPON

Established 1906

GOLDEN GATE
HOTEL & CASINO • ONE FREMONT STREET • LAS VEGAS

FREE Deck of Cards

Receive a FREE deck of cards from Las Vegas' Most Historic Hotel at One Fremont Street.

See reverse side for full details.

CASINO COUPON

AMERICAN CASINO GUIDE

$10 in FREE Slot Play!

New members only, present this coupon at the Club Palms booth, sign up for the Club Palms card and receive $10 in FREE slot play. See reverse for complete details.

CASINO COUPON

AMERICAN CASINO GUIDE

Guaranteed Free Slot Play!
Join the New York-New York Players Club & receive:

• $5 - $500 in Slot Free Play • A Free One-of-a-kind Cab Cap

NEW YORK NEW YORK

Expires 12/22/03

CASINO COUPON

AMERICAN CASINO GUIDE

Manhattan Express®
Roller Coaster
Up to $6 Off

Please present this pass at the Manhattan Express®
ticket booth prior to boarding the ride and receive
$3 off each paid admission up to (2) people.

Expires 12/22/03

CASINO COUPON

New members present this voucher to the Club Palms booth and receive $10 in FREE slot play.

Must be 21 years of age or older. Not valid in conjunction with any other offer. Management reserves the right to cancel or change this offer at any time. Offer expires 12/31/03.

Las Vegas' Newest Resort Destination
(702) 942-7777 • 1-866-942-7777
On Flamingo West of the Strip
Easy Access Convenient Parking
www.palms.com

$5 - $20
Blackjack
Matchplay

Present this coupon and your Barley's Player Rewards Card to any Blackjack table prior to the start of a game and **we'll match your bet of $5 to $20** if you win. See reverse for complete details.

CASINO COUPON

AMERICAN CASINO GUIDE

One FREE
Pizza!

Bring this coupon directly to the Brickhouse Pizza Kitchen, show your Barley's Player Rewards Card, and get an 8" pizza with up to two toppings for FREE!. See reverse for complete details.

CASINO COUPON

AMERICAN CASINO GUIDE

FREE
Fun Book

Redeem this coupon for your FREE Fun Book at the One Club Booth located in the center of the Casino. See reverse for more details.

CASINO COUPON

4500 E. Sunset Road #30
Henderson, NV 89014
(702) 458-2739
www.stationcasinos.com

One coupon per person, per day. Must be a Barley's Player Rewards member and must present original coupon (no photocopies).

Cannot be redeemed for cash. Must be 21 or older. Non-transferable. Cannot be combined with any other offer or promotion. Not responsible for lost or stolen coupon. Management reserves all rights. Offer may be changed or discontinued at anytime at the discretion of management. Expires December 26, 2003.

4500 E. Sunset Road #30
Henderson, NV 89014
(702) 458-2739
www.stationcasinos.com

Must be 21 or older. Must be a Barley's Player Reward member and must present original coupon (no photocopies). Not valid on Holidays. Tax and Gratuity not included. Offer has no cash value. Limit: one pizza per person. Two toppings 8" pizza maximum. Additional toppings extra. Non-transferable. Not responsible for lost or stolen coupon. Management reserves all rights. Not valid with any other offer or promotion. Offer may be changed or discontinued at anytime at the discretion of management. Offer expires December 26, 2003.

3850 Las Vegas Blvd. S.
Las Vegas, NV 89145
(702) 597-7777 • (800) 937-7777
ww.excaliburcasino.com

Present original coupon (no photocopies) to One Club representative. Coupon not redeemable for cash. One fun book per person. Offer subject to change or cancellation at the discretion of management. Must be 21 years of age or older. This coupon expires December 31, 2003.

AMERICAN CASINO GUIDE

2 for 1 Buffet

Present to buffet cashier. Must purchase one buffet
to receive the second one free.
Settle to public comp # 404.

Expires December 30, 2003   Casino Guide

CASINO COUPON

AMERICAN CASINO GUIDE

$10 off next stay

Sunday - Thursday. Based on availability.
Not valid during holidays or conventions. Reservations required.
Must present coupon at check-in.

Expires December 30, 2003   Casino Guide

CASINO COUPON

AMERICAN CASINO GUIDE

Join the Player's Club
and receive

1,000 FREE points

Must join club. Please allow 72 hours before points will be available.
Existing club members receive 250 points free. One coupon per person.

Expires December 30, 2003   Casino Guide

CASINO COUPON

AMERICAN CASINO GUIDE

 **$20 Match Play**

Play this coupon with a minimum of $20 on any even-money bet on any of our table games and we'll match it with a FREE $20 bet. See reverse for details.

CASINO COUPON

AMERICAN CASINO GUIDE

 **$10 Match Play**

Play this coupon with a minimum of $10 on any even-money bet on any of our table games and we'll match it with a FREE $10 bet. See reverse for details.

CASINO COUPON

AMERICAN CASINO GUIDE

 **FREE Upgrade to Lake View Room**

When you stay at the Hyatt Lake Las Vegas present this coupon at the check-in desk to receive a FREE upgrade to a lake view room. See reverse for details.

CASINO COUPON

101 Montelago Boulevard
Las Vegas, NV 89011
(702) 567-1234 • (800) 55-HYATT
www.lakelasvegas.hyatt.com

Name/Address/City/State/Zip

All information must be completed prior to redemption. Coupon to be played with a minimum $20 wager. Match play valid on all even-money bets on table games only. Limited to one match play coupon at a time and to one $20 match play per person, per day. Coupon will be replaced with $20 in gaming tokens on all winning bets. Must be 21 or older. Non-transeferable or refundable. Coupon cannot be redeemed for cash. Management reserves the right to alter, change or cancel without notice. Void if duplicated or altered. Valid until 12/31/03.

101 Montelago Boulevard
Las Vegas, NV 89011
(702) 567-1234 • (800) 55-HYATT
www.lakelasvegas.hyatt.com

Name/Address/City/State/Zip

All information must be completed prior to redemption. Coupon to be played with a minimum $10 wager. Match play valid on all even-money bets on table games only. Limited to one match play coupon at a time and to one $10 match play per person, per day. Coupon will be replaced with $10 in gaming tokens on all winning bets. Must be 21 or older. Non-transeferable or refundable. Coupon cannot be redeemed for cash. Management reserves the right to alter, change or cancel without notice. Void if duplicated or altered. Valid until 12/31/03.

101 Montelago Boulevard
Las Vegas, NV 89011
(702) 567-1234 • (800) 55-HYATT
www.lakelasvegas.hyatt.com

Present this coupon to the front desk when checking in at the Hyatt Lake Las Vegas and you will receive an upgrade to a lake view room at no additional charge. This offer is based on availability and is subject to change or cancellation without notice. Not valid New Year's Eve or New Year's Day. Must present original coupon (no photocopies accepted). Offer expires 12/31/03.

2-For-1 Buffet

Present this coupon to the cashier at the *French Market Buffet* to purchase one breakfast, lunch or dinner buffet at regular price and receive a second buffet for FREE (or 50% off when dining alone). See reverse for more details.

CASINO COUPON

2-For-1 Fajita Dinner

Present this coupon to your server at *Don Miguel's* to purchase one beef or chicken fajita dinner at regular price and receive a second beef or chicken fajita dinner of equal or lesser value for FREE (or 50% off when dining alone). See reverse for complete details.

CASINO COUPON

Two FREE Cocktails at any Casino Bar

Present this coupon to the server at any casino bar in the Orleans Hotel & Casino to receive two FREE cocktails. See reverse for details.

CASINO COUPON

4500 W. Tropicana Ave.
Las Vegas, NV 89103
(702) 365-7111
(800) ORLEANS
www.orleanscasino.com

Must be 21 years of age or older. Not valid on holidays. Not valid with any other offer. Limit one coupon per person. Resale prohibited. Original coupon must be presented (no photocopies). Discount is 50% off when dining alone. Gratuity not included. Management reserves the right to cancel or alter this coupon without prior notice. Offer expires 12-30-03.

4500 W. Tropicana Ave.
Las Vegas, NV 89103
(702) 365-7111
(800) ORLEANS
www.orleanscasino.com

Must be 21 years of age or older. Not valid on holidays. Not valid with any other offer. Limit one coupon per person. Resale prohibited. Original coupon must be presented (no photocopies). Discount is 50% off when dining alone. Gratuity not included. Management reserves the right to cancel or alter this coupon without prior notice. Offer expires 12-30-03.

4500 W. Tropicana Ave.
Las Vegas, NV 89103
(702) 365-7111
(800) ORLEANS
www.orleanscasino.com

Must be 21 years of age or older. Excludes specialty drinks in souvenir glasses. Excludes Showroom and restaurant bars. Gratuity not included.

Please present before ordering. Original coupon must be presented (no photocopies). Resale prohibited. Management reserves the right to cancel or alter this coupon without prior notice. Offer expires 12-30-03.

AMERICAN CASINO GUIDE

Las Vegas

Hilton

Like no other.

$10 in FREE Promotional Chips

Play any way you like on your favorite table games! Present this coupon and your Park Place Connection card at the Casino Cage for $10 in non-negotiable gaming chips. If you do not have a Park Place Connection card, sign-up at our Park Place Connection Booth to begin earning player rewards. See reverse for more details.

CASINO COUPON

AMERICAN CASINO GUIDE

THE

BUFFET

Buy One Buffet Get One FREE

Present this coupon to the cashier at the buffet at the Las Vegas Hilton to buy one buffet and get one FREE. See reverse for more details.

CASINO COUPON

AMERICAN CASINO GUIDE

Las Vegas

Hilton

Like no other.

$40 Room Rate

Stay at the Las Vegas Hilton for only $40 per night (Sunday through Thursday). Just call (800) 457-3307 and ask for the American Casino Guide exclusive room offer for new players. See reverse for more details.

CASINO COUPON

Las Vegas Hilton

Like no other.

3000 Paradise Road
Las Vegas, NV 89109
(702) 732-5111 • (800) 732-7117
www.lvhilton.com

Must present this original coupon. Limit one per customer. Even money bets only. To be used at designated locations. Non-transferable. Non-redeemable for cash. Las Vegas Hilton management reserves the right to change or cancel this promotion at any time. Must be 21 years of age or older to gamble or consume alcohol. Expires 12/28/03. #1072

Las Vegas Hilton

Like no other.

3000 Paradise Road
Las Vegas, NV 89109
(702) 732-5111 • (800) 732-7117
www.lvhilton.com

Not valid with any other offers. Gratuity not included. Original coupon must be presented when placing order. Limit one couple per coupon. Not valid for parties of one. Nontransferable. Nonredeemable for cash. Las Vegas Hilton management reserves the right to change or cancel this promotion at any time. Must be 21 years of age or older to gamble or consume alcohol. Expires 12/28/03. #1073

Las Vegas Hilton

Like no other.

3000 Paradise Road
Las Vegas, NV 89109
(702) 732-5111 • (800) 732-7117
www.lvhilton.com

Rate is $40 for one room - maximum two night stay. Original coupon must be surrendered upon check-in. New players club members only. Subject to availability. Promotion may be canceled without notice. Las Vegas Hilton management reserves all rights. Limit one coupon per guest. Non-transferable. Offer valid Sunday through Thursday only. Offer not valid on holidays, social events, conventions or in conjunction with any other offer. Taxes not included. Must be 21 years of age or older. Expires 12/26/03. All rights reserved.

2-For-1 Buffet

Present this coupon to the cashier at the *Ports O' Call Buffet* to purchase one breakfast, lunch or dinner buffet at regular price and receive a second buffet for FREE (or 50% off when dining alone). See reverse for more details.

CASINO COUPON

Stay Two Nights and Get a Third Night FREE

Purchase two nights at the Gold Coast Hotel & Casino at the regular rate and receive a third night FREE! See reverse for details.

CASINO COUPON

Two FREE Cocktails at any Casino Bar

Present this coupon to the server at any casino bar in the Gold Coast Hotel & Casino to receive two FREE cocktails. See reverse for details.

CASINO COUPON

Gold Coast Hotel & Casino
4000 W. Flamingo Road
Las Vegas, NV 89103
(702) 367-7111 • (800) 331-5334
www.goldcoastcasino.com

Must be 21 years of age or older. Not valid on holidays. Not valid with any other offer. Limit one coupon per person. Resale prohibited. Original coupon must be presented (no photocopies). Discount is 50% off when dining alone. Gratuity not included. Management reserves the right to cancel or alter this coupon without prior notice. Offer expires 12-30-03.

Gold Coast Hotel & Casino
4000 W. Flamingo Road
Las Vegas, NV 89103
(702) 367-7111 • (800) 331-5334
www.goldcoastcasino.com

Advance reservations required by calling 1-888-402-6278. Sunday-Tuesday arrivals only. Must present coupon at check-in. Original coupon must be presented (no photocopies). Excludes conventions, sporting events and holiday periods. Management reserves the right to cancel or alter this coupon without prior notice. Subject to availability. Not valid for groups. Must be 21 years of age or older. Not alid with any other offer. Resale prohibited. Offer expires 12-30-03.

Gold Coast Hotel & Casino
4000 W. Flamingo Road
Las Vegas, NV 89103
(702) 367-7111 • (800) 331-5334
www.goldcoastcasino.com

Must be 21 years of age or older. Excludes specialty drinks in souvenir glasses. Excludes Showroom and restaurant bars. Gratuity not included. Please present before ordering. Original coupon must be presented (no photocopies). Resale prohibited. Management reserves the right to cancel or alter this coupon without prior notice. Offer expires 12-30-03.

AMERICAN CASINO GUIDE

Blackjack $5 Match Play

(with your Passport Players Club Card)

Make a $5 bet at any "21" table with this coupon and your Passport Players Club Card and receive a FREE $5 Match Bet! See reverse for more details.

CASINO COUPON

AMERICAN CASINO GUIDE

2-For-1 Menu Item

Present this coupon at the Restaurant or BBQ in the Ellis Island Casino & Brewery to receive one FREE menu item when you purchase one item at the regular price. See reverse for more details.

CASINO COUPON

AMERICAN CASINO GUIDE

1,000 FREE Points for New Members of the Passport Players Club!

Present this coupon at the Passport Players Club desk inside the Ellis Island Casino & Brewery to receive 1,000 FREE points when you join the Club. See reverse for more details.

CASINO COUPON

4178 Koval Lane
Las Vegas, NV 89109
(702) 733-8901
www.ellisislandscasino.com

Must be 21 years of age or older and a Passport Players Club Member. Make a $5 minimum bet at an Ellis Island Casino "21" table, along with this original coupon (no photocopies), and receive a $5 Match Bet. Valid for one hand only and coupon must be surrendered after the hand. No Cash Value. Limit: one coupon per customer. Not valid with any other offer. Management reserves all rights. Expires 12/30/03.

4178 Koval Lane
Las Vegas, NV 89109
(702) 733-8901
www.ellisislandscasino.com

Present this original coupon (no photocopies) to the hostess in the restaurant or the BBQ, along with your Passport Players Club Card, to receive one FREE menu item from the regular menu with the purchase of another menu item at the regular price. The FREE item must be of equal of lesser value. Limit: one coupon per customer. No cash value. Must be 21 years of age or older. Tax and gratuity not included. Management reserves all rights. Offer expires 12/30/03.

4178 Koval Lane
Las Vegas, NV 89109
(702) 733-8901
www.ellisislandscasino.com

Present this coupon at the Passport Players Club desk inside the Ellis Island Casino & Brewery to receive 1,000 FREE points when you first join the Passport Players Club. Must be 21 years of age or older. Only valid for new memberships. Not valid with any other offer. Management reserves all rights. Expires 12/30/03.

2-For-1 Room Offer!

Buy one room night (Sunday-Thursday) at the regular rate and receive the second night FREE! See reverse for details.

CASINO COUPON

FREE Funbook
includes Free Breakfast!

Present this coupon at the Promotions Desk inside the El Cortez Hotel & Casino for your FREE Funbook. See reverse for details.

CASINO COUPON

FREE Draft Beer or Wine!

Present this coupon to the server at any bar or lounge in the El Cortez Hotel & Casino to receive one FREE glass of draft beer or wine.See reverse for details.

CASINO COUPON

600 E. Fremont Street
Las Vegas, NV 89101
(702) 385-5200
(800) 634-6703
www.elcortezhotelcasino.com

Offer valid for adults 21 years of age or older. Advance reservations required. Call 1-800-634-6703 to make your reservations and ask for the **American Casino Guide** 2-For-1 discount. Not valid with any other offers or discounts. Management reserves all rights. Coupon must be presented upon check-in. Offer expires 12/25/03.

600 E. Fremont Street
Las Vegas, NV 89101
(702) 385-5200
(800) 634-6703
www.elcortezhotelcasino.com

Offer valid for adults 21 years of age or older. Coupon must be presented at promotions desk to receive FREE funbook. Limited to one funbook per person, per day. This offer is subject to change or cancellation without notice. Offer expires 12/30/03.

600 E. Fremont Street
Las Vegas, NV 89101
(702) 385-5200
(800) 634-6703
www.elcortezhotelcasino.com

Offer valid for adults 21 years of age or older. Coupon must be presented to server to receive FREE drink. Limited to one FREE glass of draft beer or wine per person, per day. This offer is subject to change or cancellation without notice. Offer expires 12/30/03.

JERRY'S NUGGET

Blackjack $5 Match Play
with your More Club Plus Card

Make a $5 bet at a "21" table and receive a $5 Match Bet ($5 minimum bet required). See reverse for full details.

CASINO COUPON

JERRY'S NUGGET

FREE Bingo With your More Plus Card!

Redeem this coupon for a FREE $3 BLUE CARD.
Sessions at 11am, 1pm, 7pm, 9pm and 11pm
See reverse for full details.

CASINO COUPON

JERRY'S NUGGET

FREE Gift <u>and</u> FREE 100 BONUS POINTS
For New Members! Join More Club Plus today,
the only player's club that gives you more!

See reverse for full details.

CASINO COUPON

1821Las Vegas Boulevard North
N. Las Vegas, NV 89030
(702) 399-3000 • www.jerrysnugget.com

Blackjack $5 Match Play

Limit one coupon per customer. Must be a More Club Plus member. Make a $5 minimum bet at a Jerry's Nugget '21' table, along with this coupon and receive a $5 match bet. Coupon surrendered after first hand. Good for one hand, one wager. Cannot be redeemed for cash. Not valid with any other offer. Must be 21 years of age or older to redeem. Management reserves all rights. Offer expires 12/30/03.

1821Las Vegas Boulevard North
N. Las Vegas, NV 89030
(702) 399-3000 • www.jerrysnugget.com

FREE $3 BINGO

Limit one coupon per customer. Must be a More Club Plus member. T.E.D. purchase includes $1.25 extra charge. Valid only during regular sessions. Cannot be redeemed for cash. Not valid with any other offer. Not valid on holidays. Must be 21 years of age or older to redeem. Management reserves all rights. Offer expires 12/30/03.

1821Las Vegas Boulevard North
N. Las Vegas, NV 89030
(702) 399-3000 • www.jerrysnugget.com

FREE Gift <u>and</u> FREE 100 BONUS POINTS!

Limit one coupon per customer. New More Club Plus members only. Must be 21 years of age or older to redeem. Present this coupon at the More Club Center, sign up for the More Club Plus and receive your free gift and 100 bonus points. Must present valid ID. Offer expires 12/30/03.

Hit Four-of-a-Kind and Receive a FREE Buffet Dinner!

Present this coupon to the Slot Supervisor when you win a four-of-a-kind (no wild cards) on any denomination video poker machine at the Suncoast Hotel and Casino. Your Club Denaro card must be properly inserted while playing and you must be playing maximim coins in order to receive this buffet bonus. See reverse for complete details.

CASINO COUPON

Join Club Denaro and receive 1,000 FREE Bonus Points!

Present this coupon to the Club Denaro desk at the Suncoast Hotel and Casino to recive 1,000 FREE bonus points when you join!. Valid for new enrollments only. See reverse for complete details.

CASINO COUPON

$4 Bingo Bucks FREE with purchase!

Present this coupon at the Bingo Hall at the Suncoast Hotel and Casino to receive $4 in Bingo Bucks FREE with the purchase of one regular price pack. Excludes Bonanza, Cashball or any validation. Use this coupon for credit towards additional bingo packs. See reverse for complete details.

CASINO COUPON

9090 Alta Drive
Las Vegas, NV 89145
(702) 636-7111 • (877) 677-7111
www.suncoastcasino.com

Four-of-a-kind must be verified by slot supervisor at time of jackpot and original coupon must be presented (no photocopies). No game recalls. Based on maximum coins played. No wild cards. Multi-line poker machines must hit on base line only. One bonus per player only. Cannot be used with any other offers. Must be 21 years of age or older. Offer expires 12-30-03.

9090 Alta Drive
Las Vegas, NV 89145
(702) 636-7111 • (877) 677-7111
www.suncoastcasino.com

One 1,000-point bonus per player. Original coupon (no photocopies) must be presented at time of enrollment. Cannot be used in conjunction with any other offer. Coupon has no cash value. Must be 21 years of age or older. Offer expires 12-30-03.

9090 Alta Drive
Las Vegas, NV 89145
(702) 636-7111 • (877) 677-7111
www.suncoastcasino.com

Limit: one per guest. Coupon has no cash value. Original coupon (no photocopies) must be presented at time of purchase. Cannot be used in conjunction with any other offer. Must be 21 years of age or older. Offer expires 12-30-03.

**18 E. Fremont Street
Las Vegas, NV 89101
(702) 385-1664
(800) 634-6532
www.playatlvc.com**

Offer valid on a space available basis for adults 21 years of age or older. Advance reservations required. Call 1-800-634-6532 to make your reservations and ask for the **American Casino Guide** 2-For-1 discount. Not valid with any other offers or discounts. Management reserves all rights. Original coupon must be presented upon check-in. Limited to one coupon per customer. Offer expires 12/25/03.

**18 E. Fremont Street
Las Vegas, NV 89101
(702) 385-1664
(800) 634-6532
www.playatlvc.com**

Offer valid for adults 21 years of age or older and for new slot club members only. Original coupon (no photocopies) must be presented at promotions desk to receive your 4,000 FREE slot club points and free deck of cards. Limited to one 4,000 FREE slot club points offer and one free deck of cards per person, per account. This offer is subject to change or cancellation without notice.Management reserves all rights. Offer expires 12/25/03.

**18 E. Fremont Street
Las Vegas, NV 89101
(702) 385-1664
(800) 634-6532
www.playatlvc.com**

Offer valid for adults 21 years of age or older. Original coupon (no photocopies) must be presented to server to receive FREE drink.

Limited to one FREE glass of draft beer or wine per person, per day. This offer is subject to change or cancellation without notice. Management reserves all rights. Offer expires 12/25/03.

3595 Las Vegas Blvd. S.
Las Vegas, NV 89109
(702) 737-7111
(888) 227-2279
www.barbarycoastcasino.com

Must be 21 years of age or older. Not valid with any other offer. Resale prohibited. Limit one coupon per person. Gratuity not included. Original coupon must be presented (no photocopies).

Management reserves the right to cancel or alter this coupon without prior notice. Offer expires 12-30-03.

3595 Las Vegas Blvd. S.
Las Vegas, NV 89109
(702) 737-7111
(888) 227-2279
www.barbarycoastcasino.com

Must be 21 years of age or older. Excludes specialty drinks in souvenir glasses. Excludes restaurant bars. Gratuity not included. Please present before ordering. Original coupon must be presented (no photocopies accepted). Resale prohibited.

Management reserves the right to cancel or alter this coupon without prior notice. Offer expires 12-30-03.

CIRCUS CIRCUS®

2880 Las Vegas Boulevard South
Las Vegas, NV 89109
(702) 734-0410
Reservations (800) 444-2472

Second Room Night FREE!

Buy one room night at the regular rate and receive the second night FREE! See reverse for details.

CASINO COUPON

FREE Drink at Any Casino Bar

Present this coupon at any Plaza Casino Bar to receive your FREE glass of draft beer, wine, or bottle of water. See reverse for more details.

CASINO COUPON

One FREE Progressive Bonanza (with any buy-in)

8 sessions daily from 9:00 a.m. until 11:00 p.m.

Present this coupon in our Bingo Room to receive a FREE Progressive Bonanza Card with any buy-in. See reverse for more details.

CASINO COUPON

1 Main Street
Las Vegas, NV 89101
(702) 386-2110
(800) 634-6575
www.plazahotelcasino.com

Offer valid on a space available basis for adults 21 years of age or older. Advance reservations required. Call 1-800-634-6575 to make your reservations and ask for the **American Casino Guide** 2-For-1 discount. Not valid with any other offers or discounts. Management reserves all rights. Original coupon (no photocopies) must be presented upon check-in. Limit to one coupon per customer. Offer expires 12/25/03.

1 Main Street
Las Vegas, NV 89101
(702) 386-2110
(800) 634-6575
www.plazahotelcasino.com

Offer valid for adults 21 years of age or older. Original coupon (no photocopies) must be presented to bartender to receive your FREE drink. Limited to one FREE glass of draft beer, wine, or bottle of water, per person, per day. This offer is subject to change or cancellation without notice. Management reserves all rights. Offer expires 12/25/03.

1 Main Street
Las Vegas, NV 89101
(702) 386-2110
(800) 634-6575
www.plazahotelcasino.com

Offer valid for adults 21 years of age or older. Limit one coupon per person per session. Original coupon (no photocopies) must be presented to attendant to receive FREE Progressive Bonanza Card. Coupon has no cash value. This offer is subject to change or cancellation without notice and is not valid with any other offer. Management reserves all rights. Offer expires 12/25/03.

Receive a FREE Buffet with qualifying slot club play!

Present this coupon at the Rewards Center to receive a FREE breakfast, lunch or dinner buffet when you earn 500 points in the same calendar day. Valid at either Arizona Charlie's location. See reverse for more details.

CASINO COUPON

Receive up to $20 OFF at the Yukon Grille Steakhouse!

Present this coupon to the cashier at the Yukon Grille Steakhouse at either Arizona Charlie's West or Arizona Charlie's East to receive $5 off per person on your check. Maximum discount is $20. See reverse for more details.

CASINO COUPON

Receive a FREE Ham & Eggs Meal or
Steak & Eggs Meal with qualifying slot club play!

Present this coupon at the Rewards Center to receive a FREE Ham & Eggs Meal when you earn 279 points in the same calendar day, or a FREE Steak & Eggs Meal when you earn 299 points in the same calendar day. Valid at either Arizona Charlie's location. See reverse for more details.

CASINO COUPON

4575 Boulder Highway
Las Vegas, NV 89121
(702) 951-9000 • (800) 362-4040
www.arizonacharlies.com

740 S. Decatur Boulevard
Las Vegas, NV 89107
(702) 258-5200 • (800) 342-2695
www.arizonacharlies.com

Must be 21 or older. Surrender this original coupon (no photocopies) at the Rewards Center. Cannot combine offers. Limit: one buffet coupon per player account. Management reserves all rights. Offer expires December 31, 2003. Settle to: 33-7028.

4575 Boulder Highway
Las Vegas, NV 89121
(702) 951-9000 • (800) 362-4040
www.arizonacharlies.com

740 S. Decatur Boulevard
Las Vegas, NV 89107
(702) 258-5200 • (800) 342-2695
www.arizonacharlies.com

Must be 21 or older. Must present your Charlie's Rewards card and surrender this original coupon (no photocopies) to the cashier before being seated. Receive a discount of $5 per person, for up to 4 people. Minimum check amount of $20 per person. Cannot combine offers. Offer expires December 31, 2003. Settle to: 33-7028

4575 Boulder Highway
Las Vegas, NV 89121
(702) 951-9000 • (800) 362-4040
www.arizonacharlies.com

740 S. Decatur Boulevard
Las Vegas, NV 89107
(702) 258-5200 • (800) 342-2695
www.arizonacharlies.com

Must be 21 or older. Surrender this original coupon (no photocopies) at the Rewards Center. Cannot combine offers. Limit: one ham & eggs or Steak & eggs coupon per player account. Management reserves all rights. Offer expires December 31, 2003. Settle to: 33-7028.

Jackie Gaughan's

400 E. Ogden Avenue
Las Vegas, NV 89101
(702) 384-8444
(800) 634-6703
www.goldspikehotelcasino.com

Offer valid on a space available basis for adults 21 years of age or older. Advance reservations required. Call 1-800-634-6703 to make your reservations and ask for the **American Casino Guide second night FREE offer.** Not valid with any other offers or discounts. Management reserves all rights. Original coupon (no photocopies) must be presented upon check-in. Limit: one coupon per customer. Offer expires 12/25/03.

Jackie Gaughan's

400 E. Ogden Avenue
Las Vegas, NV 89101
(702) 384-8444
(800) 634-6703
www.goldspikehotelcasino.com

Offer valid for adults 21 years of age or older 24 hours a day. Original coupon (no photocopies) must be presented to server to receive your FREE meal. This offer is limited to one FREE meal (includes: one entree, one drink and one dessert) per person, per day. This offer is subject to change or cancellation without notice. Management reserves all rights. Offer expires 12/25/03.

Jackie Gaughan's

400 E. Ogden Avenue
Las Vegas, NV 89101
(702) 384-8444
(800) 634-6703
www.goldspikehotelcasino.com

Offer valid for adults 21 years of age or older. Original coupon (no photocopies) must be presented to attendant at the Casino Bar or the Snack Bar to receive your FREE drink. This offer is limited to one FREE glass of draft beer, wine, or soft drink, per person, per day. This offer is subject to change or cancellation without notice. Management reserves all rights. Offer expires 12/25/03.

AMERICAN CASINO GUIDE

2-For-1 Feast Buffet

Present this coupon to the cashier at *The Feast Buffet* at any of the above casinos. Pay for one buffet and get the second buffet FREE! Valid Sunday through Thursday only. Offer expires 12/26/03. Settle to comp BS 11-942, GVR 200-101, PS 28-115, SS 413-279, TS 82-295. See reverse for details.

CASINO COUPON

AMERICAN CASINO GUIDE

FREE Fun Book

Present this coupon at our Front Desk to receive a FREE Fun Book - a $100 value!. Offer expires 12/30/03.

CASINO COUPON

AMERICAN CASINO GUIDE

$39.99 Room Rate

A great $39.99 room rate at Santa Fe Station Hotel & Casino! Offer valid Sunday through Thursday, based on availability. Black out dates apply. Must have advance reservations. Limit one coupon per check in. No exceptions. Holiday and convention periods excluded. Management reserves all rights. No cash value. Offer expires December 26, 2003. See reverse for complete details.

CASINO COUPON

AMERICAN CASINO GUIDE

2-For 1 Room

Pay for one night and get the second night FREE! Good Sunday through Thursday. Holidays and convention periods excluded. Black out dates may apply. Subject to availability. Offer expires December 26, 2003. See reverse for complete details.

CASINO COUPON

AMERICAN CASINO GUIDE

2 FOR 1 Breakfast or Lunch Buffet

Use this coupon to receive your second buffet meal FREE.

CASINO COUPON

AMERICAN CASINO GUIDE

pay **$49** for your first night

get your second night **FREE**

CASINO COUPON

4111 Boulder Highway
Las Vegas, NV 89121
(702) 432-7777
(800) 683-7777
www.stationcasinos.com

Advance reservations required. Call: 1-800-683-7777 and ask for Operator #103. This voucher entitles the bearer to one free room night at the Boulder Station Hotel & Casino, with the purchase of one night at the prevailing rate. Must present original voucher upon check-in (no photocopies). Not valid in conjunction with any other offer. Management reserves the right to cancel this promotion at any time. Credit card or cash deposit required. Guest is responsible for tax, telephone, room service and all other additional charges. Must be 21 or older. Limit one free room per person. Offer expires 12/26/03.

733.7000
4100 Paradise Rd.
Las Vegas, NV • 89109
www.terribleherbst.com

Present this coupon along with your Terrible's Player Card to the Cashier at the Buffet when paying for your meal. Receive one FREE breakfast or lunch buffet with the purchase of another at the regular price. Must be a Players Cub Member. One coupon for up to a party of two. Non-transferable. No cash value. Must be 21 years of age or older. Tax and gratuity not included. Management reserves the right to modify, change or cancel this offer at anytime without prior notice. Expires 12/31/03.

call1.800.640.9777
for **RESERVATIONS**
4100 Paradise Rd.
Las Vegas, NV • 89109

Call 1-800-640-9777 to make your reservation. Offer is good only after purchasing first nights stay at $49. This offer is valid Sunday through Wednesday arrival only. No cash value. One coupon per customer. Must be 21 years of age or older. Based on availability. Management reserves the right to modify, change or cancel this offer at anytime without prior notice. Expires 12/31/03.

www.terribleherbst.com

AMERICAN CASINO GUIDE

2-For-1 Entree
at Mahoney's Cafe

CASINO • BOWLING CENTER • RV PARK

Buy one entreee at Mahoney's Cafe and receive the second entree of equal or lesser value for FREE. Valid for breakfst, lunch or dinner. Cafe open from 6:00 a.m. to Midnight. See reverse for more details.

CASINO COUPON

AMERICAN CASINO GUIDE

$10 Refund For
New Slot Club Members

CASINO • BOWLING CENTER • RV PARK

Present this coupon at the Club Center and become a new Silver Nugget slot club member. Then, if you should lose $20.00 in slot, video poker or keno machines on the day you join the club, you will receive a $10 refund! See reverse for more details.

CASINO COUPON

AMERICAN CASINO GUIDE

2-For-1
Bowling

CASINO • BOWLING CENTER • RV PARK

Buy one game of bowling and receive one game FREE! Also, receive shoe rental for only $1.00 with this coupon. See reverse for more details.

CASINO COUPON

2140 Las Vegas Blvd N.
N. Las Vegas, NV 89030
(702) 399-1111
www.mahoneyscasino.com

- Must be 21 years of age or older.

- Present original coupon (no photocopies) to server before ordering.

- Cannot be used with any other offer.

- Management reserves all rights.

- Offer expires 12/30/03.

2140 Las Vegas Blvd N.
N. Las Vegas, NV 89030
(702) 399-1111
www.mahoneyscasino.com

- Must be 21 years of age or older.

- Present original coupon (no photocopies) at Club Center. Membership is FREE and the Club is open from 8:00 a.m until Midnight.

- Valid for new slot club members only.

- Receive $10 refund after play is verified.

- Management reserves all rights.

- Offer expires 12/30/03.

2140 Las Vegas Blvd N.
N. Las Vegas, NV 89030
(702) 399-1111
www.mahoneyscasino.com

- Present original coupon (no photocopies) at bowling desk.

- Valid 9 a.m. to 5 p.m. Monday through Friday.

- Valid for up to four players per coupon.

- Cannot be used with any other offer.

- Management reserves all rights.

- Offer expires 12/30/03.

AMERICAN CASINO GUIDE

2-For-1 Room

Pay for one night and get the second night FREE! Good Sunday through Thursday. Holidays and convention periods excluded. Black out dates may apply. Subject to availability. Offer expires December 26, 2003. See reverse for complete details.

CASINO COUPON

AMERICAN CASINO GUIDE

One FREE Game of Bowling Anytime!
(including Cosmic Bowling)

The bearer of this coupon is entitled to one FREE game of bowling anytime (including Cosmic Bowling). One coupon per person, per day. Management Reserves All Rights. Offer expires December 26, 2003. See reverse for complete details.

CASINO COUPON

AMERICAN CASINO GUIDE

Pay for one night at prevailing rate, get a second night at half-price!

Present this coupon when you check in at the front desk Monday through Thursday. Pay for one night at the prevailing rate and get the second night at half-price. See reverse for complete details.

CASINO COUPON

2101 Texas Star Lane
N. Las Vegas, NV 89032
(702) 631-1000
(800) 654-8888
www.texasstation.com

Advance reservations required. Call 1-800-654-8888 and ask for Operator #325. This voucher entitles the bearer to one free room night at the Texas Station Hotel & Casino, with the purchase of one night at the prevailing rate. Must present original voucher upon check-in (no photocopies). Not valid in conjunction with any other offer. Management reserves the right to cancel this promotion at any time. Credit card or cash deposit required. Guest is responsible for tax, telephone, room service and all other additional charges. Must be 21 or older. Limit one free room per person. Offer expires 12/26/03.

2101 Texas Star Lane
N. Las Vegas, NV 89032
(702) 631-1000
(800) 654-8888
www.texasstation.com

This coupon entitles the bearer to one FREE game of bowling anytime at the Texas Station Hotel & Casino Bowling Center.

Must present original voucher (no photocopies). Not valid in conjunction with any other offer. Management reserves the right to cancel this promotion at any time. Limit one free game per person, per day. Offer expires 12/26/03.

3330 W. Tropicana Ave.
Las Vegas, NV 89103
(702) 740-0000
(800) 634-3488

Advance reservations required. Call (702) 367-2441 and ask for Operator #623. This voucher entitles the bearer to one room night at half-price at the Wild Wild West Gambling Hall & Hotel, with the purchase of one night at the prevailing rate. Offer good Monday through Thursday. Must present original voucher upon check-in (no photocopies). Holidays and convention periods are excluded. Must have advance reservations. Limit one coupon per check in. No exceptions. Management reserves all rights. No cash value. Must be 21 or older. Offer expires December 31, 2003.

AMERICAN CASINO GUIDE

Buy one Breakfast, Lunch or Dinner entrée, get the second entrée FREE!

Buy one entrée at the Gambler's Grill and enjoy a second entree of equal or lesser value FREE.. Offer expires December 31, 2003. See reverse for complete details.

CASINO COUPON

AMERICAN CASINO GUIDE

Up to $8 off the Festival Buffet!

Present this coupon to the cashier at the Festival Buffet to receive $2 off, per person on lunch or dinner at the Festival Buffet. Valid at either Fiesta Rancho or Fiesta Henderson. See reverse for details.

CASINO COUPON

AMERICAN CASINO GUIDE

Sign up for an Amigo Card and receive 1,500 bonus points!

Present this coupon to the Amigo Club when you sign up for an Amigo Card and receive 1,500 bonus points! Valid at either Fiesta Rancho or Fiesta Henderson. See reverse for details.

CASINO COUPON

3330 W. Tropicana Ave.
Las Vegas, NV 89103
(702) 740-0000
(800) 634-3488
www.stationcasinos.com

- Present original coupon (no photocopies) to server prior to ordering.

- Limit one coupon per person.

- Management reserves all rights.

- No Cash Value.

- Offer expires December 31, 2003.

- Settle to comp #10187

777 W. Lake Mead Drive
Henderson, NV 89015
(702) 558-7000 • (866) 469-7666
www.stationcasinos.com

2400 N. Rancho Drive
Las Vegas, NV 89130
(702) 631-7000 • (866) 731-7333
www.stationcasinos.com

Must be 21 or older. Management reserves all rights. Not a line pass. Tax and gratuity not included. Coupon valid for up to four people. Original coupon (no photocopies) must be presented to the cashier. Not transferable or redeemable for cash. Not valid on holidays. Valid through 12/26/03. Settle to comp# FH 41353/FR 33-513.

777 W. Lake Mead Drive
Henderson, NV 89015
(702) 558-7000 • (866) 469-7666
www.stationcasinos.com

2400 N. Rancho Drive
Las Vegas, NV 89130
(702) 631-7000 • (866) 731-7333
www.stationcasinos.com

Offer only valid for first time sign up for the Amigo Card. Original coupon (no photocopies) must be presented at Amigo Club. Must be 21 or older. Management reserves all rights. One coupon per person. Valid through December 26, 2003.

AMERICAN CASINO GUIDE

2-For 1 Room

Pay for one night and get the second night FREE! Good Sunday through Thursday. Holidays and convention periods excluded. Black out dates may apply. Subject to availability. Offer expires December 26, 2003. See reverse for complete details.

CASINO COUPON

AMERICAN CASINO GUIDE

2 for 1 BUFFET

Brunch - Monday through Friday. 7a.m. to 3p.m.
Not valid for weekends or holiday brunch.
Dinner - Good seven days a week, 4p.m. to 10p.m.

One coupon per person. Coupon may not be duplicated and has no cash value. Coupon cannot be combined with any other offer. Management reserves the right to modify or cancel this promotion at any time. Each member of party must be 21. Offer expires December 23, 2003.

Comp #183

CASINO COUPON

AMERICAN CASINO GUIDE

$5.00 OFF THRILL PASS

Unlimited Rides, All Day Long!
Quicken your pulse with unlimited rides on these great attractions!
Regular price $19.95

Coupon may not be duplicated. Coupon has no cash value. Coupon cannot be combined with any other offer. Management reserves the right to modify or cancel this promotion at any time. Offer expires December 30, 2003.

CASINO COUPON

SUNSET STATION
HOTEL · CASINO

1301 W. Sunset Road
Henderson, NV 89014
(702) 547-7777
(888) 786-7389
www.sunsetstation.com

Advance reservations required. Call 1-888-786-7389 and ask for Operator #205. This voucher entitles the bearer to one free room night at the Sunset Station Hotel & Casino, with the purchase of one night at the prevailing rate. Must present original voucher upon check-in (no photocopies). Not valid in conjunction with any other offer. Management reserves the right to cancel this promotion at any time. Credit card or cash deposit required. Guest is responsible for tax, telephone, room service and all other additional charges. Must be 21 or older. Limit one free room per person. Offer expires 12/26/03.

Sahara Hotel and Casino
2535 Las Vegas Blvd., South
Las Vegas, NV 89109

1-702-737-2111

www.saharavegas.com

NASCAR Cafe
2535 Las Vegas Blvd., South
Las Vegas, NV 89109

1-702-734-7223

www.saharavegas.com

2411 W. Sahara Avenue
Las Vegas, NV 89102
(702) 367-2411
(800) 634-3101
www.stationcasinos.com

Advance reservations required. Call 1-866-767-7772 and ask for operator #57.

Must present original voucher upon check-in (no photocopies). Not valid in conjunction with any other offer. Management reserves the right to cancel this promotion at any time. Credit card or cash deposit required. Guest is responsible for tax, telephone, room service and all other additional charges. Must be 21 or older. Limit one free room per person. Offer expires 12/30/03.

2411 W. Sahara Avenue
Las Vegas, NV 89102
(702) 367-2411
(800) 634-3101
www.stationcasinos.com

Redeem this original coupon (no photocopies) at the Palace Station Rewards Center one hour prior to showtime.

Subject to availability. Must be 21 years or older to redeem. Tax not included. Valid Monday through Thursday. Showtimes are 7:30 pm & 10:00 pm. One drink minimum per show. Laugh Trax is a non-smoking showroom. Management reserves all rights. No cash value. Offer expires December 30, 2003.

Show times 7:30 & 10:30 nightly except Sundays
Show reservations (702) 794-3261 • Toll-Free (800) 777-7664

Not valid in combination with any other discounts. Must present coupon at the Imperial Palace's Show Reservations Desk (main casino floor) for discount. Tickets for show must be purchased at least one hour prior to show time. Legends In Concert is not responsible for lost or stolen coupons. Good for up to a party of six. Offer expires December 30, 2003.

LAS VEGAS CASINO & HOTEL

1-800 HARRAHS / *www.harrahs.com*

3475 Las Vegas Blvd., South • Las Vegas, Nevada 89109

LAS VEGAS CASINO & HOTEL

1-800 HARRAHS / *www.harrahs.com*

3475 Las Vegas Blvd., South • Las Vegas, Nevada 89109

LAS VEGAS CASINO & HOTEL

1-800 HARRAHS / *www.harrahs.com*

3475 Las Vegas Blvd., South • Las Vegas, Nevada 89109

AMERICAN CASINO GUIDE

The Way Las Vegas Was Meant To Be

$10 Off Early Show
$5 Off Late Show
Folies Bergere

Redeem this ticket at the Tropicana Box Office to receive $10 off the 7:30 pm show or $5 off the 10 pm show. See reverse for details.

CASINO COUPON

AMERICAN CASINO GUIDE

The Way Las Vegas Was Meant To Be

$5 Off
The Magic of
Rick Thomas

Redeem this ticket at the Tropicana Box Office.
See reverse for full details.

CASINO COUPON

AMERICAN CASINO GUIDE

The Way Las Vegas Was Meant To Be

Casino Legends Hall of Fame
FREE Admission to the
World's Largest
Gambling Museum
Over 15,000 Exhibits!

A Gang of Gamblers • A Gallery of Gangsters • A Montage of Movies
The Smithsonian of Showgirls • Vegas Visionaries • Hall of Headliners
Fires & Implosions • See reverse for full details.

CASINO COUPON

The Way Las Vegas Was Meant To Be

3801 Las Vegas Blvd. S.
Las Vegas, NV 89109
(702) 739-2222

Reservations (800) GO-2-TROP

This coupon is good for a maximum of two people. Special discounted prices are not applicable to booth seating. Subject to availability. Tax included in price. Management reserves the right to cancel or modify this offer without prior notice. Must present coupon at time of purchase.

Offer expires 12/11/2003. For more information call (702) 739-2411

The Way Las Vegas Was Meant To Be

3801 Las Vegas Blvd. S.
Las Vegas, NV 89109
(702) 739-2222

Reservations (800) GO-2-TROP

This coupon is good for a maximum of two people. Special discounted prices are not applicable to booth seating. Subject to availability. Tax included in price. Management reserves the right to cancel or modify this offer without prior notice. Must present coupon at time of purchase.

Offer expires 12/30/2003. For more information call (702) 739-2411

The Way Las Vegas Was Meant To Be

3801 Las Vegas Blvd. S.
Las Vegas, NV 89109
(702) 739-2222

Reservations (800) GO-2-TROP

Casino Legends
Hall of Fame
Open Daily
9 a.m. - 9 p.m.
For more information
call (702) 739-5444

Redeem this coupon at the museum. Coupon good for up to four people. Must be 18 unless accompanied by an adult. Offer expires 12/30/2003.

RIVIERA Hotel & Casino
The Entertainment Center of Las Vegas
The Alternative for Grown-Ups

2901 Las Vegas Blvd. S. • Las Vegas, NV • (702) 734-5110

Coupon must be presented to Riviera box office. Must be 21. Not valid Saturdays or Saturdays and Sundays of a holiday weekend or with any other offer. One coupon per person. Offer may be cancelled at any time without notice. No cash value. Offer expires 12/30/2003.

RIVIERA Hotel & Casino
The Entertainment Center of Las Vegas
The Alternative for Grown-Ups

Riviera Comedy Club
Las Vegas' Original Comedy Showcase

2901 Las Vegas Blvd. S. • Las Vegas, NV • (702) 734-5110

Coupon must be presented to Riviera box office. Must be 21. Not valid Saturdays, or Saturdays and Sundays of a holiday weekend, or with any other offer. One coupon per person. Offer may be cancelled at any time without notice. No cash value. Offer expires 12/30/2003.

IMPERIAL PALACE
HOTEL & CASINO • LAS VEGAS, NEVADA
Center Strip • (702) 731-3311

The Imperial Palace Auto Collections & Collectibles. Over 350 inspired works of automotive design on display and for sale daily. This offer is subject to cancellation at any time. Management reserves all rights.

2000 Las Vegas Blvd. S. • Las Vegas, NV 89104
(800) 99-TOWER • (702) 380-7777

Must be at least 5 years of age to attend show. Some material may be inappropriate for children; parental discretion recommended. Minors must be accompanied by an adult. Subject to availability. Show times subject to change. Offers cannot be combined. Management reserves all rights. Not for resale. Valid through December 27, 2003. **(Coupon must be presented at the Stratosphere's Ticket Center.)**

2000 Las Vegas Blvd. S. • Las Vegas, NV 89104
(800) 99-TOWER • (702) 380-7777

Must be at least 5 years of age to attend show. Some material may be inappropriate for children; parental discretion recommended. Minors must be accompanied by an adult. Subject to availability. Show times subject to change. Offers cannot be combined. Management reserves all rights. Not for resale. Valid through December 27, 2003. **(Coupon must be presented at the Stratosphere's Ticket Center.)**

Coupon valid Monday through Friday. Limit one coupon per person, per cruise. Offer not valid with any other discount or coupon. Not valid on holidays or selected cruises. Subject to change or cancellation without notice. Coupon expires 11/30/03.

For cruise schedules and reservations:
(800) 842-0115

Golden Isles Cruise Lines, Inc.
1 St. Andrews Court, Brunswick, GA 31520
(BRUNSWICK, GEORGIA IS LOCATED MIDWAY BETWEEN SAVANNAH, GA AND JACKSONVILLE, FL.)
SHIP'S REGISTRY: PANAMA

Name

Address

City, St, Zip

1- Must be 21, or older, to board. 2-Advance reservations required. 3-This coupon is not combinable with any other Stardancer offer 4-Coupon must be presented at ticket booth on day of sailing. 5-Limit (4) people per coupon. 6-Certain restrictions apply. 7- Offer subject to change without notice. 8- Coupon expires on date indicated. 9-This coupon is not transferable

---

(954) 453-3333
1-877-SEA-ESCAPE (1-877-732-3722)
www.seaescape.com
(SYMBOL:SEPI)

For reservations ask for code "CG"

SeaEscape 2003 Party Cruises
Departs from Fort Lauderdale

Sail with us 13 times a week on a five, or six-hour cruise and thrill to the action of Slots, Roulette,Craps, Blackjack, Poker, Pai Gow Poker, Caribbean Stud, Let It Ride and Video Gaming.

*No cash value. One coupon valid for up to 4 people per sailing. Restrictions apply. Advance reservations required. $3 federal departure tax and $3 security charge additional. Cannot be combined with any other offer. Photo ID required.

Ship's registry Bahamas.

1-800-474-DICE

No other ships pay out more!

**Hollywood • Key Largo
Jacksonville • Port Canaveral
Daytona Beach • John's Pass, T.I.
N. Myrtle Beach, South Carolina**

Just like Las Vegas only offshore!

Offer valid for two persons on SunCruz CASINOS at any of the above locations. Coupon cannot be combined with any other offers. Reservations are required. Government tax per person is additional. For reservations or information call 1-800-474-DICE. Offer expires 12/30/03.